C000017582

RESCUE R

About *Rescue Remedy*, a unique natural stress reduction formula made from English wildflowers, developed by Dr. Edward Bach in the early 1930s. Contains new material and photographs hitherto unpublished.

Bach and *Rescue Remedy* are trade marks belonging to The Bach Centre, England.

NOTE TO THE READER

Neither the author nor the publisher of this book make any claims as to the medicinal effectiveness of the Bach Flower Rescue Remedy. The material presented in this work represents a compilation of information, which was researched by the author both in the United States and Great Britain.

The author is not a physician and is not able to reply to any correspondence or questions about the use of the Rescue Remedy. However, if you know of additional sources of information, or have used the Rescue Remedy and wish to share your experiences for possible inclusion in future editions of this book, contact Gregory Vlamis, P.O. Box A3237, Chicago, Illinois 60690, U.S.A.

Rescue Remedy

The Healing Power of Bach Flower Rescue Remedy

Gregory Vlamis

Foreword by Dr Charles K. Elliott
(Formerly Physician to Her Majesty
Queen Elizabeth II)

Thorsons
An Imprint of HarperCollins*Publishers*

Thorsons
An Imprint of HarperCollins*Publishers*
77–85 Fulham Palace Road,
Hammersmith, London W6 8JB
1160 Battery Street,
San Francisco, California 94111–1213

First published as *Flowers to the Rescue* 1986
Published as *Flower Remedies to the Rescue* 1990
This edition 1994
3 5 7 9 10 8 6 4 2

A catalogue record for this book
is available from the British Library

ISBN 0 7225 2948 1

Printed in Great Britain by
HarperCollinsManufacturing Glasgow

DEDICATION

To those who suffer and are in distress; to Dr. Edward Bach, and to his spirit; to the Bach Centre for carrying on his good work; to my daughter, Roxanne Vlamis; to my father, Constantine Vlamis, and especially to my mother, Roxanne Vlamis Santos—for her tremendous caring and support.

'Gregory Vlamis has made a fine contribution to the understanding of the Bach Flower Remedies and one which will greatly increase our awareness of these wonderful healing agents. His account of their development by Edward Bach, supplemented by very practical descriptions of their use, forms a valuable treatise for which we are grateful.' — *Maesimund Panos, MD, DHt, former President, National Center for Homeopathy, Washington, D.C.; co-author of 'Homeopathic Medicine at Home' (Tarcher).*

'I am glad that Gregory Vlamis has taken the trouble to collect all these testimonies to the Bach Flower Remedies. Medical research into them is long overdue.' — *Alec Forbes, MA, DM, FRCP, formerly member Expert Advisory Panel on Traditional Medicine, World Health Organization; medical director Bristol Cancer Help Centre, and author of 'The Bristol Diet: a Get Well and Stay Well Eating Plan' (Century).*

'An outstanding reference work, *Rescue Remedy* is both a reference tool and reader for all those interested in the Bach Flower Remedies and especially Dr. Bach's combination formula Rescue Remedy. Mr Vlamis has excelled in bringing together numerous case studies on the current use of Rescue Remedy, many by top physicians in the field. Additionally, the inclusion of two out-of-print philosophical works by Dr. Edward Bach makes this book a *must* for all those interested in whole person healing.' — *Leslie J. Kaslof, author of 'Wholistic Dimensions in Healing' (Doubleday) and President of the Dr. Edward Bach Healing Society, North America.*

'. . . a valuable record of how Dr. Bach's work has continued in the 50 years since his death. It is a well organized book of impressive and thorough research.' — *Julian Barnard, author of 'A Guide to the Bach Flower Remedies' (C. W. Daniel).*

'*Rescue Remedy* shows us the impressive range of experience from health professionals and consumers with the Bach Flower Remedies. This book provides strong testimony to the value of these flower remedies and encourages us all to use them for the various trials and tribulations of modern life.' — *Dana Ullman, MPH, co-author of 'Everybody's Guide to Homeopathic Medicines' (Tarcher), and Director of Homeopathic Educational Services, Berkeley, California.*

'This book will be of great interest to many veterinarians. The wonderful accounts of the efficacy of Rescue Remedy in animals is particularly fascinating'. — *Richard H. Pitcairn, DVM, PhD, author of 'Dr. Pitcairn's Complete Guide to Natural Health for Dogs and Cats' (Rodale Press).*

Contents

Contents

Acknowledgements

A great many people helped to put this book together. I am especially indebted to:

Nickie Murray, formerly Co-Director and Curator of the Dr Edward Bach Centre, and John Ramsell, currently Trustee-Curator and Managing Director, for their co-operation, general support and permission to use case studies from their files, and the right to reproduce *Ye Suffer From Yourselves* and *Free Thyself* by Dr. Edward Bach.

Leslie Kaslof for his wisdom, advice, encouragement, and pioneering of the Bach Flower Remedies in North America.

Ralph Kaslof for his commitment to the work.

Mary Hayden, Dr. Bach's sister and Evelyn Varney, his daughter, for sharing their memories and photographs.

Dr. Charles K. Elliott for his kind comments and foreword.

Dr. J. Herbert Fill for the introduction.

Andrewjohn and Eleni Clarke for their hospitality in the United Kingdom.

Deborah Mills for her meticulous typing.

I wish to deeply thank the many who responded to my letters and questionnaires, as well as those hundreds of people throughout the world who provided case studies, kind words and encouragement for the completion of this work.

The following, whom I warmly thank, have contributed in one way or another:

Anne Catherine, Didier and Georgette Basilios, Mark Blumenthal, Michael Bookbinder, Bruce Borland, Thomas Boyce, Mary Carter, Robert and Sharon Corr, Marsha DeMunnik, Sonny Delmonico, Leonard and Nilda Durany, Ron Eager, Gloria Early, Marilyn Preston Evans, Professor Norman R. Farnsworth, Marie Firestone, Demos Fotopoulos, Dr. Benjamin G. Girlando, Fred Hahn, Yvonne Hillman, Judy Howard, Celia Hunting, Jeanne

Janssen, Margie Kuyper, Stewart Lawson, Dr. Robert Leichtman, Sanna Longden, Linda Nardi, Robert Krell, Nancy Madsen, Marilyn Marcus, Dick and Rita Marsh, Molly Morgan, Malcolm Murray, Beverly Oldroyd, Ann Parker, Dr. Richard Pitcairn, Katherine Prezas, Victoria Pryor, Melanie Reinhart, Mary Rita, John-Roger, the Royal London Homoeopathic Hospital, London, England, Vera Rugg, George Santos, Sue Smith, Mrs. Spalding, Robert Stevens, Serita Stevens, the University College Hospital Medical School, London, England, Ginny Weissman, Bette, Eileen and Francis Wheeler, Ingrid Williams, and Jennifer Wright.

A special thank you to Bonnie Corso, Elinore Detiger, Faye Waisbrot Honor, Jack Honor, Bobbie Philip, and Lisa Sperling.

Most of all an exceptional acknowledgement to Sharon Steffensen for being the inspiration for this work.

Preface

During the past fifty years, many prominent medical doctors, homoeopaths,[1] and other health care professionals have reported the successful treatment of adult patients, children, and animals with the thirty-eight flower remedies discovered by the late Dr. Edward Bach.

Prepared from the flowers of wild plants, bushes, and trees, the Bach Flower Remedies do not directly treat physical disease, but help stabilize the emotional and psychological stresses reflecting the root cause. The stress factors include such things as fear, loneliness, worry, jealousy, and insecurity. Carried to the extreme, these emotions lower the body's natural resistance to disease. By assisting the integration of emotional, psychological, and physiological patterns, the remedies produce a soothing, calming effect, thereby allowing the body to heal itself.

These flower remedies are simple to use, and relatively inexpensive; moreover, they have reportedly been shown to be consistently effective when chosen correctly.

All thirty-eight of the Bach Flower Remedies have been included in the *Supplement to the Eighth Edition of the Homoeopathic Pharmacopeia of the United States*[2], and are officially recognized as homoeopathic drugs. This was primarily due to the efforts of Leslie J. Kaslof, author, researcher, and pioneer in the field of holistic health.

---

1. For editorial consistency the traditional spelling "homoeopathy" has been used wherever the word appears except when "homeopathy" (a more contemporary spelling) is used in a book's title.

2. Official compendium of homoeopathic drugs.

Most widely known of all the Bach remedies is the Rescue Remedy, a combination of five of the Bach flowers. Rescue Remedy is the emergency first aid remedy. It is extremely useful in many situations and generally works very quickly.

I first observed the effects of Rescue Remedy on a friend who was grieving over his father's death. So dramatic was his relief that I felt compelled to explore Bach's discoveries in more depth. Eventually, this led me on a four-month journey through the United Kingdom, where I came upon rare photographs, unpublished writings and letters of Dr. Bach's, all kindly supplied to me by his relatives and close friends.

I have been most impressed by the consistent reports of success in the use of Rescue Remedy, both in simple and complicated circumstances. These reports justify further investigation and controlled studies.

Though Rescue Remedy is called for in diverse circumstances, it is not a panacea or a replacement for orthodox medical care. It is used during minor stressful periods to develop emotional and psychological equilibrium, and during crisis situations, to ease emotional and psychological stress before and during emergency medical treatment. Many medical doctors, homoeopaths, other physicians and health care professionals throughout the world, carry the Rescue Remedy in their emergency kits or on their person for use in such circumstances.

The case studies contained in this book are authentic and based on extensive research and personal interviews. They illustrate, however, only a small part of the Rescue Remedy's versatility.

If only a few people obtain relief from their suffering and distress through the use of the Rescue Remedy, the purpose of this work will have been accomplished.

Gregory Vlamis
Chicago, Illinois
25 January 1986

Foreword

Dr. Edward Bach's (1886-1936) contribution to medicine—his system and philosophy known as the Bach Flower Remedies—provides us with an ideal of health beyond the absence of symptoms. True well-being comes from within. Like Hippocrates, Paracelsus, and Hahnemann, Bach knew that good health depended on spiritual, mental, and emotional factors being in harmony.

The effects of disharmony are shown by negative moods and thoughts that assail each of us at times. Bach understood that these, in turn, can affect the body, depleting it of strength and vitality by blocking the life force necessary to our existence at all levels. True healing—restoring harmony—opens up the channel for this vital flow of life.

Dr. Bach astutely noted that illness is ultimately beneficial and constitutes a period of true refinement and purification.

Heal Thyself, Bach's brilliant essay, published by C. W. Daniel, 1931, should be mandatory for every student of health. In it Bach states: "There is a factor which science is unable to explain on physical grounds, and that is why some people become affected by disease whilst others escape, although both classes may be open to the same possibility of infection. Materialism forgets that there is a factor above the physical plane which in the ordinary course of life protects or renders susceptible any particular individual with regard to disease, of whatever nature it may be."

Devoted and inspired research, coupled with Bach's unique background as a physician, pathologist, immunologist, and bacteriologist, led him to create one of the most comprehensive state-of-the-art systems of healing known, a gentle, simple system that works and is available to all.

3

The Bach Flower Remedies can be used with orthodox or complementary, alternative systems of medicine. Nature's wisdom is always added to any treatment employed. In ancient wisdom, medicine existed in closest communion with spiritual vision. Today, Dr. Edward Bach's holistic system embodies this ancient ideal.

Current scientific research is proving that a person's mental and emotional state can influence, positively or negatively, ills ranging from the common cold to cancer.

This new field of research, psychoneuroimmunology, is rapidly gaining the respect of the medical establishment. Mental states and emotions are now seriously considered in the total treatment of most illness.

I hope that progressive scientists examine the varied merits of the Bach Flower Remedies. Bach's philosophy of health offers us inner peace, harmony, and hope for the future.

Charles K. Elliott, MB, BCh,
MFHom, MRCGP, MLCO, AFOM RCP,
London; Former Physician to
Her Majesty Queen Elizabeth II

Introduction

I have been using the Bach Flower Remedies in my practice for over ten years and have found them, including the Rescue Remedy, invaluable when used correctly. I use them almost exclusively instead of tranquilizers and psychotropics, and in many cases they alleviate the problem when all else has failed. The Bach Flower Remedies are extremely sophisticated in their alleviation of specific moods, gentle and yet potent in balancing the body's subtle energy fields. Though subtle in their action, the Bach Flower Remedies are not placebos.

The Bach Flower Rescue Remedy deserves its special place in the Bach literature. Its action is unique, as the reader will discover in the subsequent pages. Until this present work, little has been made available on this subject.

In writing this book, Gregory Vlamis has produced a well-written summary for the professional as well as the general public. The reader is given practical information on how to use the Bach Flower Rescue Remedy in dealing with the crises of everyday life, from acute to chronic. *Flowers to the Rescue: The Healing Vision of Dr. Edward Bach* is easily readable and abundantly filled with case accounts, illustrating the great variety of applications of this amazing gift of nature. As a psychiatrist, I distinctly appreciate the preventive value of the Bach Flower Remedies and Rescue Remedy as a powerful and safe alternative to tranquilizers without their characteristic side effects.

It is my sincere wish that all, especially my colleagues and medical students, become aware of the Bach Flower Rescue Remedy and Bach's work in order to experience the remedy's efficacy and to confirm the insights of a modern medical genius.

With many people now losing faith in modern medicine, this is the right era for us to learn about this time-honored method of healing that uses preparations obtained from English wildflowers.

Thanks to the author, we have been given a valuable opportunity to become aware of a most precious adjunct to medicine. This book and the Bach Flower Rescue Remedy should be in every health care professional's armamentarium, in every home, vehicle, and first aid kit.

J. Herbert Fill, MD, psychiatrist;
former New York City Commissioner
of Mental Health; author of
The Mental Breakdown of a Nation
(New York: Franklin Watts, 1974)

PART I

Dr. Edward Bach:
Healing Pioneer

The spirit of Edward Bach lives in the lush green country-side of England—in the trees, plants, and flowers he used for his remedies.

Born on September 24, 1886, at Moseley, outside Birmingham, he was the eldest of three children.

Independent in outlook, even from his earliest years, Bach had a great sense of humor, which sustained him through many trials. As a child, he loved to meditate, and he often roamed the countryside alone, pausing just to sit and to contemplate the beauty of nature. As he grew, his love for nature and life developed into a great compassion for all living things, especially those in pain or distress. His overwhelming desire to help the suffering compelled him to become a physician.

Even before he began his medical studies, Bach observed that standard medical treatment was often more palliative than curative. He became convinced that there had to exist a simpler method of healing, one that could be applied to all diseases, including those regarded as chronic or incurable. He decided that he would search out those long-forgotten truths of the healing arts.

To accomplish this he sought medical training. In 1912, Bach obtained the Conjoint Diploma of MRCS, LRCP, and in 1913 he received his MB and BS[1] degrees from the Univer-

---

1. MRCS—Member Royal College of Surgeons; LRCP—Licentiate of the Royal College of Physicians; MB—Bachelor of Medicine; BS—Bachelor of Surgery.

Dr. Edward Bach, 1921. (Courtesy E. Varney)

sity College Hospital Medical School, London. In 1914, he received the Diploma of Public Health from Cambridge.

Though occasionally referred to as batch; his family, close friends and colleagues called him bache as in the letter H, meaning little one, petite, or dear. Today, most people, unaware of this specific pronunciation, commonly pronounce Bach as they would the name of the well-known musical composer.

In the early years of his practice, Bach became a respected pathologist, immunologist, and bacteriologist. Still, he was never satisfied with the results of orthodox medical treatment. Bach observed that although pills, drugs, and surgery were helpful in relieving specific symptoms, they did little to fight long-term and chronic disease. At this time, Bach set out to find and develop a treatment for the relief of chronic illness. In 1915 he accepted a position at University College Hospital as assistant bacteriologist. There he discovered that certain strains of intestinal bacteria had a specific relationship to the cause of chronic disorders. He began preparing vaccines from these bacteria. The results of his research exceeded all expectations.

Complaints such as arthritis and severe headaches were alleviated, and patients began to report remarkable improvements in their general health.

Pleased with these results but not with the side effects of vaccination, Bach searched for a method of treatment that would be gentle yet effective.

In 1919, after taking a position at London Homoeopathic Hospital, he discovered the works of Dr. Samuel Hahnemann, the founder of homoeopathy.[2] Bach found much of Hahnemann's philosophy similar to his own. It was similar to the same principles and philosophy which had inspired him from the beginning of his medical career. Hahnemann's concept—"treat the patient and not the disease"—was to become the basis of Bach's system of healing, a system he was to discover many years later.

Bach began preparing his bacterial vaccines homoeopathically and administered them orally. These oral vaccines, or nosodes, as they are called, seemed to fulfill all his

---

2. A system based on the theory and practice that disease is cured by remedies which produce in a healthy person effects similar to symptoms in the patient. The remedies are normally administered in minute or even infinitesimal doses, thus minimizing the potential for toxic side effects often found with the use of most allopathic drugs.

expectations.. Hundreds of chronic cases were treated, yielding exceptional results.

Welcomed enthusiastically by the medical profession, these vaccines became widely used, and they are still used today by homoeopaths and medical doctors in England, America, and Germany. Bach's works on intestinal toxemia appeared in the *Proceedings of the Royal Society of Medicine,*[3] 1919-1920, and in 1920-1921 additional works appeared in the *British Homoeopathic Journal.*[4] During his career, Bach contributed many other original articles to the British medical and homoeopathic journals. Of particular acclaim was his book *Chronic Disease: A Working Hypothesis* (London: H.K. Lewis & Co., Ltd., 1925), co-authored with Dr. C.W. Wheeler, his highly respected homoeopathic colleague.

Despite these successes, Bach was still not satisfied. He felt that by treating only physical disorders, he was overlooking the real issues of health and the cure of disease.

Disease, he concluded, was the result of disharmony between a person's physical and mental state; illness, the physical manifestation of negative states of mind. Bach noted that deep disharmony within the sufferer, such as worry, anxiety, and impatience, so depleted the individual's vitality that the body lost its natural resistance and became vulnerable to infection and other illnesses. Though Bach came to this understanding in his own right, it had been propounded in the past by such noted individuals as Hippocrates, Maimonides, and Paracelsus, and more recently substantiated by the research of Drs. Hans Selye, O. Carl Simonton, and many others working in the field of stress-related disorders. In light of the tranquillity and inner har-

---

3. "The Nature of Serum Antitrypsin and Its Relation to Autolysis and the Formation of Toxins," and "The Relation of the Autotryptic Titre of Blood to Bacteria Infection and Anaphylaxis," Teale, F.H. and Bach, E. *Proc. of the Royal Society of Medicine*, (13) December 2, 1919, pp. 5, 43, respectively.

4. "The Relation of Vaccine Therapy to Homoeopathy," and "A Clinical Comparison Between the Actions of Vaccines and Homoeopathic Remedies," *British Homoeopathic Journal*, 10:2 April 1920 p. 6, 11:1 January 1921 p. 21, respectively.

mony Bach always experienced when out in nature, he felt that the solution to disease-causing states was to be found among the plants, trees, and herbs of the field.

Obeying his intuition, which had proved successful in his earlier experiments, Bach decided to visit Wales in 1928.

There, by a mountain stream, he gathered the flowers of Impatiens (*Impatiens glandulifera*) and Mimulus (*Mimulus guttatus*). Later that year, he discovered the wild Clematis (*Clematis vitalba*). Preparations of these flowers were later administered to his patients, producing immediate and noteworthy results.

At this time, Dr. Edward Bach was at the height of his medical career. But in 1930, again following his inner conviction, Bach courageously closed his laboratory, left his London home, and spent his remaining years traveling throughout Wales and Southern England, perfecting his new system of medicine. Walking hundreds of miles in his search for curative plants, he discovered thirty-eight remedies—all, with one exception, derived from flowering plants and trees he found in the English countryside.

As his work progressed, he realized that his own senses were becoming more refined. For several days before he found a remedy, he would intensely experience the physical and mental symptoms of the disease that this remedy was to cure. Then he would go into the fields and find the appropriate healing flower. He could place a petal or flower in his palm or on his tongue and experience the effects of the plant on his mind and body. Coupled with extensive research and application, the newly found remedies proved extremely successful.

Bach immediately published his discoveries in the leading homoeopathic journals of the day. It was also his intention that this new system be made available to the lay person as well as to the professional community. Bach described his system of medicine in inexpensive booklets, the first three entitled *Heal Thyself*, *Free Thyself*, and the *Twelve Healers*. (See page 159 for references.)

Dr. F.J. Wheeler, a close friend and colleague, verified

Bach's findings by using many of the flower remedies in his own practice. He gave Bach valuable feedback and encouraged him to continue his research.

Bach treated many patients, particularly during the winter months, with his new remedies and his unique system of diagnosis. He developed a special love for the people of Cromer (Norfolk, East Anglia, England), where he settled and took up practice, feeling especially close to the fishermen and lifeboat men. What Bach most admired about these men was their 'down-to-earth' lives. Not caring for money, Bach often received gifts of fish, eggs, or vegetables in payment for his medical services.

It was at Cromer, during a terrible storm, that Bach first used three of the flowers found in the Rescue Remedy to aid an ailing crew member of a ship wrecked in the storm. Unconscious, foaming at the mouth, and almost frozen, the

The Bach Centre, Mount Vernon. (Courtesy Here's Health)

man seemed beyond hope. At repeated intervals, Dr. Bach moistened the patient's lips with the remedies as the unconscious fisherman was being carried up the beach to a nearby house. Within minutes, the patient regained consciousness.

Bach continued with his work in this small community until 1934 when, at Sotwell near Wallingford, Oxfordshire, England, he located a small house named Mount Vernon. Here he was to spend the final two years of his life.

Bach's humanity, as much as his genius, drew people to him. Believing that anyone who needed help or sought it for others should be given the tools for healing, he advertised his remedies in local newspapers. As a result, in 1936 the General Medical Council threatened to remove him from its register. In his reply, Dr. Bach wrote, "I consider it the duty and privilege of any physician to teach the sick and others how to help themselves....My advertisements were for the public good, which, I take it, is the work of our profession." Reconsidering its charge, the General Medical Council never did remove Dr. Bach's name from its register, and to this day Bach's work has been a major source of inspiration to doctors and the general public worldwide.

For further information on Dr. Bach's life, the reader is encouraged to consult *The Medical Discoveries of Edward Bach, Physician*, by Nora Weeks (London: C.W. Daniel, 1940), published in the United States by Keats, New Canaan, Connecticut, 1979.

The Work of Bach Continues

Following Dr. Bach's passing in 1936, Victor Bullen and Nora Weeks carried on his work at Mount Vernon. Nora, who during her years as trustee of the Bach Centre at Mount Vernon wrote *The Medical Discoveries of Edward Bach, Physician* was, along with Victor Bullen, mainly responsible for the growth of Bach's work until their respective deaths in 1978 and 1975.

Victor Bullen and Nora Weeks worked with Dr. Bach, carrying on his work at Mount Vernon, after Bach's passing in 1936. (Courtesy Bach Centre)

Nickie Murray and John Ramsell in the days when they worked together at the Bach Centre. (Courtesy Bach Centre)

In the early 1960s, Nickie Murray became closely acquainted with Nora Weeks and Victor Bullen, and was invited in 1970, along with her brother John Ramsell, to join them at the Bach Centre as their chosen successors. They both worked with Victor Bullen and Nora Weeks, and after Nora's passing continued on as equal partners in the Bach Flower Remedies Ltd. and as trustees and co-directors, with the same devotion and commitment as their predecessors.

In 1988 Nickie Murray severed her connection with the Bach Centre. John Ramsell, presently Trustee-Curator and Managing Director, then appointed Judy Howard, his daughter, to serve as Co-Director and Secretary.

During their walks about the country, Bach had taught Victor and Nora the names of every wildflower and every tree, saying, "You must recognize them by the leaves of their seedlings so that you can know them and make friends with them from their very beginning."

To this day, the Bach Flower Remedies are prepared exactly as Dr. Bach had done, taken from Bach's original wildflower locations. In addition to preparing the Bach remedies and overseeing appointed distributors in many parts of the world, the Dr. Edward Bach Centre answers inquiries from around the world and publishes *The Bach Remedy News Letter.*

Mount Vernon will always be the center of Dr. Bach's work. Before Bach departed, he made it a point to emphasize: "Though the work will ever increase, keep your life and the little house as it is, for simplicity is the keyword to this system of healing."

Dr. Edward Bach, c.1931-32. (Courtesy Bach Centre)

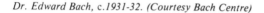

The Philosophy of Bach on Health and Disease

For many years, since he had come upon the works of Samuel Hahnemann, Bach had concentrated on "treating the patient, not the disease." His personal philosophy on health and disease was an important element in his discovery and development of the flower remedies.

Bach himself was deeply religious, believing all mankind was created in a state of perpetual Unity with God. Man's Soul—the real Self—is most directly connected to the Creator and ever leads man to a higher good. Although the physical body is temporary, the soul is everlasting. Moreover, the soul infuses and guides the personality, comprising the mind and the body as a whole.

Dr. Bach also believed that each person has a mission in life. He wrote:

> "...this divine mission means no sacrifice, no retiring from the world, no rejecting of the joys and beauty of nature; on the contrary, it means a fuller and greater enjoyment of all things; it means doing the work we love to do with all our heart and soul whether it be housekeeping, farming, painting, acting or serving our fellow-man in shops or houses. This work, whatever it may be, if we love it above all else, is the definite command of our soul."

Taking this idea a step further, Bach defined health as perfect harmony between the soul, mind, and body. Disease, then, results from a lack of harmony between these elements.

When we do not follow the dictates of our soul by following our intuition—our knowledge of "good"—disease develops in our body as a result of our resistance. This resistance occurs, "when we allow others to interfere with our purpose in life, and implant in our minds doubt, or fear, or indifference." Emotions such as fear and anger, as well as cruelty and rigidity of thought, surface when we are diverted from the soul's purpose, and, consequently, from the personality's true development.

But disease, according to Bach, is paradoxically a healing process because it warns us against carrying our wrong actions too far. Once disease has manifested itself, we must modify our erring mental state and bring it back into line with the convictions of our soul, if we are to be healed. When this realignment begins, so does the physical healing; and both will continue until mind and soul are again in tune and the body is well.

Thus, Bach argued that disease is not an evil, but a blessing in disguise whose purpose is "solely and purely corrective." Indeed, the area where we have physical difficulties is a mirror of our mental difficulties. Bach wrote:

> "If you suffer from stiffness of joint or limb, you can be equally certain that there is stiffness in your mind; that you are rigidly holding on to some idea...which you should not have. If you suffer from asthma, you are in someway stifling another personality; or from lack of courage to do right, smothering yourself....The body will reflect the true cause of disease such as fear, indecision, doubt—in the disarrangement of its systems and tissues."

Complete healing Bach said, depended on four factors:

• The realization of the Divinity within us, and our consequent knowledge that we have the ability to overcome all harm.

• The knowledge that disease is due to disharmony between our personality and our soul.

• Our desire and ability to discover the fault that is causing the conflict.

• The removal of that fault by our developing the opposing virtue.

Over and over again, Bach emphasized that if we want to return to health, we must expect change. Disease was not to be conquered by direct fighting, since "darkness is removed by light, not by greater darkness." To help us make the necessary changes in our personalities, he urged that we learn to replace our weaknesses with strengths, such as substituting acceptance for intolerance.

Bach realized, of course, that "certain maladies may be caused by direct physical means, such as those associated with some poisons, accidents, and injuries, and gross excesses; but disease in general is due to some basic error in our constitution—the conflict of personality and soul..."we have so long blamed the germ, the weather, the food we eat as the causes of disease; but many of us are immune in an influenza epidemic; many love the exhilaration of a cold wind and many can eat cheese and drink black coffee late at night with no ill effects. Nothing in nature can hurt us when we are happy and in harmony."

Believing that physical disease manifested as a result of negative mental and emotional states, Bach opposed those aspects of modern medicine that directed efforts only toward the healing of the physical. He felt that drugs were often counter-productive because the temporary relief they produced in many instances suggested a complete return to health while negative mental and emotional patterns continued unchecked. True healing was postponed, and the inevitable result was more serious illness later on.

When Bach developed his flower remedies, his aim was to effect a healing on a much deeper level than just the physical. Bach, referring to the remedies once wrote:

"they are able...to raise our very natures, and bring us nearer to our Souls.... They cure, not by attacking disease, but by flooding our bodies with the beautiful vibrations of our Higher Nature in the presence of which disease melts as snow in the sunshine."

As a physician, Bach believed that doctors should play the part of adviser and counselor to a patient, providing guidance and insight. The patient must come to realize that he has responsibility for his own healing. He must be prepared to face the truth that his illness was caused by faults that lie within himself, and he must have the desire to rid himself of those faults.

One of the unique advantages of the Bach Flower Remedies is that they can be applied before the first signs of physical illness, thereby preventing disease before it takes hold in the body. Bach noted that "before almost all [serious] complaints there is usually a time of not being quite fit, or a bit run down; that is the time to treat our conditions, get fit and stop things going further." Even a temporary state of conflict between the personality and soul may render the body susceptible to infectious agents that are ready to attack when the body's normal defenses are weak.

A more in-depth explanation on Dr. Bach's Philosophy can be found in *Heal Thyself,* by Edward Bach (London: C.W. Daniel, 1931), and in *The Bach Flower Remedies,* by Drs. Edward Bach and F.J. Wheeler (New Canaan, Connecticut: Keats, 1977). Previously unavailable philosophical writings, *Ye Suffer From Yourselves* and *Free Thyself* are included in appendices A & B.

The Thirty-eight Bach Flower Remedies

The following chapter provides an overview of the various conditions and situations to which all thirty-eight of the Bach Flower Remedies apply.

Additional information on the use of the entire thirty-eight remedies, may also be found, either in *The Twelve Healers and Other Remedies*, by Edward Bach (London: CW. Daniel, 1933) or in *The Bach Flower Remedies* (New Canaan, Connecticut: Keats, 1977).

Since 1936, the thirty-eight flower remedies discovered by Dr. Bach have been used to restore emotional and psychological equilibrium to individuals during periods of both mild and intense stress. Within his system, Bach classified the following seven major emotional and psychological states:

- **FEAR**
- **UNCERTAINTY**
- **INSUFFICIENT INTEREST IN PRESENT CIRCUMSTANCES**
- **LONELINESS**
- **OVERSENSITIVE TO INFLUENCES AND IDEAS**
- **DESPONDENCY OR DESPAIR**
- **OVERCARE FOR THE WELFARE OF OTHERS.**

Within every classification, he described their variations.

The following is a brief summary of all the thirty-eight Bach Flower Remedies and their uses. These are listed within their appropriate categories. This list is not intended as a definitive explanation of all the Bach remedies and their uses. For further information consult the references listed above.

1. FEAR

*Rock Rose (*Helianthemum nummularium*) for extreme terror, panic, hysteria, fright, and nightmares.

*Mimulus (*Mimulus guttatus*) for known fears; for example, fear of heights, pain, darkness, poverty, death, being alone, of other people, etc. Also for timidity and shyness.

Cherry Plum (*Prunus cerasifera*) for fear of losing mental and physical control; inclination to uncontrollable rages and impulses, with fear of causing harm to oneself or others, for example suicidal tendencies,** or losing one's temper.

Aspen (*Populus tremula*) for vague fears and anxieties of unknown origin, a sense of foreboding, apprehension, or impending disaster.

Red Chestnut (*Aesculus carnea*) for excessive fear or overconcern for others—especially loved ones, for example; overconcern during their illness, automobile trips, etc., always anticipating that something unfortunate may happen to them.

2. UNCERTAINTY

*Cerato (*Ceratostigma willmottianum*) for those who doubt their own ability to judge and make decisions. They are constantly seeking others advice and are often misguided.

---

*One of the original twelve healers.

**The Bach Flower Remedies and Rescue Remedy are not meant to take the place of emergency medical treatment. In all cases requiring psychiatric or medical attention, a licensed physician should be called immediately.

*Scleranthus (*Scleranthus annuus*) for those who are indecisive, being unable to decide between two choices, first one seeming right then the other. They may also be subject to energy or mood swings.

*Gentian (*Gentianella amarella*) for those easily discouraged, in whom even small delays may cause hesitation, despondency and self-doubt.

Gorse (*Ulex europaeus*) for feelings of despair, hopelessness, and futility.

Hornbeam (*Carpinus betulus*) for that Monday-morning feeling of not being able to face the day; for tiredness and a tendency towards procrastination; for those who feel that some part of their bodies or minds need strengthening.

Wild Oat (*Bromus ramosus*) for those dissatisfied in their current career or life style, their difficulty however, is in determining exactly what career to follow.

3. INSUFFICIENT INTEREST IN PRESENT CIRCUMSTANCES

*Clematis (*Clematis vitalba*) for those who tend toward escapism living more in the future than in the present; for lack of concentration, daydreaming, lack of interest in present circumstances, and spaciness.

Honeysuckle (*Lonicera caprifolium*) for those dwelling too much in the past, reminiscing about the "good old days;" nostalgia, and homesickness.

Wild Rose (*Rosa canina*) for those who are apathetic and have resigned themselves to their circumstances, making little effort to improve things or to find joy.

Olive (*Olea europaea*) for total mental and physical exhaustion and weariness; for sapped vitality from a long illness or personal ordeal.

White Chestnut (*Aesculus hippocastanum*) for persistent, unwanted thoughts, mental arguments, or preoccupation with some worry or episode.

Mustard (*Sinapis arvensis*) for deep gloom that comes on for no apparent reason, bringing sudden melancholy and heavy sadness.

Chestnut Bud (*Aesculus hippocastanum*) for those who fail to learn from experience, continually repeating the same patterns and mistakes.

4. LONELINESS

*****Water Violet** (*Hottonia palustris*) for those whose preference is to be alone; seemingly aloof, proud, reserved, self-reliant, sometimes 'superior' in attitude. Capable and reliable they will advise, but not get 'personally' involved in others affairs.

*****Impatiens** (*Impatiens glandulifera*) for those quick in thought and action but often impatient, especially with those who are slower than they; for those who show irritability through lack of patience.

Heather (*Calluna vulgaris*) for those talkative persons who constantly seek the companionship of anyone who will listen to their troubles. They are self-absorbed, generally poor listeners, and have difficulty being alone for any length of time.

5. OVERSENSITIVITY TO INFLUENCES AND IDEAS

*****Agrimony** (*Agrimonia eupatoria*) for those not wishing to burden others with their troubles, covering up their suffering with a cheerful facade; they often seek escape from pain and worry through the use of drugs or alcohol.

*****Centaury** (*Centaurium umbellatum*) for those who have difficulty in saying no, often becoming subservient in their desire to serve others; anxious to please they can be easily exploited, neglecting their own interests.

Walnut (*Juglans regia*) for stabilizing emotions during periods of transition, such as teething, puberty, adolescence, and menopause; for breaking past links and adjusting to new beginnings, such as new jobs, adjusting to new residence, cultures, or even relationships.

Holly (*Ilex aquifolium*) for negative feelings such as envy, jealousy, suspicion, revenge, and hatred; for all states showing a need for more love.

6. DESPONDENCY OR DESPAIR

Larch (*Larix decidua*) for those who, despite being capable, lack self-confidence. Anticipating failure, they often do not make a real effort to succeed.

Pine (*Pinus sylvestris*) for those not satisfied with their own efforts, who are self-reproachful and suffer much from guilt and the faults they attach to themselves, feeling they should or could have done better. They are often quick to blame themselves for the mistakes of others.

Elm (*Ulmus procera*) for those who over extend themselves and become overwhelmed and burdened by their responsibilities.

Sweet Chestnut (*Castanea sativa*) for those who feel they have reached the limits of their endurance; for dark despair, when the anguish seems to be unbearable.

Star of Bethlehem (*Ornithogalum umbellatum*) for mental and emotional stress during and following such traumatic experiences as grief, loss and accidents.

Willow (*Salix vitellina*) for those who have suffered from some misfortune or circumstance they feel was unjust or unfair. As a result, they become resentful and bitter toward others.

Oak (*Quercus robur*) for those who despite illness and adversity never give up. They are brave and determined to overcome all obstacles in order to reach their intended goal.

Crab Apple (*Malus pumila*) for feelings of shame, uncleanliness, or fear of contamination; for poor self-image, particularly as it relates to parts of or growths on the body. Will assist in detoxification and the cleansing of wounds, both internal and external.

7. OVERCARE FOR WELFARE OF OTHERS

*__Chicory__ (*Cichorium intybus*) for those who are overfull of care and possessive of those close to them; they can be demanding and self-pitying, with a need for others to conform to their ideals.

*__Vervain__ (*Verbena officinalis*) for those who have strong opinions, always teaching and philosophizing. They are easily incensed by injustices, and when taken to the extreme can be overenthusiastic, argumentative, and overbearing.

Vine (*Vitis vinifera*) for those who are strong-willed leaders in their own right. However, when carried to extremes, they can become autocratic, dictatorial, ruthless, and dominating.

Beech (*Fagus sylvatica*) for those who, while desiring perfection, easily find fault with people and things. Critical and intolerant at times, they may fail to see the good within others, overreacting to small annoyances or other people's idiosyncrasies.

Rock Water (*Aqua petra*) for those who are strict and rigid with themselves in their daily living. They are hard masters to themselves, struggling toward some ideal or to set an example for others. This would include strict adherence to a life style or to religious, personal, or social disciplines.

PART II

The cure of the part should not be attempted without treatment of the whole. No attempt should be made to cure the body without the soul, and, if the head and the body are to be healthy, you must begin by curing the mind.... For this is the great error of our day in the treatment of the human body, that physicians first separate the soul from the body.

Plato (427-347 B.C.) *Charmides*

Rescue Remedy: Bach's Emergency Medicine

R escue Remedy was named by Dr. Bach for its calming and stabilizing effect on the emotions during a crisis.

The following chapter describes the composition of Rescue Remedy, its historical origin, its scope of application, and use.

Rescue Remedy is made up of the following five Bach Flower Remedies.

*Impatiens (*Impatiens glandulifera*) for the impatience, irritability, and agitation often accompanying stress. This may sometimes result in muscle tension and pain.

*Clematis (*Clematis vitalba*) for unconsciousness, spaciness, faintness, and out-of-the-body sensations, which often accompany trauma.

*Rock Rose (*Helianthemum nummularium*) for terror, panic, hysteria, and great fear.

Cherry Plum (*Prunus cerasifera*) for fear of losing mental or physical control.

Star of Bethlehem (*Ornithogalum umbellatum*) for trauma, both mental and physical.

Dr. Bach first used three (Rock Rose, Clematis and Impatiens) of the five ingredients in the Rescue Remedy with two men shipwrecked in a gale off the beach at Cromer on

---

*One of the original twelve healers.

the Norfolk coast of England, where Bach did much of his work. The men had lashed themselves to the mast of their wrecked barge and survived for five hours in a howling gale before a lifeboat could reach them. The younger man was almost frozen, delirious, and foaming at the mouth. Dr. Bach ran into the water, meeting the rescuers, and began to apply these remedies to the man's lips. Even before the sailor could be stripped of his wet clothes and wrapped in a blanket, his relief became apparent as he sat up and began conversing. After a few days of hospital rest, he had recovered completely. Bach later combined the remedies Cherry Plum and Star of Bethlehem, for their particular virtues, to the first three remedies, thereby completing the formula we know today as the Rescue Remedy.

Using the Rescue Remedy

Rescue Remedy is available in both liquid concentrate and cream form. It can be used alone or in combination with any other of the Bach Flower Remedies. In addition, it has been deemed effective when used with other remedial agents and various therapeutic modalities such as chiropractic, dentistry, and massage. As reported in the case studies, Rescue Remedy has been shown to be non-toxic, non-habit-forming, and free from side effects. However, it should be noted that **Rescue Remedy is not meant to be a panacea or a substitute for emergency medical treatment.** In serious situations such as accidents, a doctor or ambulance should be called immediately. Many times during emergencies, however, before qualified medical assistance can arrive, the sufferer may experience a variety of emotional and psychological disturbances. These can include fear, panic, severe mental stress, and tension. Rescue Remedy used during this critical period, has been reported to significantly assist in stabilizing the victim emotionally until help arrives.

Additionally, Rescue Remedy is reported to have a positive calming and stabilizing effect in a broad range of stressful situations including nervousness, anxiety, and the stress arising from bereavement, great fright, hysteria, anguish, and desperation.

Even minor incidents that cause stress, such as arguments, exams, speeches, and job interviews, are made easier with Rescue Remedy.

Application

1. Place four drops of Rescue Remedy concentrate into a quarter glass of liquid.

2. Sip every three to five minutes or as often as necessary. Hold in mouth a moment before swallowing.

If water or other beverages are not available:

1. Rescue Remedy may be taken directly from the concentrate bottle (dilute if alcohol-sensitive) by placing four drops under the tongue. Drops may also be added to a spoonful of water if desired.

2. Hold liquid in mouth a moment before swallowing.

For those unable to drink:

• Rub the remedy directly from the concentrate bottle on the lips, behind the ears, or on the wrists.

NOTE: Rescue Remedy, as with all Bach Flower Remedies, assists in restoring emotional balance. Once balance is achieved, the need for and the effect of the remedy diminishes. Therefore, no discernible effect will be noticed if a person takes Rescue Remedy when he is not distressed.

External Use

Rescue Remedy cream is prepared in a neutral, homoeopathic, non-allergenic and non-abrasive cream base. It has been reported extremely effective when applied to bruises, bumps, sprains, scratches, hemorrhoids, minor burns, insect bites, and minor inflammations. It has also been reported useful in healing minor cuts when applied directly. Using the liquid Rescue Remedy orally, in conjunction with Rescue Remedy cream, will help ease emotional upset associated with any of the above conditions. **If Rescue Remedy cream is unavailable the liquid may also be applied externally with equal effectiveness, especially for painful blows, minor burns, sprains, etc.** In addition, the cream rubbed on is said to be effective in reducing acute muscle stiffness. To use:

• Apply by smoothing gently into the affected area, or by applying on a piece of gauze to wounds or abrasions. Use as often as required, continuing applications for a short time even after the condition has improved.

Veterinary Use

Mix four drops of Rescue Remedy in an animal's drinking water or food. In the case of large animals such as cows and horses, ten drops to a bucket of water have been reported to be greatly beneficial in those conditions calling for the use of Rescue Remedy. Examples include accidents, pre- and postsurgical conditions, and birthings. If an animal is traumatized or unconscious, Rescue Remedy may be used directly from the concentrate bottle or diluted in a small glass of water and rubbed on and in the mouth or beak, behind the ears, or on other soft points of the body.

Plant Use

Researchers, such as Cleve Backster, as reported in the book *The Secret Life of Plants*, by Peter Tompkins and Christopher Bird (New York: Harper & Row, 1973), have shown plants to be affected by environmental stimuli, as well as interrelations between them and other forms of life. It comes as no surprise, then, that the Rescue Remedy has also been used to ease trauma in transplanted botanicals, drooping flowers, and injured trees. Ten drops in a watering can or sprayer, applied regularly for a day or two, will help reduce the very real shock that plants can experience and help revitalize them. In the vegetable garden, the addition of five to ten drops in the water at planting time or at any other point in the growing season has been reported of benefit to crops.

Case Studies: Professional and Consumer Use

The following case studies have been meticulously compiled and researched by the author over a three-year period. Because of the highly personal and sensitive nature of these accounts, measures were taken to protect the privacy of individual contributors using the Rescue Remedy at home. This was accomplished by listing only their city, state, or country in place of personal names. Additionally, personal consumer reports were edited when necessary, for grammatical consistency and clarity; still remaining true to the intent and experience originally described. Subsequently, quotation marks have not been included in any of the personal consumer case reports.

Wherever cases involving the professional use of Rescue Remedy appear, names of the contributing doctors or health care professionals are included, along with the names of their cities, states, or countries reported to us at the time.

All professional testimonies and case studies appear here with the full knowledge and written consent of the contributing doctors and health practitioners. Except for minor grammatical changes, indicated by editors brackets[ ] these testimonies and case studies appear verbatim.

All case studies included in this book were obtained through personal interviews, questionnaires, and letters from contributors in the United States and abroad. In addition, the Bach Centre's newsletter files were consulted and used.

NOTE: Rescue Remedy is not meant to take the place of emergency medical treatment. In all instances requiring proper medical attention, a competent physician should be notified at once.

Cases where only the name of a country was available, were primarily extracted from published Bach Centre newsletters.

It should be noted that while many of the case studies included here are impressive, they are meant only to serve as a reference—not to sensationalize or make unfounded claims of efficacy for the Rescue Remedy.

From the hundreds of reports available, every effort was made to present the reader a balanced representation of cases. Though great attention was paid to categorizing these case studies, some overlapping occurs.

Professional Testimonies

The following is a compilation of professional reports on the use of Rescue Remedy both in the United States and abroad. Highly valued, Rescue Remedy is clearly an important healing tool, used by physicians as well as by many other health care professionals worldwide.

All testimonies, as well as professional case studies and consumer reports appear in arbitrary order in their respective sections and categories.

Professional use and reports on Rescue Remedy are prolific; though seeming extensive, the statements presented here represent only a fraction of its overall use.

Physicians practicing in the United Kingdom often have numerous titles and credentials; wherever these references appear in the text, the style of the British Medical Journal was followed, whereby only the two highest medical degrees are listed. While there are many medical doctors (MD's) practicing in the United Kingdom, many British physicians have distinguishing credentials other than MD. Ninety-eight percent of the British testimonials and case studies included in this book were written by practicing physicians of one degree or another. Since all professional credentials are abbreviated, the following glossary has been included to clarify their meaning.

AFOM	—Associate Faculty Occupational Medicine (UK)
BAc	—Bachelor of Acupuncture (UK)
BAO	—Bachelor of the Art of Obstetrics (UK)
BCh	—Bachelor of Surgery (UK)
BChir	—Bachelor of Surgery (UK)
BS	—Bachelor of Surgery (UK)
BVetMed	—Bachelor of Veterinary Medicine (UK)
CA	—Certified Acupuncturist (USA)
ChB	—Bachelor of Surgery (UK)
DC	—Doctor of Chiropractic (USA & UK)
DCH	—Diploma in Child Health (UK)
DDS	—Doctor of Dental Surgery (USA & UK)
DM	—Doctor of Medicine (same as MD) (UK)
DN	—Doctor of Naprapathy (USA)
DPH	—Diploma in Public Health (UK)
DO	—Doctor of Osteopathy (Different Lic.Requirements in USA & UK)
DObst RCOG	—Diploma Royal College Obstetricians and Gynaecologists (UK)
DVM	—Doctor of Veterinary Medicine (USA)
DVSM	—Doctor of Veterinary Surgery and Medicine (UK)
FRCP	—Fellow Royal College of Physicians (UK)
LRCP	—Licentiate Royal College of Physicians (UK)
LRCS	—Licentiate Royal College of Surgeons (UK)
MB	—Bachelor of Medicine (UK)
MD	—Medical Doctor (USA & UK)
MFHom	—Member Faculty of Homoeopathy (UK)
MLCO	—Member London College of Osteopathy (UK)
MRCP	—Member Royal College of Physicians (UK)
MRCGP	—Member Royal College of General Practitioners (UK)
MRCS	—Member Royal College of Surgeons (UK)
MRCVS	—Member Royal College of Veterinary Surgeons (UK)
ND	—Naturopathic Doctor (USA & UK)
PhD	—Doctor of Philosophy (USA & UK)
(UK)	—United Kingdom
(USA)	—United States of America

"As a healer I choose to use only those systems of healing that prove themselves to be effective in my work. It is well known by all people of knowledge that disease begins on a much deeper level than the physical. This, great men have taught for thousands of years. One such man in our time was the English physician and scientist Dr. Edward Bach, who not only taught this truth but became a great herbalist, discovering those special plants and healing waters which work on this deepest of levels. His system is respected and known as the Bach Flower Remedies.

"I have used these Bach remedies and the combination Rescue Remedy for over eight years and have found them to be gentle but powerful healing medicines. Emotional upsets ranging from the deepest fear to pride and jealousy are gently resolved within and scattered like the dust in a wind. We would not want to be without the Rescue Remedy for emergencies. Hysteria and grief, or the trauma resulting from accidents, are quickly stabilized by the oral administration of Rescue Remedy and, when required, the topical use of the cream. It will even soothe the minor upsets of the child who is crying and irritable.

"Though there are many healing tools for good, Dr. Bach's combination, Rescue Remedy, is one of the finest for emergencies and trauma. I strongly encourage all people, those who have pets and range animals, and especially those with children, to keep the Rescue Remedy at home or on their person, for emergencies happen when they are least expected."

Sun Bear, medicine chief,
Bear Tribe, Spokane, Washington

"I use the Bach remedies extensively in my practice. They have proven very helpful with patients wishing to clarify issues in their minds, develop their potential, and see the positive qualities within themselves.

"Rescue Remedy is very useful in calming children who are having temper tantrums, and it alleviates their apprehension when they have to get shots. I also use it with good results for the fears and anxieties that patients experience in my office.

"I keep Rescue Remedy in my car, in my house, and in every room of my office. I even take it myself when I have a hard schedule."

G.S. Khalsa, MD,
Lathrup Village, Michigan

"The Bach Flower Remedies are underused in practice and are long overdue to be researched. I have found them extremely useful in a large number of cases. I would use Rescue Remedy without hesitation in any acute situation in addition to any other appropriate measure indicated by the circumstance."

Julian Kenyon, MD, director,
Center for Alternative Therapies,
Southampton, England

"In my experiences at the Old London Homoeopathic Hospital, now the Royal London Homoeopathic Hospital, I have found Rescue Remedy and the Bach Flower Remedy, Star of Bethlehem to be of great value."

Margery G. Blackie, MD,
former Physician to
Her Majesty Queen Elizabeth II;
author of *The Patient: Not the Cure*
(London: Macdonald & Janes, 1979;
also published in the USA by
Woodbridge Press, 1978)

"In my practice, I treat the whole person but specialize in skin and allergic diseases. I have seen many older, despondent patients sit around and scratch themselves almost raw. With kindness, patience, and the use of the Bach remedies, especially Rescue Remedy, many of these people have been remarkably helped without the use of lotions and drugs."

James Q. Gant Jr., MD,
Washington, D.C.

"I always carry Rescue Remedy in my purse. You never know when an emergency may arise and you will need it."

Maesimund Panos, MD,
Tipp City, Ohio;
former president, National Center for
Homeopathy, Washington, D.C.;
co-author of *Homeopathic Medicine at Home*
(Los Angeles, California: Tarcher, 1981)

"I have used the Bach Flower Remedies for over thirty years and have found them, especially the Rescue Remedy, to be of great value in my practice. I recommend that everybody carry the Rescue Remedy, as one never knows when it may be needed in an emergency. Dr. Bach made a great contribution to the world; he was indeed an absolute medical genius. The Bach Flower Remedies are a missing key to the new medicine of the future."

Aubrey Westlake, MB, BChir,
Fordingbridge, Hampshire, England;
president of The Psionic Medicine Society;
author of *The Pattern of Health*
(London: Shambhala Press, 1961)

"The Rescue Remedy is a very useful first aid remedy when used for acute crises, anxieties, and fears. I have often been surprised at the good results it has achieved when other measures have failed. I consider the Bach Flower Remedies a major contribution to medicine."

Robin G. Gibson, FRCP, DCH,
consultant physician to the
Glasgow Homoeopathic Hospital,
Glasgow, Scotland

"I have used the Rescue Remedy for myself and my family, as I prefer this type of 'trial' prior to deciding if a treatment is appropriate for my professional use. I have found Rescue Remedy extremely effective in relieving a wide variety of acute emotional stresses. I have also found the Rescue Remedy cream equally valuable when applied topically to bruises, bumps, sprains, swellings, etc."

Richard E. Behymer, MD,
Camptonville, California

"I would like to say how marvelous the Rescue Remedy is, both in cream and liquid form. I always carry them both with me. It never ceases to amaze me how well they work. I recommend it to many of my patients and am always hearing of its good results."

Nicola M. Hall, principal,
The Bayly School of Reflexology,
Worcester, England

"I have had amazing results, both with the individual Bach Flower Remedies and especially with Rescue Remedy. I've seen the Rescue Remedy used on people who have had accidents as well as other traumatic experiences. It works almost instantly to calm them down, and when either the Rescue Remedy liquid or cream is applied directly on the affected area, it quickly reduces any swelling or trauma there."

Eugene C. Watkins, ND,
Southfield, Michigan

"I find the Bach Flower Remedies very effective in treating anxiety, depression, mental upsets, and emotional problems. I use them in combination with other homoeopathic medicines and dietary modifications when called for, especially in cases of hyperactivity in children."

S.J.L. Mount, MB, MRCP,
former consultant to the
Royal London Homoeopathic Hospital,
London, England; medical consultant to the
London Natural Health Clinic, London, England;
author of *The Food and Health of Western Man*
(New York: John Wiley and Son, 1971)

"In my practice I often use a technique that treats imbalances of the temporal mandibular joint in the jaw. With most people, there is usually tremendous emotional tension stored in this area, and during treatment a patient may bring emotions to a conscious level. One dose of Rescue Remedy usually has an immediate and profound calming effect on them."

Gerald Brady, DC,
St. Paul, Minnesota

"I use the Rescue Remedy frequently, particularly for acute wounds such as cuts, bruises, swellings, etc. It works almost immediately to calm the system and take away nausea, faintness, or hysteria. It is also very useful during acute asthma attacks. The remedy quiets the patient almost immediately. I have also used it for morning sickness in pregnant women and in many cases of animal injury, especially with birds that fly into glass doors or windows. However, it should not be counted on as the only means of treatment, but as an aid to remove panic and trauma, giving the physician time to prepare for more specific procedures."

James E. Williams, CA,
DelMar, California

"I use quite a lot of Rescue Remedy for myself and my patients. Anyone who uses it while under pressure and stress will find that it works far better than any tranquillizer."

Elizabeth Ogden, LRCPI, LRCSI,
Dublin, Ireland

"In my experience I have seen positive results from the use of the Bach Flower Remedies, including Rescue Remedy, and feel that they definitely merit further investigation."

Jonathan Shore, MD,
Mill Valley, California

"We use a great deal of Rescue Remedy, both the liquid and cream, and find that the liquid, taken internally, helps to reduce emotional upsets, while the cream hastens the healing of conditions ranging from cuts to scalds; we also massage the cream into painful joints to alleviate discomfort. We find all the Bach remedies, especially the Rescue Remedy, to be invaluable in our work here, and would not want to be without them."

Beryl James, physical therapist,
The Roy Morris Clinic,
Oswestry and Wigan, England

"I am a volunteer in a local hospice program [a place where terminally ill people can go to spend their last days, without the use of life-support systems], and Rescue Remedy really comes in handy for the families I deal with. I give it to people who are going through emotional or physical difficulties, and it always makes them feel better."

B.J.D.,
San Antonio, Texas

"I use the Bach Flower Remedies quite extensively in my practice. Most patients tell me that within the first few days of taking the remedies they feel a greater sense of emotional balance. I find the Rescue Remedy as useful with my own family as with my patients. Any time there is a trauma, it will often calm a person down to the point where nothing else is needed. Rescue Remedy liquid is also extremely useful in dealing with grief, emotional upset, or when one is nervous or off-center.

"I have also used the Rescue Remedy cream for sprains, muscle strains, bruises, bumps, and minor burns and find it to be remarkably effective in reducing the pain, swelling, and inflammation of these conditions. I recommend that Rescue Remedy be in everyone's first aid kit. It's easy to use, inexpensive and produces no toxic side effects."

Kirby Hotchner, DO,
Des Moines, Iowa

"The most useful treatment for trauma that I know is Dr. Bach's Rescue Remedy. It is [an] invaluable first aid (along with proper medical treatment) for the victims of accidents, [and for] injuries [and] fright—especially in children—or [in] sudden bad news. The liquid comes in a handy little dropper bottle which [practically] lives in my bag. I also keep a bottle in my car [for similar situations]."

> **Barbara Griggs,** London, England;
> author of *The Home Herbal: A Handbook
> of Simple Remedies* (London: Pan, 1983;
> originally published by Jill Norman &
> Hobhouse, Ltd., 1982); and *Green
> Pharmacy: A History of Herbal Medicine*
> (London: Jill Norman & Hobhouse Ltd., 1981;
> also published by Viking Press, New York, 1981)

"I recommend that Rescue Remedy be kept on hand especially during childbirth, both for the mother and those attending. I have found it extremely valuable for relieving tension in a crisis. Rescue Remedy is an absolute must, used in childbirth, especially if there's a long labour or if forceps are used. In addition, Rescue Remedy can also be used for the newborn to assist with the trauma of the birth experience. It can be rubbed on the wrists, temples, scalp, or navel area."

> **Lorraine Taylor,** BAc,
> Oxford,England

"I use the Rescue Remedy as an alternative to prescribing Valium. It sometimes proves to be of invaluable assistance."

> **D. McGavin,** MRCGP, DCH,
> Maidstone, Kent, England

"Of the various remedies and techniques used in this office, none are more valued and respected than the Bach remedies."

> **Nicholas Ashfield,** DC,
> Toronto, Canada

"I find the Rescue Remedy very useful in calming and assisting patients, particularly during the transitional effects of strong treatment procedures. We often use Rescue Remedy during extensive cranial work and in other mechanical adjustments.

"I feel that Rescue Remedy helps to minimize the physiological, mental, and emotional stress that often accompanies manipulative procedures. It is an important adjunct for the doctor as well as facilitating the patient's healing response."

Joseph Unger Jr., DC,
St. Louis, Missouri

"I use Rescue Remedy with elderly patients who live alone; it seems to assist them in handling their lives more effectively. When these patients face a task they must struggle with, Rescue Remedy calms and stabilizes them quite effectively. I recommend Rescue Remedy for use in the later years and to calm and stabilize in all forms of stress."

Hilda Saenz de Deas, BAc,
Oxford, England

"I have used the Bach Flower Remedies in my clinical practice for over twenty-five years and have had very good results, especially in conjunction with other modalities. In raising my own family of four boys, my wife and I found that certain remedies were very helpful indeed."

Brian K. Youngs, ND, DO,
Harrow, England

"I have used the Bach remedies regularly for over ten years, both personally and with patients. They have certainly proven their healing powers in accidents and for functional ailments and skin conditions."

K.J. Noblett, MB, ChB,
Blackpool, England

"I have used Rescue Remedy extensively in my chiropractic work, especially with patients in acute pain as a result of emotional distress. It helps amazingly in enabling patients to focus, listen to instructions, and relax— allowing the healing process to evolve. I have used [Rescue Remedy] personally in times of emotional crisis and have given it to my dog when she has been sick, always with positive results. It definitely allows for a calming and recentering, and I would be lost without it.

"Rescue Remedy cream has also been quite helpful in speeding the healing of abrasions and contusions as well as in relieving the joint pain of arthritis and bursitis in the acute phases. I use it automatically with my other modalities, like ultrasound and galvanic currents, in order to work it into the deeper tissues."

Barbara Dorf, DC,
Culver City, California

"I have been using the Bach Flower Remedies, including Rescue Remedy, for quite some years. I find them to be of remarkable service in stabilizing emotional upset during most traumatic situations. In our applied kinesiological testing, we have found the remedies to correct not just one, but three muscles (our criteria for their use), allowing a person to be more relaxed and receptive to other corrective procedures."

George Goodheart, DC,
Detroit, Michigan;
pioneer and developer of applied kinesiology;
author of numerous articles and text books
in the field of applied kinesiology

"I have used the Bach Flower Remedies, and the Rescue Remedy, [for] over thirty years, mostly for stress and emotional problems, with excellent results. A high percentage of patients, once they return to the office, report they are able to handle stress with much greater ease."

Harold J. Wilson, MD,
Columbus, Ohio

"In approximately ninety percent of the patients I've used the Bach Flower Remedies with, there has been a dramatic shift within a month in their basic attitudes toward themselves and others. This [shift] has resulted in greater self-acceptance and the realization that they are responsible for, and have control over, their own lives.

"I always use the Rescue Remedy when there's been any kind of accident that has resulted in emotional, psychological, or physical trauma. Following this, my patients have found that within a few hours, and most always within a few days, they have begun shaking off the effects of the accident."

Jeff Migdow, MD,
Kripalu Center, Lenox, Massachusetts

"The Bach Flower Remedies have been an integral part of my practice for the last two years, and the clinical results I have seen range from good to remarkable."

Louis I. Berlin, DC,
Atlanta, Georgia

"If I had to pick only one set of remedies of all the many systems of healing in the world, I would choose the Bach Flower Remedies alone. I believe these remedies to be many decades ahead of their time, and I am sure we will see a much more extensive use of them by doctors and the public alike. They have in some way a subtle effect on the inner self, often evinced quickly, whereas psychotherapy would have taken years, if ever, to achieve the same positive change."

C.K. Munro, MB, BAO,
Londonderry, Northern Ireland

"In my experience, the Bach Flower Remedies [chosen for the underlying emotional stress] have been helpful in classroom phobia, agoraphobia, sexual phobia, and premature ejaculation. The Rescue Remedy is good to start with for any anxiety, acute stress, and acute mental states. I've also seen Rescue Remedy alleviate tension in youngsters, especially before they take driving and classroom exams.

"I regard the Bach medicines as an essential extension of homoeopathic practice. One reason for this is that, unlike other homoeopathic medicines, they may be repeated, if necessary, with impunity. I highly recommend that every family have a bottle of Rescue Remedy, one for the home and another to be carried in their automobile for road emergencies."

Anthony D. Fox, MRCGP, DCH
Barton-on-Sea, England

"…I have used Rescue Remedy in many childbirth cases, always with satisfactory results. In some cases, I have recommended Rescue Remedy to women who were very nervous and uneasy about having natural childbirth. I suggested that they take it whenever they felt anxious during the days approaching delivery. Many did this and later shared with me how remarkably easy the births were. It is the single most important tool I carry in my treatment bag."

Marsha Woolf, ND,
Newton Corner, Massachusetts and
Providence, Rhode Island

"I have been using the Bach Flower Remedies for about seven years now and cannot imagine practicing without them. They continue to play an important and growing role, and sometimes their effects are astounding. Many patients tell me how remarkably positive their changes are after they begin using the remedies.

"I constantly use the Rescue Remedy in situations ranging from simple emotional upsets to heavy emotional trauma, with remarkable results. I also use the Rescue Remedy cream to massage onto bruises, bumps, tension headaches, and acute muscle and spinal pains with equally exceptional results."

Mark Smith, DC,
Vienna, Virginia

"I have had positive experiences with the Bach Flower Remedies. For example, I've treated a number of patients who have had a variety of gastrointestinal disorders, many of them long- standing. These individuals were helped dramatically by the Bach Flower Remedies. Though the remedies are not used specifically for physical ailments, in most cases where there is an underlying emotional problem, as there is in most [simple] gastrointestinal dysfunctions, we generally get excellent results."

Catherine Smith, MD,
Abingdon, Virginia

"I use the Bach Flower Remedies and Rescue Remedy in ninety percent of my practice, both before and after most dental procedures. I especially find them effective after surgery and reconstructive work and in easing the patients' trauma and stabilizing their condition.

"I find the Bach remedies and Rescue Remedy to be excellent for alleviating apprehension, both in adults and children, and especially for those suffering from temporal mandibular joint (TMJ) dysfunction. Many TMJ conditions are related to emotional imbalance, with fear a key element. There is not an emotionally based condition I have come across in my practice that the Bach Flower Remedies have not in some way been able to help. I wish that more dentists knew about the gentle yet consistently positive effects that the Bach remedies and Rescue Remedy have proven in my practice. If they did, they would not hesitate to use them themselves."

Maurice Tischler, DDS,
Woodstock, New York

"I have been using the Bach Flower Remedies for ten years as a part of my general medical practice. I have prescribed these remedies to well over two thousand patients and have found them to be of immense help in overcoming the negative emotional and mental states that seem to afflict us all.

"There is no doubt that the Bach remedies are capable of restoring the patient to emotional balance. The remedies, particularly the Rescue Remedy, are excellent in relieving acute states of distress resulting from sudden changes or catastrophes. The remedies also remove fear and anger and assist one in developing a more positive direction in life.

"I personally carry a bottle of Rescue Remedy with me at all times, and have used it during numerous emergencies, with immediate results. When grief occurs in the home, as from the loss of a dear one, there is no need for a potent sedative. Even here, Rescue Remedy proves extremely safe and effective.

"As a concerned physician, it is my hope that one day the Bach remedies will be a part of every doctor's healing practice."

Abram Ber, MD,
Phoenix, Arizona

"I have used the Bach remedies for nearly twenty years and have taken hundreds of patients off drugs (antidepressants, sedatives, tranquillizers) through their use. I use the remedies regularly at the Cancer Help Centre in Bristol, England, and find them to be most helpful in alleviating the emotional and psychological stress many of these patients experience. The remedies have also helped me personally through many family crisis situations as well. They are therapeutic agents I would never be without."

Alec Forbes, MD, FRCP,
formerly member, Expert Advisory Panel on
Traditional Medicine, World Health
Organization; medical director, Bristol Cancer
Help Centre, Bristol, England; author of
The Bristol Diet: Get Well and Eating Plan
(London: Century, 1984)

"I use the Rescue Remedy liquid concentrate internally, for calming emotional upset; and the liquid concentrate or cream externally, applied to lacerations or cuts, [this] seems to speed up the healing process. Often these wounds do not need to be sutured. A few drops of the remedy or application of the cream is all it takes. I find Rescue Remedy to be a very effective and powerful healing tool."

Joe D. Goldstrich, MD,
former medical director,
Pritikin Longevity Center,
Santa Monica, California;
author of *The Best Chance Diet*
(Atlanta: Humanics, 1982)

"In my former capacity as Dr. Margery Blackie's assistant [former physician to Her Majesty Queen Elizabeth II], both Dr. Blackie and I used the Rescue Remedy with very good results to treat people under stress. I have found it quite effective, without a doubt."

Charles K. Elliott, MB, BCh,
MFHom, MRCGP, MLCO, AFOM RCP,
London: Former Physician to Her Majesty Queen Elizabeth II;
co-editor of *Classical Homoeopathy* (Beaconsfield:
Beaconsfield Publishers Ltd., 1986)

"I have been using the Bach Flower Remedies primarily for insomnia, depression, and other nervous disorders and have found them to be extremely effective. I have found the Bach remedies, especially Rescue Remedy, to be valuable adjuncts to my homoeopathic practice."

Andrew H. Lockie, MRCGP, DObst RCOG,
Guildford, England

"I always keep a bottle of Rescue Remedy in my desk drawer for personal use and for friends and office staff, whenever there is any traumatic emotional or physical incident."

Richard Crews, MD, president,
Columbia Pacific University,
Mill Valley, California

"The Bach Flower Remedies are extremely sophisticated in their action. They are unusually gentle yet at the same time profoundly potent....I use the Bach Flower Remedies almost exclusively instead of tranquilizers and psychotropics, and I get excellent results. In many cases, they alleviate the problem when all else has failed."

J. Herbert Fill, MD, psychiatrist,
New York City, New York; former
New York City Commissioner of Mental Health;
author of *Mental Breakdown of a Nation*
(New York: Franklin Watts, 1974)

Emergencies: Professional and Consumer Use

The following section consists of emergency cases involving the professional and consumer use of Rescue Remedy. Emergencies are those situations that generally require immediate first aid or assistance.

Rescue Remedy is not meant to be a panacea or a substitute for emergency medical treatment. In all emergencies requiring medical attention, an ambulance or licensed physician should be called immediately.

Emergencies: Professional Use

"Recently, while traveling on a ship, I was called to treat a woman who wouldn't come out of her cabin. She was having an emotional crisis and was depressed and crying, saying she just couldn't face things. I administered a dose of Rescue Remedy and was then called away. One hour later, the woman approached me on deck, explaining how remarkably effective the remedy was in helping her overcome her terrible ordeal."

Alec Forbes, MD, FRCP,
Bristol, England

"We had just given a local anesthetic injection to a patient who told us that he didn't like Novocaine. Within a minute he began to shake and turn pale, apprehensive, and sweaty; he looked as though he were going to faint. I reached for the oxygen mask and the ammonia, but before I could get them to the patient my assistant had put four drops of Rescue Remedy liquid into the patient's half-open mouth. Instantly, he stopped shaking, his color returned, and he opened his eyes. He was completely recovered! Nothing but Rescue Remedy was used."

Steve Ross, DDS,
Wappinger Falls, New York

"A dentist friend and I were hiking in the woods when he was bitten by close to a hundred fire ants, over his arm and hands. These are extremely painful, itchy bites for most people, and my friend had been suffering for forty-five minutes before we were able to return to our cabin where I had some Rescue Remedy. If I had had the Rescue Remedy cream I would have used it, but since I didn't, I placed about ten to fifteen drops of Rescue Remedy liquid into a cup of spring water and applied this mixture to the bitten areas. Fire ant bites usually cause irritation to people for one to three days, or more. To our amazement, within a short time almost all itching, swelling, and inflammation ceased."

J. Hunter Lilly, ND, PhD,
Winter Haven, Florida

"During the first five days of an ocean voyage to Saudi Arabia, I was informed that a woman passenger was suffering from seasickness. I suggested to her husband that Rescue Remedy would be helpful for her. I gave him a bottle, instructing him to administer a dose under his wife's tongue every five minutes. Within the hour there was a marked improvement, and the next morning the woman was up and about, walking on deck. She had no recurrence of seasickness during the rest of the journey."

Ahmaed bin Embun, health practitioner,
Singapore, Malaysia

"I do chiropractic work with brain-damaged children, and many have responded well to Rescue Remedy. In several instances, these children were screaming and out of control when they came in for treatment. I administered a few drops of Rescue Remedy under their tongues, and their behavior improved immediately, like throwing a switch. It is quite amazing to watch."

Terry Franks, DC,
Burnsville, Minnesota

"One day, one of my patients who suffers from bouts of alcoholism came to see me. She was shaking, delirious, and completely out of control. During our two-hour session, I gave her repeated doses of liquid Rescue Remedy directly under her tongue. After the second dose, her tremors stopped, [and] she became increasingly coherent and able to function during the remaining part of the session. I gave her the rest of the bottle to take daily, which she did. Later that week at our next appointment, she said she felt better, and indeed she looked brighter than I had seen her look in a long time."

Joe Ann Cain, psychotherapist,
Encino, California

Emergencies: Consumer Use

I am a member of the Sri Chinmoy Marathon Team. After sixteen miles into a marathon, I usually become tired, irritable, and lightheaded. In my squirt bottle I carry a dilution of Rescue Remedy and water, which I usually drink during the last ten miles. It gives me energy and alleviates mental weariness and depression.

While running, I also apply Rescue Remedy cream to my knees to alleviate recurring pain, and I rub it on my calf muscles and ham strings, to relieve the muscle tightness I experience during the course of the race.

During my last race, I gave some Rescue Remedy cream to a friend who was also having knee pain midway through the race. A month before, he had had the same pain, and it had forced him to quit. This time, a few minutes after using the cream, he said his knee was fine. Following the race, he said he never would have finished if he hadn't used the Rescue Remedy.

Jamaica, New York

One day my sister and her son were digging a hole for a fence post. Accidentally she caught her leg in the equipment and ended up with a compound fracture. She quickly called out to her other son to bring the Rescue Remedy which was kept for emergencies. During the next five minutes, she promptly took repeated doses. The remedy immediately alleviated the worst effects of the trauma so that my sister was able to calmly organize her trip to the hospital.

Loudonville, New York

My oldest son cut his left thumb severely. Shortly after he became pale, dizzy, and nauseated, I gave him Rescue Remedy liquid orally and also applied it to the thumb full-strength and wrapped the finger with gauze. Within a short time my son's color returned, and he felt fine. No stitches were needed. He even complained afterwards about not having a scar to show for the cut.

Montgomery, Texas

I find the Rescue Remedy cream invaluable here in the tropical climate of Singapore, since cuts, wounds, or bruises sometimes take months to heal. The cream clears up a cut or bruise in one to two days.

Singapore, Malaysia

57

I used Rescue Remedy to counter my reaction to a skin cream, which had caused my eyes to become puffy and my face to become swollen and discolored. Hoping for relief, I first tried using a cold washcloth over my face; I also spent a lot of time in bed, dozing. In a couple of days, the redness and swelling abated, but my skin was scaly and itchy, as if I had a bad sunburn.

Then someone gave me some liquid Rescue Remedy, which I applied to my face several times. By evening I noticed a visible improvement, although I was still very anxious. The next morning, the improvement was more pronounced. I continued to apply the remedy every half-hour; at the end of the day not only was my anxiety gone, but I could see that my face was going to be all right.

Los Angeles, California

My mother recently slipped on a patch of ice in a parking lot, striking her head just above the temple, against the corner of a car. She blacked out completely for several seconds, then seemed to regain consciousness but was unable to say her name or respond in any way. She was very pale, as though in shock. I got her into the car, covered her with a blanket, and then gave her several drops of Rescue Remedy liquid which I always carry.

The effect was immediate. She became more conscious and asked for another dose. She was able to respond to questions, and although she still felt cold, her condition began to stabilize. Not surprisingly, she had a very bad headache. Seeing that she was okay, I took her home, where she soaked in a hot bath laced with a dropper full of Rescue Remedy. The next day her headache was almost gone, and she was able to go to work. Besides a chiropractic adjustment, no further treatment was needed.*

Ballston Lake, New York

---

*Blows to the head may result in a fracture or other complications, in all conditions requiring medical attention a physician should be consulted immediately.

One month ago, after carelessly touching a hot oven and burning myself, I immediately plunged my scorched hand into a jar of Rescue Remedy cream. Additionally, I took the liquid remedy as I massaged the cream onto the burned area. The next day I put in a twelve-hour shift at the hospital where I work as a nurse. My hands were constantly in and out of water, but there was no tenderness, just a slight redness. I continued to apply Rescue Remedy to the burned spot, and within one week I could not even see where the burn had been.

Kansas City, Missouri

Quite recently, while doing some work in my home, I hit my thumb with a hammer. The pain was very bad, and a throbbing sensation quickly developed in the thumb. My wife applied Rescue Remedy cream, and within moments the pain and throbbing were almost gone. It was quite remarkable.

We also use the Rescue Remedy with our children; it always seems to bring relief and comfort to them following their usual mishaps.

Kent, England

Our six-month-old baby had an injury on the foreskin of his penis—a painful place! He cried every time he urinated. We decided to try the Rescue Remedy and gave him four drops in some water orally, at the same time applying the Rescue Remedy cream to the injury. Our son fell into a sound and peaceful sleep almost immediately. After a few more applications over the next two days, the injury healed completely.

East Hampton, New York

When my four-year-old grandchild was bitten behind the ear by a dog, I immediately gave the child and his mother some Rescue Remedy, since they were both badly shaken. They became visibly calm within moments as preparations for emergency care were being made.

Tipp City, Ohio

59

Last summer, I was cutting hedges when a large branch flew up in my face, pushing my upper tooth through a half-inch of my lower lip, which started bleeding quite a bit. I held open the wound while my husband put two drops of full-strength Rescue Remedy on it. The bleeding slowed, and after several repeated doses over the next ten minutes it stopped completely. The wound healed in one week. Although I still have a knot in my lip, there is no scar at all.

Hull, Georgia

Preparing for extensive dental surgery, my wife put twenty drops of Rescue Remedy into a glass of water, which she sipped throughout the day before and after her surgery. She did not feel any pain on the day of surgery or on the days following it, nor did she have to take any codeine or aspirin. Sleep came naturally and easily without medication that first night and on the following nights as well. My wife visited the dental surgeon two days after the surgery, and he was astounded at how quickly she had healed.

California

We couldn't get through a summer without the Rescue Remedy ointment. It instantly relieves all types of insect stings.

Washington, D.C.

One night my husband began hemorrhaging. The amount of blood he was vomiting terrified both of us. I gave him some Rescue Remedy as soon as he could keep it down, and he was soon able to walk calmly out of the bathroom. I'm a nurse, so I know that in a situation like this it is imperative that the patient be calmed. I also took a dose of Rescue Remedy myself every ten or fifteen minutes so that I, too, could stay calm. It helped us both very much; I was easily able to get my husband to the emergency room without either of us panicking.

Salisbury, North Carolina

My husband and I went for a long drive last week and were badly shaken up by a near-accident. The car ahead of us stopped very suddenly, and my husband jammed on the brakes just in time. We were very shaken, but we put some drops of the Rescue Remedy on our tongues and were genuinely surprised at the speed which it worked and with which our nervousness disappeared.

California

My friend and I used Rescue Remedy to help ourselves get through a rough climb up Mount Cruach Ardrain, in Scotland. About halfway up, it began to get very cold, and we became extremely exhausted. But we knew we had to continue if we were going to complete the climb. I took a sip from the small bottle of Rescue Remedy that I had in my coat and told my companion that he must take some if we were to make it through the climb. After remaining motionless for a few minutes, we felt sufficiently recovered to complete a final patch, returning safely, in a time that was something of a record. I am quite certain that we would not have completed that climb had it not been for the Rescue Remedy.

Scotland

One of the students in my cooking class cut her finger quite badly. Despite our prompting she refused to go to a doctor, and rather than argue with her, I gave her several drops from my Rescue Remedy bottle. I also had her lie down, and packed her finger with Rescue Remedy cream. This dressing I changed every few hours. The next day, the wound was still open but looking pink and alive. I put on a new dressing and told my student to change it every day. When she showed it to me four days later, I couldn't believe my eyes. The skin had completely healed; there wasn't even a line where it had been cut. Except for the fact that my student's nail was partially gone, there was no sign of the wound.

Amsterdam, Holland

My five-year-old niece fell off her bicycle, tearing skin off her nose, bruising both lips badly, and leaving a front tooth dangling. She screamed with pain as we squirted some Rescue Remedy straight into her mouth and headed for the nearest hospital. The remedy didn't seem to have any effect on her. We gave her a few more doses while waiting for the doctor, but that didn't help. Then it dawned on me that she was spitting blood—and the Rescue Remedy along with it. I immediately started applying the drops behind her ears, and the result was almost instantaneous; my niece stopped screaming and became very cooperative. The look of disbelief on the nurse's face was an absolute study.

In another incident: I gashed my left hand with a can opener, near the joint between the thumb and index finger. The cut was deep and half an inch long. I applied Rescue Remedy cream immediately and then covered my hand with a Band-Aid. Three days later, I found that the cut was healing. I took off the covering on the fifth day, and all that was left was a little scar. This surprised me greatly, since other cuts I've had have always healed extremely slowly.

Victoria, Australia

I burned the inside of my mouth with some very hot food. I have done this before and usually it means agony for at least two days and discomfort for another week or two. This time I rubbed some Rescue Remedy liquid on the burned spot and got relief within seconds. I applied a few more doses; before the day was over, the pain was gone.

London, England

I am physically handicapped from polio and have to walk with crutches. One day, while reaching for a jar on a high shelf, I stretched too far and felt a sudden, violent pain in my middle finger and my wrist. My hand became swollen and remained painful for the next ten days; gradually, it started to become numb.

On the tenth day I saw my doctor, who became concerned because the finger was not only swollen but was starting to curve in. An X-ray, however, showed nothing wrong. Ten days later—my hand still hurting—a friend suggested that I try my Rescue Remedy. I immediately put the cream on the finger, and in about two hours the pain was virtually gone. At this time I again applied more cream, and the next morning the pain and swelling were all but gone. I was able to stretch my hand and fingers normally. It was miraculous. Neither the pain nor the swelling has returned since then.

Herefordshire, England

A young girl of seven with a history of travel sickness was due to go on a holiday to Spain. Her parents, who were worried that they had to journey for three hours in a bus before they reached their destination, had asked if I had any ideas which might help. I suggested the girl use the Rescue Remedy, which I knew to be somewhat effective in these circumstances, along with the Bach remedy Scleranthus. After obtaining a mixture, the mother later told me that she had administered it frequently, both before and during the trip, which proceeded without any mishap whatsoever.

Pinner, England

Whenever I go to San Francisco, I spend half my time soaking my hot, swollen feet, which can't seem to take the constant trudging up and down the steep hills. Last time, however, I obtained and smoothed on the Rescue Remedy cream. The relief was immediate. The heat left my feet at once, and the swelling was reduced shortly thereafter. I continued to use the Rescue Remedy during the rest of my trip and was not bothered with foot problems for the remainder of my stay.

Everett, Washington

After a recent operation, I found it difficult to sleep. I would jerk and toss continuously. My various surgical wounds hurt me, and my brain seemed to be on fire. At one point, my wife gave me a dose of Rescue Remedy; within minutes I quieted down, shortly afterwards falling into a peaceful sleep. It was miraculous.

For two days and nights I was able to lie still. I was so tranquil that the bed clothes were left undisturbed. My mind was at peace, and I lay contentedly, not reading and rarely speaking, just enjoying the peace. By the third day, I was feeling much better and more relaxed. The Bach remedies have helped me tremendously.

USA

I was working on a fluorescent fixture and did not know that someone had forgotten to turn off the power. After grabbing the exposed wires, I got an intense electrical shock. Quite shaken up, I located my bottle of Rescue Remedy and immediately took four drops under my tongue, and several more within the next half-hour. The effects of the shock disappeared within minutes; in a half-hour, I was fine.

Philadelphia, Pennsylvania

Emotional and Psychological Stress: Professional and Consumer Use

The following section consists of cases specifically involving the use of Rescue Remedy for acute emotional and psychological stress.

Emotional and psychological stress includes, but is not limited to anxiety, nervousness, panic, and non-clinical depression. The stress may result from everyday situations, such as visiting a dentist, taking an exam, receiving bad news, or as a result of accidents.

Emotional and Psychological Stress: Professional Use

"I have my patients sip Rescue Remedy in warm water, and it always seems to calm them. One very disturbed patient, who had been on numerous tranquilizers with poor results, described to me his experience with the Rescue Remedy. He stated that Rescue Remedy assisted him in feeling calm and natural, and that it has helped him more than anything else he has ever tried for his nervous condition."

Catherine R. Smith, MD,
Abingdon, Virginia

"I prescribe Rescue Remedy liquid for the sense of internal panic brought on by the diagnosis of cancer. It helps both the patient and family cope more easily with the situation. In the acute phase of bereavement, Rescue Remedy is of definite value. One man whose thirty-two-year-old wife had suddenly died used Rescue Remedy as often as every two hours for many weeks and reported that it always eased his panic and tears.

"Rescue Remedy is excellent as a convalescent tonic, when given [four] drops four times daily, especially for the elderly."

D.T.H. Williams, MB, DObst RCOG,
Chiddingfold, Surrey, England

"Recently, a thirty-seven-year-old woman who was attempting to reduce a sixteen-year dependency on Valium came to see me. Withdrawal was causing her extreme pain in her muscles and joints, and feelings of suffocation. She had already seen several physicians who offered her no relief. I suggested that she try the Bach Rescue Remedy. After five to six doses at fifteen-minute intervals before bedtime, she would sleep quite well. After taking Rescue Remedy for two months, along with counseling during the crisis periods, she has considerably reduced her Valium intake, along with her extreme tension and worry. Now, after further Bach remedies, and counseling, she has been off Valium for over a year."

Doug Lancaster, health practitioner,
Kingston, Ontario, Canada

"An extremely depressed thirty-eight-year-old man came to me for treatment; he was nervous, exhausted, unclean, and was exacerbating his problems by smoking two to three packs of cigarettes a day. He had very low self-esteem worsened by his feeling that he lacked sufficient will-power to control his smoking.

"I gave him one dose of the Rescue Remedy at the beginning of our session, and he sat for three hours without reaching for a cigarette. He said it was the first time in years he hadn't felt like smoking.... [Following our session he later reported] that after taking the Rescue Remedy for just a short time he had begun to develop a much deeper level of self-respect and a greater sense of well-being."

Loretta Hilsher, PhD, DN,
president and founder of
Hyperactive Children's Institute,
Chicago, Illinois

"In our office we have a dropper bottle of Rescue Remedy by each chair. Before any injection or stressful treatment, we give the patient a few drops of the remedy. We explain to the patient that the Rescue Remedy is a helpful, herbal remedy without side effects. We find that the Rescue Remedy helps raise a patient's resistance to stress while at the same time having a great calming influence. We have also adopted a policy of offering a bottle of Rescue Remedy to any patient we refer to an oral surgeon or endodontist."

Jerry Mittelman, DDS,
New York City, New York

"I treated a violinist who had severe stage fright before a performance, feeling that she could not go on. I gave her some Rescue Remedy to take before going on stage, and now she says she actually enjoys performing.

"Another musician, who plays the flute, said she would be tense for two weeks before a performance. For a while, regular doses of Rescue Remedy during the days before a concert made her performances better, her experiences exciting and enjoyable. Now she finds she feels this way with only a few doses prior to a performance."

Jeff Migdow, MD,
Kripalu Center, Lenox, Massachusetts

"A forty-nine-year-old client went through a traumatic divorce, lost his medical practice, and had an emotional and physical breakdown. Though various kinds of treatments have helped him, he still has occasional periods of great emotional agitation. During these episodes, Rescue Remedy improves his ability to function and to continue his work day."

David Winston, nutritional consultant,
Franklin Park, New Jersey

Emotional and Psychological Stress: Consumer Use

A month ago my sister rammed into a Coca-Cola truck with her new VW. I received a call from the hospital and got very nervous and shaky. Immediately I took four drops of Rescue Remedy; very quickly I stopped shaking and was able to turn my attention to my sister's well-being.

Upon my arrival at the hospital I found that my sister had only minor cuts and bruises, but she was emotionally out of control. She was crying and hysterical, worried about our parents' reproaches and her unpaid-for car. I gave her a dose of Rescue Remedy, and she immediately stopped crying. With a deep breath, she relaxed and closed her eyes. Fifteen minutes later, she was anxious again, so I repeated the dose. We continued in this way for an hour and a half.

My sister was released from the hospital, laughing and back to her old self. There was no further need for the remedy after that, and within a week the cuts and bruises were completely healed.

New Mexico

The local bakery burned down a few weeks ago. When my friend, who lives next door to the baker, went in to see if she could help, she found the baker's wife completely traumatized. My friend immediately gave her two or three doses of Rescue Remedy; within a short time, the woman was back to her normal self. Her colour had completely returned, and she has not shown any signs of disturbance since then.

Ascot, England

A Japanese passenger sitting alongside us on a recent airplane trip was obviously terrified. His body was doubled up, his head buried in his hands, his meal untouched. We gave him a few drops of Rescue Remedy in water, and he became relaxed almost immediately; he soon fell asleep. He awoke quite a long time afterwards and ate the next meal quite well. Since he spoke no English, he passed on his grateful thanks for the special 'medicine' via a bilingual hostess.

Australia

I am a registered nurse working in an in-patient mental health facility. I began using Rescue Remedy regularly in February 1981, when I was a medical staff nurse under a great deal of stress. At the time, I was close to a nervous breakdown, suffering from what was eventually diagnosed as adrenal exhaustion and hypoglycemia. For several months, in addition to experiencing insomnia and depression, I would feel extremely anxious and panic-stricken whenever my blood sugar fluctuated. I used the Rescue Remedy many times throughout this period to alleviate my feelings of panic and acute anxiety. It seemed to help stabilize both my mind and my body.

Moreover, I feel that the Rescue Remedy has been invaluable to my personal growth and transformation, helping me gain a greater sense of understanding and self-awareness throughout some rough periods in my life.

Fort Wayne, Indiana

My youngest son, now six-years-old, used to be a thin, emotional child, at times very sweet and reasonable, at other times a holy terror. Touchy and sensitive, he would sometimes have a screaming tantrum over nothing. I ordered some Rescue Remedy liquid, and during the next emotional outburst I gave him four drops. Within five minutes, right before our eyes, he calmed down; his face softened and became rounded, and his demeanor changed so much that my fourteen-year-old son exclaimed, 'If it will do that for him, fix me some.'

Montgomery, Texas

Recently, my three-year-old daughter had to have a front tooth refilled. We gave her a dose of Rescue Remedy just before going to the dentist. Both my wife and the doctor were amazed at how thoroughly calm and cooperative she was throughout the process. Even while the dentist used his drill, my daughter never once winced or cried.

Mount Shasta, California

Recently, two of my friends were in similar situations of breaking up with their mates and experiencing severe emotional trauma. I gave each of them a bottle of Rescue Remedy and told them to take doses daily. Afterwards, they both reported feeling much calmer and told me how the remedy helped them through their difficult periods.

San Diego, California

Some friends of mine made the difficult decision to divorce. When they told their twelve-year-old son, he became extremely upset and frightened. He paced around, shouting and crying, hitting the walls and furniture. His mother gave him several doses of Rescue Remedy, and within twenty minutes he calmed down and was able to discuss the situation rationally.

Albuquerque, New Mexico

A young Indian girl, frightened by her first menstrual period, became deeply disturbed after a friend laughed at her and told her that she should be ashamed of herself for bleeding. For two weeks, the girl sat in a dark corner, crying and refusing to speak to anyone, even her mother. Doctors were treating the girl with vitamins and tranquilizers, but to no avail.

Fortunately, when I arrived on the scene, I had my little bottle of Rescue Remedy, and since the mother had lost faith in the treatment applied so far, she agreed to put the remedy to the test. After the first day, the girl started to speak. On the fourth day after her treatment with Rescue Remedy, the girl was completely well; she did not cry, and she said she no longer felt afraid.

Honduras

Recently, I moved from suburbia to my dream house in the mountains. While moving, I experienced total physical exhaustion, financial disaster, confusion, burnout, and sheer terror, along with an indescribable feeling of elation and joy. Close to a complete nervous breakdown, I began taking Rescue Remedy every five minutes. Within a short time, I noticed a core of strength that I had never realized before. My emotions evened out, and I felt an inner calm and a renewed self-control emerging.

Santa Barbara, California

While I was going through an intensive, five-day personal-growth training program, I began to feel a great deal of stress. Also, since the sessions lasted from early in the morning to late at night, I was getting very little sleep. I decided to try the Rescue Remedy, and after taking regular doses for about three days, I noticed a sense of well-being that surprised me. The remedy definitely helped stabilize my emotions during a particularly rough period in my personal life.

Philadelphia, Pennsylvania

As a rule, I am terribly nervous when I have to speak in public. However, the last lecture I gave was a wonderful experience. I took a dose of the Rescue Remedy upon waking that day, another at midday, and one just before I went on the platform. To my surprise and delight, I had no dry lips or butterflies in my stomach and not a twinge of fear.

Sussex, England

My whole family took Rescue Remedy every day during the first month of mourning after my mother died. It didn't change the quality of our grief, but we were able to deal with it and accept what had happened more easily.

Newton Corner, Massachusetts

Rescue Remedy has come to my rescue many times. However, my favorite Rescue Remedy story happened when my new car was stolen. I was at a gas station, paying for my gas, when two boys jumped into my car and drove off. My purse, along with my Rescue Remedy, was on the front seat. Standing there, feeling shocked and confused, I became outraged when I realized that they had stolen my Rescue Remedy, and I needed it!

Miami, Florida

In addition to being a nutritionist, I'm an actress working on a show right now. I have a highly emotional presentation at the end of scene two, which is immediately followed by a scene showing me four days later, happy and carefree. Rescue Remedy is the only thing that calms me down during the transition between scenes. I exit from one side of the stage, shaking and crying, walk around the other side of the theater, pass my dressing room, take my Rescue Remedy and three deep breaths, and go on in the next scene, relaxed and happy.

New York City, New York

My flatmate and I are both policewomen. We once interviewed a rape victim who had great difficulty recalling specific details of her recent ordeal. My partner gave the woman a dose of Rescue Remedy, and the change was almost immediate. The sequence of events became coherent, an excellent statement was obtained, and the victim's very accurate description of the offender led to his arrest a short time later.

Victoria, Australia

One of my twelve-year-old pupils played the goal position on our school football team. Before each game he would become quite upset and nervous, since the boys would tease him if he let the ball through the goal. Though skeptical, he finally agreed to sip some Rescue Remedy two hours before our next game. The following day I was thrilled when this very skeptical child, grinning from ear to ear, stated before the class, 'Your magic stuff is great; I wasn't nervous at all, even when I did let the ball go through.'

London, England

My children take Rescue Remedy before their college tests and just before their on-stage performances in order to offset anxiety. I take it before I meditate; it helps me to release my stress, relax, and enhance my experience.

New York City, New York

At the hotel where I was staying in Iona, I had great success with the Bach Flower Remedies, particularly the Rescue Remedy. Four visitors arrived, disoriented and suffering from exposure after the engine of their boat had broken down during a storm. I was able to give two of them the Rescue Remedy, and their recovery was amazing. They were calm within a matter of hours, while the other two poor souls had to be confined for two to three days.

Isle of Iona, Scotland

Two children had lost their mother to cancer. The youngest was four, the oldest eight. After the funeral, their father complained that the older girl was suddenly afraid of the dark and could not sleep through the night without wetting her bed, an unusual habit for her. She had nightmares three or four times a week and thus continued to worry her father. Her younger sister also cried incessantly and had nightmares. I gave both children Rescue Remedy.

Additionally, I suggested that their father give them both four drops of the Rescue Remedy each time they woke during the night and before meals during the day. Within three nights the bed-wetting stopped, and both children slept peacefully.

Sante Fe, New Mexico

During a meeting at our Urban Health Center, seven or eight children, all strangers to one another, began to fight and cry, and the mothers responded with angry slaps and reprimands. To try and settle the furor, I gave everyone a dose of liquid Rescue Remedy. Within just a few minutes, peace and harmony were restored.

Chicago, Illinois

I noticed a woman waiting outside the intensive care unit where her mother was dying. She was in semi-shock, quite anxious and very cold. I handed her a small bottle of Rescue Remedy and told her how to use it. She began taking the liquid, and it seemed to relax her very soon after; she seemed able to accept the situation a little more calmly.

Salisbury, North Carolina

I took the Rescue Remedy before taking an exam and found it extremely helpful. I normally waste a lot of time deciding which questions to answer and what to write. But this time, I was able to write quickly, and I felt quite alert and tranquil.

England

Some severe personal problems caused me to have acute anxiety attacks nearly every day. These attacks were no doubt aggravated by my quitting smoking. To control the anxiety, I started taking tranquilizers on and off for a year. Also, for two previous years I'd had dizzy spells whose cause no doctor could find. The day I took my first dose of Rescue Remedy was the last day I needed a tranquilizer. As I continued to take the Rescue Remedy, my anxiety attacks slowly abated, then disappeared, as did my dizzy spells.

New York City, New York

Pregnancy and Childbirth: Professional and Consumer Use

The Bach Flower Remedies can be particularly helpful before and throughout pregnancy, as well as during childbirth, when a prospective mother's moods fluctuate more than usual. Since the moods are distinctly defined, they can be treated by the mother-to-be herself or by her adviser. A quiet, happy frame of mind is one of the greatest contributors to a painless and easy birth. In addition to being taken internally, Rescue Remedy can be applied externally to the wrist, temples, and navel of the newborn, when and as needed.

The Bach Flower Remedies, as well as Rescue Remedy, have also been shown to be especially valuable in dealing with children's emotional difficulties—for example, fear and restlessness—before more complex patterns have a chance to develop.

In addition, Dr. John Diamond, a psychiatrist and well-known author, in his introduction to *Handbook of the Bach Flower Remedies*, by Philip Chancellor (New Canaan: Keats, 1980), states: "The Bach remedies have tremendous power for good and are completely free of any harmful effects." This is especially important, because many substances commonly used today for most emotional difficulties have warnings about repetition and dosage.

Because of recent FDA regulations, most over-the-counter drugs require a warning for pregnant women regardless of the drug's toxicity. *It is important to check with your physician before taking any form of medication during pregnancy.* However no known side effects have been attributed to the Bach Flower Remedies or to Rescue Remedy in over fifty years of use.

Pregnancy and Childbirth: Professional Use

"Our hospital's doctor, not able to find the cause of the illness, had done all he could for a six-week-old baby who was failing quickly. Based on my experience in emergency situations, I decided to start the infant on Bach Rescue Remedy; the effect was profound. From that point on, her condition took a dramatic shift in a positive direction. The doctor could hardly believe it when a week later, the baby's condition appeared to be stabilized."

Sister Natalie, superintendent,
St. John's Hospital, Poona, India

"While I was attending a thirty-four-year-old woman who was in the second stage of labour, she was having extreme contractions. The fetal heart monitor indicated that the fetus was in distress. The patient was getting hysterical, and we were considering a Caesarean section. I applied Rescue Remedy to her lips from a cloth three times within a fifteen-minute period. The fetal heartbeat evened out, the contractions were much milder, and the whole labour process stopped for about two hours. The woman calmed down and actually slept. When she awoke, labour began again, and there was a normal delivery, with no further complications or distress."

In another case: "I was in attendance when a child was born at home, the umbilical cord twisted twice around his neck. Since the cord was too tight, it was necessary to cut and clamp it immediately. The child was not breathing, his vital signs were low, and he displayed a poor colour. We rubbed Rescue Remedy all over his face. Within a short period, though it seemed forever, he started breathing, and his normal responses quickly picked up."

Gretchen Lawlor, ND,
Tunbridge Wells, England

"Recently, I was called to the hospital where one of my maternity patients had a series of minor convulsions directly preceding her labour. When I arrived, I immediately swabbed her tongue and inside her lips with Rescue Remedy. The convulsions ceased, and I left her drinking water 'doctored' with the Rescue Remedy. I continued this treatment throughout the next day and the following morning. Later that day, my patient delivered the child, with no discomfort."

Dr. T. L.
Northampton, England

"A fifteen-month-old-girl running a high fever was recently brought to me. I applied Rescue Remedy cream to various parts of her body, and within half an hour she was fast asleep, and her fever dropped. Two days later, she had fully recovered. I've used Rescue Remedy cream and drops in similar cases of fever in children, always with good results."

Ahmaed bin Embun, health practitioner,
Singapore, Malaysia

"I recently attended a twenty-one-year-old woman who was in labour at West London Hospital with her first child. Since she was quite agitated, I administered a dose of Rescue Remedy to calm her during the second stage and especially during the transition period of labour. She had a unusually easy birth without any complications, which I attributed to the Rescue Remedy."

Sarah Moon, BAc,
London, England

"Very shortly after her daughter was born, my patient nearly passed out. Since there were complications and a lot of bleeding, I gave her a dose of Rescue Remedy, which, within moments, brought her back to clarity. The rapidity of recovery was quite amazing to witness."

G. S. Khalsa, MD,
Lathrup Village, Michigan

"A thirty-one-year-old woman patient of mine had wanted natural childbirth but was two weeks past her delivery date. She was taken to the hospital to have labour induced. This upset her. She had lower back pain; she was apprehensive, and she felt a sense of failure at not having a home birth.

"I gave her five drops of Rescue Remedy in warm water. There was an immediate dramatic change, and she said, 'I'm going to really cope with this.' She was suddenly clear and had her first baby in three hours."

Lorraine Taylor, BAc,
Oxford, England

"Recently, I gave Rescue Remedy to a young woman in the early stages of labour. She was highly nervous, but after a few sips of the remedy in water she calmed down considerably. After ten minutes, her contractions regulated and labour progressed beautifully. She gave birth within two hours in a relaxed and normal manner. Also, as a preventative to postnatal depression, there is nothing equal to Rescue Remedy."

E. Eckstein, RMH*,
England

Pregnancy and Childbirth: Consumer Use

The following letter was written to John Ramsell who, with his daughter, Judy Howard, carries on Dr. Bach's work as the current curators of the Bach Centre in England. The letter eventually appeared in *Mothering* magazine, Spring 1983, and is printed here with permission from the

* Registered Medical Herbalist

writer. An extremely moving account of one woman's coura- geous battle to save her child, the letter is included here so that the reader may share in the woman's experience. **No medical claims are implied or made here for the Bach reme- dies or Rescue Remedy, in Down's Syndrome, or any other serious medical disorder by either the author or the pub- lisher.**

Dear John,

I knew I would have a story to tell, but I had no idea it would be so dramatic. You might just want to put your feet up in one of those wonderful wooden chairs Dr. Edward Bach built, to read this one.

I had made about eight one-ounce dropper bottles full of my favorite Bach flowers—Rescue Remedy, Walnut, Mi- mulus, and Oak—the day my labor began. I took them regu- larly on my tongue, and put four or five drops on the crown of my head to even out the rough edges. I was 9¾ cm. di- lated when my labor stopped...thirty-six long, long hours later.

Since I had planned a home delivery, I did my laboring at home to the hour. Soon, I figured the son within me was not safe in his own right; otherwise, he would have been born by then. I got my bag, and off to the hospital I went with my husband, my midwives, my remedies, and the baby still within. I slipped a bottle of comfrey and chlorophyll into my medicine pouch and thought I was ready.

When I arrived at the hospital, I had a heavy contraction at the front desk, and the woman there screamed, "Are you going to have your baby right here? Right now? Get into a wheelchair and use the service elevator—it's faster!"

A fetal monitor determined that baby Anton was in dis- tress—imagine having one's head caught in the cervix for thirty-six hours—and we opted for a Caesarean section. It was performed at 9 p.m.—eight long hours later.

The remedy I continued to take every three minutes in front of all the attending doctors and nurses kept them very curious. When asked by my doctor what I was so faithfully taking, I told him it was a remedy for impatience. He laughed, and admitted that he, too, could probably use some, although he never asked to try any.

Baby Anton was born in distress. He had no lung capacity and swallowed meconium (baby's first elimination) after my waters broke early in the morning. The heart had enlarged to keep the baby alive. He was put on 100% oxygen immediately, and he looked as if he wanted to go back to the garden.

About ten minutes out of recovery, our pediatrician told us our son was born with Down's Syndrome. In addition, he had many problems and had about two hours to live. Did we want to see him? Yes, Did we make funeral arrangements at the pediatricians suggestion? Yes, we did that too. We cried mostly; this was a little much to bear, even with the remedies. I asked my husband to return home and bring back the entire set of thirty-eight remedies. I added the Bach flower Gorse...[for hopelessness] to our remedy, and we took it continually. Soon, we calmed down.

I was wheeled into Infant Intensive Care where I could not reach my son's head after my own abdominal surgery. I asked my husband to put Oak, Walnut, and Rescue Remedy on his (the baby's) knees, feet, and chest—between the EKG and catheter wires. If our son was going to die, I wanted his transition to be a peaceful one. I knew the flower Walnut would aid his transition. We told the nurses it was holy water. Even though they were incredible women, I figured the chances of their knowing about the Bach flowers were ten to one. I felt too weak to explain.

The pediatricians said they would transport baby Anton to a large city hospital sixty miles away. They would be "better equipped" there to save his life, if in fact it could be saved. Heart surgery would probably also be necessary. Jack and I said no, no, no to both.... If baby Anton was to live, he would have to pull through where he was born, here in the mountains of this small city.

That night, I stayed with him in intensive care and reached into his oxygen tent, scared to death he might die if I opened it up. I fed him my remedy, now his, through an eyedropper. He was so dehydrated he slurped it up with all the enthusiasm he could gather. Every ten minutes I gave him his remedy: on the knees, his mouth, and on the crown of his badly misshapen head. I did this for twenty-four hours. The Newborn Nursery nurses kept him warm and dry and untangled from all those wires. Then I went to bed.

When I woke the next day, eight hours later, I slightly remember the doctor saying the crisis seemed to be over. We then administered an intense stimulation program. Soon, I could hold my son with blow-by oxygen in between the wires. He had a strong suck, and breast-fed in six or seven days. Little by little, over a ten-day period in intensive care, we used six ounces of remedy. The oxygen supply was decreased from 100% eventually to room air. I added tincture of comfrey and chlorophyll to my milk. Baby's skin was rubbed down with the gel from live Aloe Vera plants three or four times every twelve hours. He was three weeks overdue, and he looked as if he had spent that time in a bathtub. His head shaped up. His skin is beautiful. We have a baby boy.

We continue our daily use of the Bach flowers. Thanks again for carrying on Bach's work. In the eight years I have used these remedies, I have never been so appreciative that Bach discovered them. With my thanks, please expect a package of herbal teas for you and all your staff, and your guests from the world over.

Most sincerely,

Alexandra Kolkmeyer
Author of *A Modern Woman's Herbal*
(Santa Fe, New Mexico: Insight Press, 1976)

Since the birth of my first child eleven years ago was such a painful and frightening experience, I grew quite terrified as the time came closer for my second child to be born. However, following sound advice, I took Rescue Remedy during labour, and the delivery was quick and easy. I became quite relaxed both during and after the birth.

Isles of Scilly, England

When the third member of our family arrived early this summer, it became evident to me that the Rescue Remedy was also the baby's remedy. I found it a wonderful and almost instantaneous cure for colic.

Three drops in a tablespoon of warm boiled water worked like magic.

Selsdon, England

Before delivering her baby, my daughter regularly took Rescue Remedy, and her labour only lasted an hour and a half. The nurses said they had never seen such a quick and easy delivery, and called her son Speedy Gonzales. She is continuing with the remedy and is so relieved that this baby, as opposed to her first, sleeps peacefully through the night.

Devon, England

I began taking Rescue Remedy with the onset of labour contractions while on the way to the hospital. The contractions started coming every three minutes, and by the time I arrived I was fully dilated and ready to push. In the delivery room my husband gave me water with the Bach Flower Rescue Remedy added. Between each contraction, I was fully aware of all that was going on. Even through the powerful contractions I had no need for painkillers and after an hour gave birth to twin boys.

I took Rescue Remedy throughout my six days in the hospital by putting a few drops in my bedside water. This helped me to cope with the overwhelming task of breast-feeding two hungry babies. I attributed the calmness and inner strength I felt throughout this intense experience to Dr. Bach's Rescue Remedy.

Derbyshire, England

"My first birth was a nightmare. There's no other word for it. Even the midwife, who attended as one of my coaches, admitted that it was 'one of the more difficult' she had seen. ...No, I was not medicated, and yes, I was a 'prepared' woman. But prepared for what? After twenty-four hours of excruciating back labor, with little or no dilation, no breathing technique could alleviate the pain and exhaustion I was suffering....

"Sensing my panic, my coach pulled a small bottle of Rescue Remedy, a Bach flower extract, from her pocket and dripped three or four drops of the dew-like liquid into my mouth....Soon after that, an unexpected surge of energy and concentration came over me. After three long pushes, my baby girl emerged in one sudden, hot, wet 'plop.'...

"...When things got bad [during my second birth], I asked my other coach for the Rescue Remedy."

Olympia, Washington (Extracted from *Mothering* magazine, Spring 1984)

Recently, I suggested Rescue Remedy to a young woman in the early stages of labour. She was highly nervous, but after a few sips of the remedy in water she calmed down considerably. After ten minutes, her contractions regulated and labor progressed beautifully. She gave birth within two hours in a relaxed and normal manner. Also, as a preventive to postnatal depression, there is nothing equal to Rescue Remedy.

England

I was ten weeks pregnant when I started to miscarry. I began to bleed so profusely that I almost passed out. All I had time to say was, 'Get the Rescue Remedy off the shelf!' I took it every few moments until I regained my strength and was able to get medical assistance. The bleeding lessened a bit, and I was able to get to the hospital in a stable condition. Rescue Remedy will always be on hand in my home for any emergency.

New South Wales, Australia

Following a loss in the family, my stress was compounded by an ectopic pregnancy [in the Fallopian tube], which had aborted. This was followed by surgical removal of the damaged tube and ovary as well. During this period, Rescue Remedy was the only thing that kept me [emotionally] stable. Shortly after my return from the hospital, my marriage began to break up, and once again Rescue Remedy proved invaluable in helping me through this time.

I have used all the Bach remedies, and they have played an important role in helping me cope with the changes I've experienced in my life. They have allowed me to change my negative thoughts and thus develop more fully as a human being. I cannot speak highly enough of Dr. Bach and his remedies.

Lancashire, England

After much debating, we took our two-month-old daughter to receive her first immunization vaccine. The after effects of this shot were dreadful. The poor little baby ran a high fever and went into a frenzy, screaming for hours. Before her second shot, we rubbed Rescue Remedy cream on the spot where the needle would go in, and she didn't feel a thing. For the rest of the day, we gave her Rescue Remedy orally, and this time she had no after effects whatsoever. We dealt with the third shot the same way, and our daughter actually seemed to enjoy her visit with the doctor.

USA

Acute and Chronic: Professional and Consumer Use

The following section consists of cases involving the professional and consumer use of Rescue Remedy for acute and chronic conditions. Acute conditions are defined here as those conditions that appear suddenly but do not require emergency assistance. Chronic conditions are those a person has lived with over a long period of time.

Acute and Chronic: Professional Use

"One of my patients was a thirty-six-year-old woman who was a heavy drinker and smoker with a history of chronic depression. I suggested that she take the Bach Flower Rescue Remedy, which she did. The next day, she reported that she had slept for the first time in two weeks and felt a sense of relief from her problems. She continued to take the remedy and after two or three weeks was able to stabilize her condition. She now takes the remedy intermittently."

Jeffrey Fine, ND, PhD,
Palm Beach Shores, Florida

"J.T. is a sixty-five-year-old ex-weight-lifter who had been having attacks of 'wooziness' and lightheadedness for the last year and a half. They would occur if he sat still for more than a half-hour or if he drove a car for over an hour and then stood up. He would then feel weak and tired for a few hours after the attack. When he came to my office, he had been seen by his family doctor, given tranquilizers and told 'to take it easy.'

"After talking with him and examining him, I suggested he take Rescue Remedy daily when these attacks occur. I also prescribed some vitamin supplements for stress. When I saw him next, he reported only two episodes in the intervening six weeks (he had been having them daily). At the beginning of both episodes, he had taken three drops of Rescue Remedy. He told me these drops seemed to clear up the wooziness quickly, and a full-blown attack never materialized.

"Additionally, he said that he knew things had changed when, during a recent bridge game, he got up to go to the kitchen after sitting for over two hours, (this normally would have created a problem for him) and became really excited when he realized that he had not been weak or woozy for weeks."

Ronald Dushkin, MD,
Kripalu Center, Lenox, Massachusetts

"A patient of mine was diagnosed as being severely hypoglycemic as well as having severe allergic responses to all kinds of foods and foreign proteins. The Rescue Remedy liquid has proven significant in terms of providing stress relief during the acute episodes, especially after [the patient takes] any offending substances."

Jim Said, DC, ND
Grants Pass, Oregon

Acute and Chronic:
Consumer Use

I have suffered from head noises for forty years, and all the doctor and ear specialists I have seen have been of little help. Two nights ago, I awoke at 3 a.m.. The noises were so terrible that I felt I couldn't take anymore and rose with the intention of trying to 'end it all.' Stepping out of bed, I noticed the little bottle of Rescue Remedy that I keep on my bedside table for emergencies. Unbelievable as this may sound, I took three small sips from the bottle, and in less than a minute my panic had subsided, allowing me to fall asleep peacefully.

Stirling, Scotland

I get a powerful allergic reaction to a combination of pollution and cats. My eyes itch; I get a rash on the back of my knees and around my eyes; I sneeze; and, if I stay in that environment, I have coughing and retching spasms. The only thing that alleviates my distress is Rescue Remedy.

East Hampton, New York

During a bout of sinusitis with associated congestion and pain, I poured a diluted dose of Rescue Remedy in my palm and sniffed it up each nostril; it was not pleasant, but it was most effective. I patted the rest of the dose over my sinuses, and the relief was almost instantaneous. I have shared this knowledge with several other folks who also report excellent results.*

Christchurch, New Zealand

---

*Rescue Remedy cream can be used here in the same way.

I began to prepare for a difficult heart operation by taking the Rescue Remedy each day. I took it full strength right before the operation, a double-bypass and mitral valve replacement, and then again each hour afterwards in the intensive care unit.

Following my operation, I had an unusually rapid recovery. This surprised the doctors, who felt it would be at least six months before I could do much of anything. I continued to take the remedy and was back at work before three months were up. Even now, during my checkups, the doctors are amazed at how swift my recovery was.

United States

A friend of mine who is an accomplished runner took regular doses of Rescue Remedy while running a thirty-one-mile marathon. After his seven-and-a-half-hour run, he had no soreness or significant exhaustion; he said he felt better than he did after any previous run.

In another incident: A thirty-eight year-old acquaintance of mine who was not used to strenuous exercise took a three-hour hike over snow, ice, and rocks, while wearing only soft moccasins. After his walk he took a hot shower, then applied the Rescue Remedy cream to his calves and to the soles of his feet. Shortly thereafter, he reported happily that there was no muscle soreness or swelling in his feet or legs.

New Mexico

My lips were chapped to the point where I could not smile, eat, or talk. My lower lip was also split about one-eighth of an inch. I applied Rescue Remedy cream to my lips, and within minutes I felt a great deal of relief from the pain—I could even smile again. I applied the cream several times that day and the next, and on the third day, I found I didn't need it any more. The split had come together, and my lips had completely healed.

New York City, New York

Years ago, my fingernails began to crack, flake, peel and split, and I tried every sort of cream and nail-hardener on the market—calcium tablets, cod liver oil, iodine, biochemic remedies. All proved ineffective. Finally, I bought a set of false nails, which I wore on social occasions. Five weeks ago, as I was rubbing Rescue Remedy cream into a bad bruise on my hand, I absent-mindedly smoothed it on my nails and cuticles. It worked! Now I am showing everyone my really lovely, healthy, strong, long fingernails. I am absolutely thrilled.

Plymouth, England

One of my co-workers was in pain during her menstrual cycle. She was sitting with her head on her desk, almost fainting. I squeezed a few drops of Rescue Remedy into a glass of water and urged her to drink it. She did, and to her great surprise, the pain diminished, then stopped almost immediately. Afterwards, she was able to finish her day's work without a recurrence of the pains or cramps.

Berkshire, England

Not getting consistent results from the various steroid creams I had been taking, I followed the suggestion of a homoeopathic physician and used the Rescue Remedy cream for an irritating eczema on my arms. I applied it two or three times a day, and after several weeks, the area improved greatly. Since last year, there have been very few recurrences, and those few promptly disappear when I apply a little Rescue Remedy cream.

Los Angeles, California

Rescue Remedy helped my wife deal with her emotional stress throughout the most severe and fearsome period of continuous illness that she has ever had. I believe that Rescue Remedy, which she took frequently during this period, stabilized her to the point that she was able to cope with her situation in a way that saved her life.

Arizona

Animals: Professional and Consumer Use

Out of thousands of case studies, some of the most extraordinary and dramatic reports have been those involving the use of the Bach Flower Remedies and Rescue Remedy with animals. The following is a compilation of cases from veterinarians and other professionals working with animals, as well as from individual consumers and pet owners.

Many veterinarians, using the Rescue Remedy as a last resort after standard procedures had failed, reported remarkable results.

It should be noted however, that the cases outlined here represent the use of Rescue Remedy with animals; and is not meant to imply its use or effectiveness for similar situations or conditions in humans.

Although the exact way in which the Bach remedies and the Rescue Remedy work is not yet known, the many animal reports outlined here strongly indicate that the remedies are not placebos. In light of this, the importance of further controlled studies cannot be emphasized enough.

Animals: Professional Testimonies

"I strongly encourage all my fellow veterinarians to use Rescue Remedy. I have used it, especially with dogs, in cases of shock, accidents, injuries, presurgical work, and tooth extractions. It does make a difference in reducing anxiety and calming the animals down so they are less susceptible to stress. In addition, it generally makes the anaesthetic procedure go a lot smoother. I believe the Rescue Remedy affects the higher centers of the brain. Dr. Bach was a medical genius; he had tremendous insight in knowing which plant would affect particular conditions."

George MacLeod, DVSM, MRCVS, England;
one of the world's foremost authorities on
the use of homoeopathic remedies for animals;
president, British Association of Homoeopathic
Veterinary Surgeons;
author of four major books on the use of
homoeopathy with animals

"We have found the Bach Flower Remedies and especially Rescue Remedy very helpful in alleviating a wide range of problems and conditions affecting all types of birds and animals. In addition, I have found the Rescue Remedy cream invaluable for insect and animal bites. We regard animals as equal to humans and they deserve equal treatment. In our experience, we have found the Rescue Remedy and the other Bach remedies an invaluable healing tool we would not want to be without."

John Bryant, former manager,
Ferne Animal Sanctuary,
Chard, Somerset, England

"Rescue Remedy, especially combined with Arnica (a homoeopathic remedy), is helpful in various types of animal emergencies, such as shock. I would encourage other veterinarians to try it. I would also like to see more work in testing and assessing the [benefits of] Rescue Remedy, for it has a tremendous potential in veterinary medicine."

Christopher Day, MB, MRCVS,
Stanford-in-the-vale, England;
author of *Homoeopathic Treatment of Small
Animals* (London: Wigmore Publications Ltd, 1984)

In his book, *Dr. Pitcairn's Complete Guide to Natural Health for Dogs and Cats,* Dr. Pitcairn recommends Rescue Remedy, for animals, used along with cardiopulmonary resuscitation, acupressure, external heart-massage, and other modalities, for various conditions.

For information on Dr. Pitcairn's recommendations, consult his book's special guide to handling emergencies, pp. 259-266.

"I have used Rescue Remedy to treat injured birds, newborn puppies, and kittens that are very weak, often with excellent results. I also use Rescue Remedy after difficult surgery, and in many cases this will make a significant difference in the animal waking up more quickly and easily."

> **Richard H. Pitcairn,** DVM, PhD,
> Eugene, Oregon;
> author of *Dr. Pitcairn's Complete Guide to Natural Health for Dogs and Cats* (Emmaus, Pennsylvania; Rodale Press, 1982)

"I use Rescue Remedy especially with newborn animals after a Caesarean section. The remedy seems particularly effective in compensating for the depressing quality of anaesthesia produced in the progeny [offspring]. Further, I consider it an outstanding aid to the harmonious survival of the young animal's family, including an anxious sire."

> **J.L. Newns,** BVetMed, MRCVS,
> Cornwall, England

"I have found the Bach Flower Rescue Remedy extremely effective in postsurgical instances. It is extraordinary in reviving pups after Caesareans. I administer Rescue Remedy during the cleanup stage once the throat is cleared; I find this to be most effective in improving the puppies' respiration and in bringing [the animals] back to normal.

"I use and recommend Rescue Remedy in situations involving the collapse of any young animal. It's a means of buying time. It's an excellent adjunct to any other treatment used for and during an immediate crisis. Try it; don't be concerned with [why or] how it works, since you might deprive yourself of a wonderful healing tool."

J.G.C. Saxton, BVetMed, MRCVS,
Leeds, England

"I use the Bach Flower Remedies on dogs that are under stress and need to relax. I also use the remedies during acupuncture therapy. Ninety percent of the time I get good to excellent results; only ten percent of the cases show little or no effect. I have used Rescue Remedy with animals that have been hit by cars or are in shock after surgery. It really does make a difference. I think that everyone, especially veterinarians, should have Rescue Remedy on hand. It is so effective yet inexpensive that it would be senseless not to try it. If it helps to get the animal out of shock, or even to calm down, it's worth it."

John B. Limehouse, DVM,
North Hollywood, California

"The Bach Flower Remedies are one of the most humane and gentle systems of healing I know. During their development, no animals were required to be sacrificed to prove the remedies' efficacy. They are a tremendous gift of healing for animals. In addition, the Bach remedies can help a person tune in to [himself] and become more sensitive to the animals.

"The more we use the remedies ourselves, the more our understanding of animals' emotions become clear. Careful observation has shown that animals tend to develop the same problems their owners have, especially psychosomatic ones. In addition, animals often have to cope with loneliness, anxiety, and fear. Rescue Remedy is highly recommended for all crises, and especially before and after surgery. We have found, when the remedies are used as indicated, that animals tend to recover very, very quickly."

Rebecca Hall, London, England;
author of *Animals Are Equal:
An Exploration of Animal Consciousness*
(London: Wildwood House, 1983) and
Voiceless Victims (London: Wildwood House,
1984)

"As a veterinary surgeon in general practice, I regularly administer Rescue Remedy for cases involving birth trauma, accident trauma, and post-Caesarean section....

"Often following a difficult birth, puppies or kittens that have been a long time in the birth canal will be slow in taking up the challenge of life. Rescue Remedy dripped on their tongues will give them that impetus to survive.

"Many animals born by Caesarean section often suffer before birth from respiratory depression as a result of the anaesthetic reaching them via their mother's blood stream. Rescue Remedy appears to stimulate their respiration and assist them in eliminating the toxic effects.

"I have had encouraging results using the remedy with lambs that have experienced a difficult birth. This is especially common with small hill ewes. Very often the newborn are suffering from bruising, exhaustion, and shock; their mothers may also be in a similar condition. For both, Rescue Remedy can be a great aid to recovery.

"I also use Rescue Remedy as a standard treatment for wild and domestic birds...[when] the animals are in shock and exhausted: birds that have been attacked by cats or hit by cars; [birds that have] flown into windows, [or fallen] out of their nests; sea birds blown ashore following severe storms; and birds recovering from anaesthetics. In these cases, I will generally administer two to three drops of the Rescue Remedy into the throat, place the bird in a dark box by a heat source, and leave it for about two hours. Often this is the only treatment required. In other cases, it will have helped the bird to be able to cope with further handling and therapy.

"I would encourage all veterinarians to have Rescue Remedy on hand. This is not a miracle medicine, but used regularly where indicated, it has much to recommend it. Inevitably there will be a case, as I have experienced, where Rescue Remedy will have such a profound and startling effect during a crisis that it will leave little doubt as to its efficacy."

Bruce Borland, BVetMed, MRCVS,
Bearsden, Scotland

"I use Rescue Remedy as a routine part of my veterinary practice in pre- and postoperative surgery. In accidents, Rescue Remedy helps animals overcome the shock of strange surroundings and assists with a more rapid recovery. The Rescue Remedy can be administered orally, put in drinking water, or dropped directly on and in the mouth. One of the great benefits of using the Bach remedies, including Rescue Remedy, is that they will not interfere with any other medicine or treatment the animal may be involved in. I would never hesitate using any of the Bach remedies.

"In my experience I have also found that one or two drops of Rescue Remedy will have an almost immediate effect on regulating and deepening an animal's breathing on coming out of an anaesthetic.

"I would further recommend that zookeepers have and use all the Bach remedies, especially Rescue Remedy. Simplicity is the key with the Bach system. I would use them [the remedies] in conjunction with other methods without reservations."

Eileen Wheeler, MRCVS,
Wales, United Kingdom

"I keep both Rescue Remedy cream and liquid available at all times, as I find them an invaluable aid in my veterinary work. They even work on wounds that would usually be slow to heal, as is the case with tortoises. The cream keeps the wounds supple, relieves pain, and speeds up the healing process. As I work with several animal rescue organizations, I am often called upon to treat sick or injured wild creatures, including foxes, badgers, and deer. Rescue Remedy liquid assists greatly by allaying their fear and panic; it also helps them to regain consciousness after being caught in wire snares.

"Birds benefit also from the Rescue Remedy; my standard treatment is to give them Rescue Remedy mixed with honey, then immediately put them into an enclosed box, in a warm, quiet place. After only twenty minutes they are calmer, stronger, and [able to] be handled with less risk of their dying from shock. I have found Rescue Remedy liquid to be extremely effective with creatures suffering emotional traumas and various forms of neuroses....I notice a significant increase in the recovery and survival rates of the wild and domestic species that I have treated since I started using the Bach remedies several years ago."

Sue Smith, veterinary nurse,
Chard, England

Animals: Professional Use

"Not long ago a colleague reported a case of a thoroughbred horse that had gone through long, drawn-out surgery involving the exploration of a tumour in the perineum area. The horse was given Rescue Remedy for three days before, and again after, the operation. During subsequent checkups, the veterinarian was staggered that the animal had recovered so quickly from such a traumatic procedure."

Eileen Wheeler, MRCVS,
Wales, United Kingdom

"Recently while I was carrying out a routine operation on a young toy poodle, it suffered an acute anaesthetic crisis with both the respiration and the heart stopping. The dog was given heart massage, artificial respiration and cardiac stimulants, but to no avail. When all else had failed, I gave the animal a few drops of Rescue Remedy under the tongue. Twenty seconds later the dog took an enormous breath and the heart started pumping. With further doses of remedy, both pulse and respiration were stabilised, the surgery was completed and the dog made an uneventful recovery. My nurse witnessed all this and looked at the poodle with disbelief. This seems a classic case where everything was traditionally done, but Rescue Remedy used as a last resort, saved the day and the dog. I was extremely impressed and continue to use the remedy in my practice."

In another case: "A Labrador bitch was presented for surgery with a ruptured diaphragm, the result of a road traffic accident. This condition always constitutes an extra anaesthetic risk. Once the animal was anaesthetised and surgery was commenced, it suffered respiratory and cardiac arrest. The dog failed to respond to orthodox methods of resuscitation but did respond to a dose of Rescue Remedy . As with the poodle, the heart started beating again and breathing was established voluntarily.

"Even effective procedures do not work in every case and I have had many cases where Rescue Remedy has been of no help. However, I am convinced of its great value and always have it to hand."

Bruce Borland, BVetMed, MRCVS,
Bearsden, Scotland

"I have recently used Rescue Remedy with a bulldog that was having a mild seizure. He was in a state of panic and was having severe respiratory difficulty. I administered Rescue Remedy at half-hour intervals for three to four hours and found it to be more effective than any sedative I could have used."

J.G.C. Saxton, BVetMed, MRCVS,
Leeds, England

"I was visiting a veterinarian friend of mine when another friend brought in a cat that appeared to be quite exhausted. The cat had been out in the rain all day and appeared frightened. We gave it one dose of Rescue Remedy, and within five minutes it was purring, cozy, and friendly."

G.S. Khalsa, MD,
Lathrup Village, Michigan

"I had a case where a dog was quite nervous and the owners wanted to tranquillize him before going on a long trip. I suggested the Bach Rescue Remedy as often as needed. Upon their return, the owners enthusiastically rang back to say that the remedy had helped remarkably to calm the animal down."

P.A. Culpin, MRCVS,
Surrey, England

"Not long ago a dog was brought into my office after being hit by a car. He wasn't very active, his gums were gray, and the time it took for his capillaries to fill was very slow. He had been hit extremely hard, but had no concussion. I gave him two doses of Rescue Remedy fifteen minutes apart. Within a short time his capillary filling time improved, and he began to perk up and recover."

John B. Limehouse, DVM,
North Hollywood, California

"I have often found Rescue Remedy very helpful for my wild bird patients. I particularly remember the case of a jackdaw suffering from severe head injuries. It was blind in one eye, infected with lice and grapeworms, thin and frail, and almost unconscious. I gave it a few drops of the Rescue Remedy on a child's paint brush, then wrapped it in wool and placed it in an electrically heated hospital cage, which I left in the dark. Soon I was handling a 'live' bird, warm and supple, conscious and alert, which I was able to attend to properly and give food. I am convinced that without the Rescue Remedy, this bird would not have regained consciousness or the will to live. In time it made a complete recovery, and its sight was saved. After it was released, it and another jackdaw used the house like a hotel for weeks, dropping in for a meal, for shelter from the rain, or just to look around."

M. Davidson,
The Bird Hospital,
Helston, Cornwall, England

Animals: Consumer Use

In the middle of March we discovered a small copper butterfly just free from her cocoon. We took her indoors, and for a whole week she remained motionless on a vase of flowers. Several times each day I sat her on a drop of Rescue Remedy on my finger. At last she unfurled her proboscis and took a long draught from the drop.

The result was immediate and almost startling. From being almost lifeless, she fluttered strongly about the room, but since the weather was still cold we kept her indoors for two more days, feeding her on fresh hyacinths and Rescue Remedy. One sunny morning at the end of that time, we opened the window and watched her fly on strong wings to freedom.

USA

My friend's dog became very lethargic when its master died. He walked around for days with his head down. Half an hour after I put four drops of Rescue Remedy on his tongue, he perked up and looked quite different. My friend continued putting drops into his drinking water for a couple of days, since then the dog has completely become himself again.

Newton Corner, Massachusetts

I use Rescue Remedy for all minor injuries that my dog and

cat sustain or when I know the animals are emotionally upset for some reason. It is the only medicine my dog doesn't shy away from; he even licks it off me when I use it.

Kansas City, Missouri

A six-month-old cat was brought in with a fishhook lodged in the pad of its right front paw. The cat was frantic and extremely difficult to control. Rescue Remedy, given orally and applied to the affected paw, calmed the cat down somewhat. Repeated applications allowed us to cut its pad with a razor blade and extract the fishhook with tweezers. I wrapped the paw in gauze and kept it wet with Rescue Remedy. During the one-week convalescence, the cat remained calm and chewed very little at the wrapping. The paw healed remarkably well.

Burkittsville, Maryland

I have an eight-month-old Labrador retriever that had cracked paws. I applied Rescue Remedy cream three times a day for one week. Compared to their normal condition, the paws remained in bad shape. But when I took the dog to the vet, I discovered that the paw condition was a result of distemper. The vet said that she had never seen paws in such good shape in a dog with distemper and wanted to know what I had been applying to them.

Madison, Wisconsin

My six-year-old male cat had a chronic abscess problem. No sooner did one abscess heal than another developed. His hair was falling out, and his eyes began to look very wild. A doctor friend told me about Rescue Remedy. I gave Thomas two doses a day, four drops in his mouth plus four drops in his drinking water. In two days the sores had new granulation and were drying; his coat felt smoother, and he was much calmer. Now he has a very smooth new coat; he is back to his normal weight; all the abscess holes are completely healed, and Thomas has his own bottle of Rescue Remedy.

Alameda, California

The Rescue Remedy cream has proved invaluable in a number of instances. A few days ago, I came across a horse that had hurt itself on barbed wire and had not eaten for two days. Its wound was raw and seemed painful to the touch. I gave the owner a jar of Rescue Remedy and told her to apply it to the affected area at regular intervals. She called one hour later, telling me that the horse began to graze. Two days later, the wound healed over.

New Mexico

I have given the Rescue Remedy to injured wild birds that dash themselves against my windows. It seems to bring them to consciousness quickly, and they fly off.

The most amazing recovery, however, was with my cat. Cats in this valley frequently get an intestinal disorder from which they eventually die. We imagine it comes from the field mice they eat. When my kitten developed the trouble, I thought of the Rescue Remedy. I administered the remedy for three consecutive mornings and nights, after which he recovered. A month later, the cat got sick again; I repeated the same treatment, and within a much shorter time he was better. Now eighteen months old, he eats mice and never seems to get sick. I've treated three of my neighbor's cats and got the same permanent results.

Yarrow, British Columbia

Oscar used to be a real fraidy cat, frightened of everything, including his own shadow. He was covered in eczema from head to tail, and we were always taking him to the vet. Six months ago, I decided to put him on the Bach remedies. I gave him the Rescue Remedy plus two other Bach remedies for his great fears. After administering three drops twice a day for nearly a week Oscar has become a changed animal. His eczema has cleared up, and he continues to be braver each week. Also, he has become extremely affectionate.

London, England

One of our Australian shepherds was running in the snow

and stepped on a broken bottle, cutting his foot. After cleaning it thoroughly and washing it in a herbal infusion, we coated the foot with Rescue Remedy cream and wrapped it. We gave the dog Rescue Remedy drops regularly and continued to coat the wound with the salve. We also dropped some of the remedy on his tongue before changing the bandage, and it always calmed him so that he didn't pull his leg away. After less than a week, his foot had completely healed without complications.

Colorado Springs, Colorado

One of my cats came bounding into the house with what looked like a dead baby chipmunk in its mouth. I pried the cat's jaws open, and the chipmunk hit the carpet with a thud. With no real hope of reviving it, I squirted some drops of Rescue Remedy into its mouth, and immediately it began to twitch and move around. It recovered so quickly that I barely had enough time to find a box for it. Fifteen minutes later, it was well enough for me to release it into the woods. Identical incidents occurred twice more during the next two months, one with a field mouse and another with a second chipmunk. Both animals revived after a dose of Rescue Remedy and were released in good health.

Ballston Lake, New York

We found a pregnant wallaby that was hit by a car on a country road. Her tiny, fully furred baby emerged. It was wriggling, struggling, and frantic. We decided to feed it, through an eyedropper, watered-down dried milk and raw sugar. The baby took the first few drops, but as the day drew on he seemed reluctant to take more. The tiny frame became skeletal and his attitude listless and dependent. We feared we were losing him.

It was then we thought of putting four drops of Rescue Remedy in his milk. Whether it was the taste of brandy, Rescue Remedy is in a brandy base, or whether he was just plain hungry, he took it until we were feeding him regularly.

Fortunately, the veterinary office was open the next day, and we took the wallaby by to show him to the vet. The doctor seemed quite surprised at the apparent health and comfort of our little friend and recommended that we continue our treatment.

For the next few days, we included the Rescue Remedy in his mixture. Today we can happily say that we have one healthy, bouncy, and bigger wallaby with us now.

Australia

We have had some marvelous experiences with the Rescue Remedy on animals. Our little Chihuahua once had a bad fall and became ill although the vet could find nothing wrong. The first dose of Rescue Remedy made a tremendous difference—the dog perked up amazingly. It was also a great help when she gave birth to her puppies. I don't know how I could manage without it.

California

Balludur was a twelve-month-old pedigree golden Labrador that completely distrusted people. No one had ever been able to touch him. Several times in a confined space he had lunged at people and bitten them.

This last time I'd gotten the idea of wetting a piece of bread with Rescue Remedy from the bottle I always carry. I did, and threw the dog a bit of the bread, which he ate. Ten minutes later, finding him still there, I wetted some more bread with the Rescue Remedy and squatted on my heels. To my amazement, he came and snatched it from my fingers and ran away. The following day, I fed him several bits by hand, and he let me rub his ears for a second before jumping away. From then on, he fed out of my hand like a normal dog and let me pat him, pull his tail, or put my hand in his mouth.

In three weeks he was behaving quite normally, contentedly stopping to sniff a trouser leg or to accept a pat or a bit of bread.

Farnborough, England

Our cat, Yarrow, caught a bird and was prevented from eating it just in time. The bird was unconscious, evidently suffering from shock. Frequent applications of the Rescue

Remedy to its head, eyes, beak, and feet helped so much that within fifteen minutes the bird was trying to fly. After another quarter of an hour, off it went.

Bermuda

I have used Rescue Remedy on one of my Lhasa Apsos that was terrified of thunder and lightning. She would panic and hyperventilate, run around looking for a place to hide, tremble, pant, and shake all over. About six months ago we began giving her a dose of Rescue Remedy as soon as she heard the first thunder. She's gotten to the point where she survives storms very well now. We don't have to keep treating her all the time. Last night we had a very bad storm, and the dog didn't bat an eyelash.

Down here we also have real flea epidemics, and my dogs get so irritated that they sometimes chew themselves incessantly. I've found that Rescue Remedy, given orally and put on the itchy spots, gives them relief. I use both the liquid and the cream. The remedy also calms them and cuts down on their frantic scratching.

St. Petersburg, Florida

We have a nine-year-old Chinese bantam chicken called Mrs., which had been trodden on by a horse. I carried Mrs. to her usual bed of hay and put Rescue Remedy around her beak and bathed her leg. I repeated this treatment frequently, until the little hen could drink water to which the Rescue Remedy and Bach remedy Crab Apple had been added.

After three days, one eye, which had closed, opened, and the chicken began to take a slight interest in tomato seeds and blackberries. I administered different Bach remedies according to her momentary moods, and her recovery is regarded as a real flower remedy miracle. She has no fear whatsoever of the ponies grazing around her now.

Godshill Ridge, England

A cat in my neighborhood was very lethargic and uncomfortable after delivering her kittens. She was barely eating and drinking, not good for a nursing mother. One night I gave her a dose of Rescue Remedy in her mouth and one during the next day. The following day, she was eating and drinking normally, happily nursing her kittens.

Albuquerque, New Mexico

Our eight-year-old Belgian shepherd, Fritz, had developed dysplasia, which hampered his ability to run and jump. After some time, his movements became more and more difficult. Our vet explained that Fritz's spinal nervous system was deteriorating and that a Vitamin C supplement might possibly improve the dog's condition. This formula worked for a period of time, but after awhile Fritz began to drag his paws, causing his toenails to be rubbed to the quick. He felt so much pain that eventually we had to carry him with a sling wrapped under his stomach. As a last resort, our vet prescribed steroids, but they had no effect.

Then one day a friend told us about Dr. Bach's Rescue Remedy. After obtaining the remedy, we put a few drops on Fritz's tongue, as our friend suggested. Fritz's first reaction was immediate; his eyes lit up, and his ears became erect.

Amazingly after some weeks of daily doses with the Rescue Remedy, Fritz's rear legs became more responsive, and he no longer needed the sling to help him. He stopped dragging his rear paws; his toenails grew back; and his spirit enlivened. Now, a year later, he walks with no difficulty.

The Dr. Bach Rescue Remedy has been a Godsend.

Chicago, Illinois

Recently, we had a bloated lamb that had reached the stage of lying on her side, gasping. She didn't have long to go when I thought of using the Rescue Remedy. I began administering it every few minutes for about an hour, when I was called away. When I returned about twenty minutes later, to my great surprise I found the lamb up and grazing as if nothing had ever happened. Since then we have saved many lambs suffering from bloat.

New South Wales, Australia

My kids were fishing off a pier when a bird fell into the water. They retrieved it and laid it down when our large dog grabbed it suddenly in his mouth. The children rescued the bird again and brought it to me. I could sense its shock and terror. I got two drops of Rescue Remedy into its beak twice before the day was over. The next day it seemed well, so we freed it, and it flew away.

DeSoto, Texas

I used to do foster work for the Great Dane Rescue League, taking in Great Danes that people could not keep. One day I took in a nine-month-old female Dane that had been living with a psychotic woman. The dog was the jumpiest, most neurotic creature I'd ever seen. For the first eight hours I couldn't get near her at all. It occurred to me to put Rescue Remedy into her drinking water, and after a day she calmed down quite a bit. I continued to treat her food and water for some weeks. Having become much more calm and stable, she was shortly thereafter adopted into a good home. I believe Rescue Remedy was the only thing that prevented her from being put to sleep.

Miami, Florida

My tortoise-shell cat, Tina, who is semi-wild, appeared one day with an enormous sheep tick behind her ear. I dropped some Rescue Remedy onto the tick's body two or three times, in addition to adding some to Tina's milk. In three days, the unpleasant parasite completely disappeared! It seemed to shrink in size and then one day just wasn't there. Evidently, ticks cannot withstand the high vibrations of the remedies.

Hampshire, England

My wife was in a hurry when she changed the water in our small goldfish bowl, adding the wrong water temperature. The fish went into shock. They were lying on their sides near the top of the bowl, apparently near death, with only sporadic movement of their gills. We put several drops of Rescue Remedy in the water, and within an hour the fish had completely recovered. The woman who handles goldfish at the pet shop assures me that it is almost unheard of for goldfish to survive the state of shock I described.

Texas

My four-year-old dog had a swollen eye and showed symptoms of allergies such as restlessness, panting, and difficult breathing. I applied several drops of diluted Rescue Remedy over her eyelid, on the tip of her nose, and in her mouth. Within a half-hour the respiratory symptoms and restlessness had abated, although the dog's eye was still swollen. Soon she became relaxed and sleepy, and after two or three more applications around the eye the swelling disappeared entirely.

Albuquerque, New Mexico

My horse's knee became swollen, and he couldn't put any of his weight on it. I rubbed some Rescue cream on it, and within fifteen minutes the horse was able to walk with a light limp. I rubbed more cream on his knee two or three times during the day. By the next day, there was no noticeable limp or swelling.

Albuquerque, New Mexico

Plants

In addition to humans and animals, the Bach Flower Remedies, as well as Rescue Remedy, are reported to be beneficial used on plants.

Plants are often affected by environmental and systemic weakness much in the same way that humans and animals are. For example, uprooting a plant without taking special precautions may result in shock, in which case the Rescue Remedy or the Bach remedy Star of Bethlehem could be helpful. Exhausted or drooping plants may be helped with either the Bach remedy Olive or Hornbeam. Infested or diseased plants may be helped, along with other appropriate treatments, by the Bach remedy Crab Apple. Other remedies may also be chosen, when a plant is 'out of sorts', by careful observation of plant behaviour and 'personality.' For example, a large overbearing plant which might give the impression of taking over the environment, may require the Bach remedy Vine; while a small delicate plant which seems to 'tremble' around people or things, may require the Bach remedy Aspen or Mimulus.

While dusting, I carelessly dropped one of our African violets face down. Sometime later it stopped drinking, its flowers fell off, and its leaves became limp. I thought it had died of shock, and I felt terrible! Shortly after this I decided to give it the Bach Rescue Remedy. In the beginning just a couple of drops at a time seemed to have a beneficial effect, though it did take a month for the plant to revive completely.

Bexhill-on-Sea, England

We had a cypress bush that was badly attacked by frost early this year. We gave it the Rescue Remedy every morning for about two weeks, and it really took a new lease on life. It is quite a happy and healthy bush now.

Manchester, England

So far, I have found several uses for Rescue Remedy in my garden. I am usually bothered with black slugs, especially on my radishes, but this year I sprinkled Rescue Remedy directly on my seeds before I covered them with earth, and I have had almost no slug activity since.

For all transplants, I put a few drops of Rescue Remedy on the roots before putting them into the ground, and then I give them a solution of five liters of water plus eight drops of Rescue Remedy. The transplants always do well after that.

This spring I've had to be away from the garden, sometimes for a week at a time. Often on my return I would find my flowers drooping quite a bit; however, I've found that if I water them that night with a solution of Rescue Remedy, they'd be bright and lovely in the morning.

Amsterdam, Holland

Our anemones were drooping and limp, looking as though they were about to die. We gave them Rescue Remedy, and within three hours they were perky; their stems had stiffened, and they looked jolly and bright.

Acton, England

One of my favourite miniature rhododendrons succumbed to the drought while we were on holiday. Completely leafless and brittle, it seemed a hopeless case. I applied the Rescue Remedy liquid to one-half of the bush. The treated section is now covered with glossy green leaves and flower buds, while the untreated section is completely dead.

Scotland

When we returned from vacation, I discovered that our favorite sansevieria had been traumatized during our absence. Left on a windowsill overnight, it had become chilled when the temperature dropped to twenty degrees. Its leaves were wrinkled and curled tight. We tried everything to revive it, but nothing worked until we watered and washed its leaves with a solution of spring water and Rescue Remedy. The next morning it started to open, and ten days later it was alive and healthy. It is doing fine now, thanks to Rescue Remedy.

Colorado Springs, Colorado

We had a young persimmon tree that was blown down by the wind and was almost completely severed to about one foot above the ground; only one thin thread of bark joined the two sections.

Without much optimism we placed the tree in an upright position, dressed the wound with bandages soaked in a solution of Rescue Remedy, and strapped the two sections tightly between wooden splints.

I kept the dressings moist with the medicine for several days, also watering the roots freely with a weak solution. Now, after this long, severe winter, our little tree is budding normally and shows no signs of the injury at all.

England

Conclusion

The reader may by now have gathered from the preceding pages that the healing effects of the Bach Flower Rescue Remedy on people, plants and animals seem remarkable, if not miraculous. The Rescue Remedy appears to work uniquely on each individual in moments of crisis, giving, for example, soothing relief from the sting of a bee, or quietness to the mind in a time of grief.

It is not the purpose of this work to claim phenomenal cures for serious conditions requiring professional treatments; nor is it to state that the Rescue Remedy should replace standard orthodox medical practice. The intent of this book is to demonstrate that the Rescue Remedy has been consistently used in the past fifty years as an invaluable healing adjunct, which is safe and has no reported side effects.

It has been shown that if standard treatment or first aid measures are not available, Rescue Remedy can make a critical difference in the recovery of the patient, especially by alleviating stressful states of mind. Case histories show that the Rescue Remedy may calm the individual and ease terror, anxiety, and fear involved with illness or injury, thereby helping the person to withstand the trauma while professional help is summoned. Even when treatment is immediately available, Rescue Remedy will augment that therapy by providing a feeling of comfort and safety. Reports indicate that psychotherapists and other health care professionals have found Bach Flower Remedies invaluable for calming anxiety or tension. As well as providing emotional comfort, the Rescue Remedy speeds the healing of physical injuries such as cuts, sprains, bruises, and other physical traumas in people, animals, and even plants.

The Rescue Remedy and Bach Flower Remedies should not be considered as drugs or addictive crutches, but as catalysts that bring about a balance in the individual's emotional and mental levels. The remedies enable some people to become more aware of their inner nature, often bringing insight which helps prevent future recurrence of problems or illness.

In today's society, lack of professional accessibility, high costs, ineffective cures, and undesirable side effects from drugs are some of the many factors contributing to a phenomenal rise of interest in medical self-care. As an indicator of this growing awareness, a report prepared by the Commission on Alternative Medicine in the Netherlands stated that the right of the individual to use an alternative/complementary medicine should be respected. Along similar lines in the United States, Joe Graedon, the Drugs Editor of "Medical Self-Care", and the author of *The People's Pharmacy* and *The People's Pharmacy II*, stated that ". . . if the remedy is harmless and inexpensive and the possible rewards are great, you may decide to conduct your own experiment without waiting for the double-blind studies. Part of self-care is being aware of the no-man's land where some pretty respectable experts say therapy 'x' works, but the final verdict isn't in . . . the final decision is yours."

To date, Rescue Remedy has not had any clinical trials. However, it is anticipated that research work will be carried out using clinical studies to prove the healing effects of the Rescue Remedy and other Bach Flower Remedies. In the interim, the testimonials included in this book from the many scientifically trained medical practitioners may serve to answer any queries concerning the Rescue Remedy's safety and effectiveness. Although some critics may consider these testimonials to be subjective reporting, it should be pointed out that the history of pharmacy is full of examples where folk medicines were subsequently validated.

The case histories reported earlier were based on the use of the Rescue Remedy that is produced by the Bach Centre in Great Britain. As with many successful quality products, there are often imitations which follow and the Bach Flower Remedies are no exception.

A month before he died, Dr. Edward Bach wrote a letter to Victor Bullen, his assistant, on 26 October 1936, foretelling that there would be others who would want to change, add to, and delete from his system of healing. He wrote:

Dear Vic,

I think now you have seen every phase of this Work.

This last episode of Doctor Max Wolf may be welcomed. It is a proof of the value of our Work when material agencies arise to distort it, because the distortion is a far greater weapon than attempted destruction.

Mankind asked for free-will, which God granted him, hence mankind must always have a choice.

As soon as a teacher has given his work to the world, a contorted version of the same must arise.

Such has happened even from the humblest like ourselves, who have dedicated our services to the good of our fellow-men, even to the Highest of all, the Divinity of Christ.

The contortion must be raised for people to be able to choose between the gold and the dross.

Our work is steadfastly to adhere to the simplicity and purity of this method of healing; and when the next edition of the *Twelve Healers* becomes necessary, we must have a longer introduction, firmly upholding the harmlessness, the simplicity and the miraculous healing powers of the Remedies, which have been shown to us through a greater Source than our own intellects.

I feel now, dear Brother, that as I find it more and more necessary to go into temporary solitude, you have the whole situation in hand and can cope with all matters either connected with patients or connected with the administration of this work of healing, knowing that people like ourselves who have tested the glory of self-sacrifice, the glory of helping our brothers, once we have been given a jewel of such magnitude, nothing can deviate us from our path of love and duty to displaying its lustre, pure and unadorned, to the people of the world.

Since then, many "people of the world" continue to benefit from his gentle system of healing.

Without Dr. Bach's deep insight into and understanding of the nature of disease, his gentle system of healing would not have evolved.

As nothing can replace Edward Bach's original writings, *Ye Suffer From Yourselves* and *Free Thyself* are provided for the reader's reflection and upliftment.

APPENDIX A

Ye Suffer
From Yourselves

by
EDWARD BACH
M.B., B.S., M.R.C.S., L.R.C.P., D.P.H.

An Address given at Southport, February, 1931.

IN coming to address you this evening, I find the task not an easy one.

You are a medical society, and I come to you as a medical man: yet the medicine of which one would speak is so far removed from the orthodox views of today, that there will be little in this paper which savours of the consulting room, nursing home, or hospital ward as we know them at present.

Were it not that you, as followers of Hahnemann, are already vastly in advance of those who preach the teachings of Galen, and the orthodox medicine of the last two thousand years, one would fear to speak at all.

But the teaching of your great Master and his followers has shed so much light upon the nature of disease, and opened up so much of the road which leads to correct healing, that I know you will be prepared to come with me further along that path, and see more of the glories of perfect health, and the true nature of disease and cure.

The inspiration given to Hahnemann brought a light to humanity in the darkness of materialism, when man had come to consider disease as a purely materialistic problem to be relieved and cured by materialistic means alone.

He, like Paracelsus, knew that if your spiritual and mental aspects were in harmony, illness could not exist: and he set out to find remedies which would treat our minds, and thus bring us peace and health.

Hahnemann made a great advance and carried us a long way along the road, but he had only the length of one life in which to work, and it is for us to continue his researches where he left off: to add more to the structure of perfect healing of which he laid the foundation, and so worthily began the building.

The homoeopath has already dispensed with much of the unnecessary and unimportant aspects of orthodox medicine, but he has yet further to go. I know that you wish to look forward, for neither the knowledge of the past nor the present is sufficient for the seeker after truth.

Paracelsus and Hahnemann taught us not to pay too much attention to the details of disease, but to treat the personality, the inner man, realising that if our spiritual and mental natures were in harmony disease disappeared. That great foundation to their edifice is the fundamental teaching which must continue.

Hahnemann next saw how to bring about this harmony, and he found that among the drugs and the remedies of the old school, and among elements and plants which he himself selected, he could reverse their action by potentisation, so that the same substance which gave rise to poisonings and symptoms of disease, could — in the minutest quantity — cure those particular symptoms when prepared by his special method.

Thus formulated he the law of ''like cures like'': another great fundamental principle of life. And he left us to continue the building of the temple, the earlier plans of which had been disclosed to him.

And if we follow on this line of thought, the first great

realisation which comes upon us is the truth that it is disease itself which is "like curing like": because disease is the result of wrong activity. It is the natural consequence of disharmony between our bodies and our Souls: it is "like curing like" because it is the very disease itself which hinders and prevents our carrying our wrong actions too far, and at the same time, is a lesson to teach us to correct our ways, and harmonise our lives with the dictates of our Soul.

Disease is the result of wrong thinking and wrong doing, and ceases when the act and thought are put in order. When the lesson of pain and suffering and distress is learnt, there is no further purpose in its presence, and it automatically disappears.

This is what Hahnemann incompletely saw as "like curing like."

COME A LITTLE FURTHER ALONG THE ROAD.

Another glorious view then opens out before us, and here we see that true healing can be obtained, not by wrong repelling wrong, but by right replacing wrong: good replacing evil: light replacing darkness.

Here we come to the understanding that we no longer fight disease with disease: no longer oppose illness with the products of illness: no longer attempt to drive out maladies with such substances that can cause them: but, on the contrary, to bring down the opposing virtue which will eliminate the fault.

And the pharmacopoeia of the near future should contain only those remedies which have the power to bring down good, eliminating all those whose only quality is to resist evil.

True, hate may be conquered by a greater hate, but it can only be cured by love: cruelty may be prevented by a greater cruelty, but only eliminated when the qualities of sympathy and pity have developed: one fear may be lost and forgotten in the presence of a greater fear, but the real cure of all fear is perfect courage.

And so now, we of this school of medicine have to turn our attention to those beautiful remedies which have been Divinely placed in nature for our healing, amongst those beneficent, exquisite plants and herbs of the countryside.

It is obviously fundamentally wrong to say that "like cures like." Hahnemann had a conception of the truth right enough, but expressed it incompletely. Like may strengthen like, like may repel like, but in the true healing sense like cannot cure like.

If you listen to the teachings of Krishna, Buddha, or Christ, you will find always the teachings of good overcoming evil. Christ taught us not to resist evil, to love our enemies, to bless those who persecute us — there is no like curing like in this. And so in true healing, and so in spiritual advancement, we must always seek good to drive out evil, love to conquer hate, and light to dispel darkness. Thus must we avoid all poisons, all harmful things, and use only the beneficent and beautiful.

No doubt Hahnemann, by his method of potentisation, endeavoured to turn wrong into right, poisons into virtues, but it is simpler to use the beauteous and virtuous remedies direct.

Healing, being above all materialistic things, and materialistic laws, Divine in its origin, is not bound by any of our conventions or ordinary standards. In this we have to raise our ideals, our thoughts, our aspirations, to those glorious and lofty realms taught and shown to us by the Great Masters.

Do not think for one moment that one is detracting from Hahnemann's work, on the contrary, he pointed out the great fundamental laws, the basis; but he had only one life: and had he continued his work longer, no doubt he would have progressed along these lines. We are merely advancing his work, and carrying it to the next natural stage.

Let us now consider why medicine must so inevitably change. The science of the last two thousand years has regarded disease as a material factor which can be eliminated by material means: such, of course, is entirely wrong.

Disease of the body, as we know it, is a result, an end product, a final stage of something much deeper. Disease originates above the physical plane, nearer to the mental. It is entirely the result of a conflict between our spiritual and mortal selves. So long as these two are in harmony, we are in perfect health: but when there is discord, there follows what we know as disease.

Disease is solely and purely corrective: it is neither vindictive nor cruel: but it is the means adopted by our own Souls to point out to us our faults: to prevent our making greater errors: to hinder us from doing more harm: and to bring us back to that path of Truth and Light from which we should never have strayed.

Disease is, in reality, for our good, and is beneficent, though we should avoid it if we had but the correct understanding, combined with the desire to do right.

Whatever error we make, it reacts upon ourselves, causing us unhappiness, discomfort, or suffering, according to its nature. The object being to teach us the harmful effect of wrong action or thought: and, by its producing similar results upon ourselves, shows us how it causes distress to others, and is hence contrary to the Great and Divine Law of Love and Unity.

To the understanding physician, the disease itself points out the nature of the conflict. Perhaps this is best illustrated by giving you examples to bring home to you that no matter from what disease you may suffer, it is because there is disharmony between yourself and the Divinity within you, and that you are committing some fault, some error, which your Higher Self is attempting to correct.

Pain is the result of cruelty which causes pain to others, and may be mental or physical: but be sure that if you suffer pain, if you will but search yourselves you will find that some hard action or hard thought is present in your nature: remove this, and your pain will cease. If you suffer from stiffness of joint or limb, you can be equally certain that there is stiffness in your mind; that you are rigidly holding on to some idea, some principle, some convention may be, which you should not have. If you suffer from asthma, or difficulty in breathing, you are in some way stifling another personality; or from lack of courage to do right, smothering yourself. If you waste, it is because you are allowing someone to obstruct your own life-force from entering your body. Even the part of the body affected indicates the nature of the fault. The hand, failure or wrong in action: the foot, failure to assist others: the brain, lack of control: the heart, deficiency or excess, or wrong doing in the aspect of love: the eye, failure to see aright and comprehend the truth when placed before you. And so, exactly, may be worked out the reason and nature of an infirmity: the lesson required of the patient: and the necessary correction to be made.

Let us now glance, for a moment, at the hospital of the future.

It will be a sanctuary of peace, hope, and joy. No hurry: no noise: entirely devoid of all the terrifying apparatus and appliances of today: free from the smell of antiseptics and anaesthetics: devoid of everything that suggests illness and suffering. There will be no frequent taking of temperatures to disturb the patient's rest: no daily examinations with stethoscopes and tappings to impress upon the patient's mind the nature of his illness. No constant feeling of the pulse to suggest that the heart is beating too rapidly. For all these things remove the very atmosphere of peace and calm that is so necessary for the patient to bring about his speedy recovery. Neither will there be any need for laboratories; for the minute and microscopic examination of detail will no longer matter when it is fully realised that it is the patient to be treated and not the disease.

The object of all institutions will be to have an atmosphere of peace, and of hope, of joy, and of faith. Everything will be done to encourage the patient to forget his illness; to strive for health; and at the same time to correct any fault in his nature; and come to an understanding of the lesson which he has to learn.

Everything about the hospital of the future will be uplifting and beautiful, so that the patient will seek that refuge, not only to be relieved of his malady, but also to develop the desire to live a life more in harmony with the dictates of his Soul than had been previously done.

The hospital will be the mother of the sick; will take them up in her arms; soothe and comfort them; and bring them hope, faith and courage to overcome their difficulties.

The physician of tomorrow will realise that he of himself has no power to heal, but that if he dedicates his life to the service of his brother-men; to study human nature so that he may, in part, comprehend its meaning; to desire whole-heartedly to relieve suffering, and to surrender all for the help of the sick; then, through him may be sent knowledge to guide them, and the power of healing to relieve their pain. And even then, his power and ability to help will be in proportion to his intensity of desire and his willingness to serve. He will understand that health, like life, is of God, and God alone. That he and the remedies that he uses are merely instruments and agents in the Divine Plan to assist to bring the sufferer back to the path of the Divine Law.

He will have no interest in pathology or morbid anatomy; for his study will be that of health. It will not matter to him whether, for example, shortness of breath is caused by the tubercle baccillus, the streptococcus, or any other organism: but it will matter intensely to know why the patient should have to suffer difficulty of breathing. It will be of no moment to know which of the valves of the heart is damaged, but it will be vital to realise in what way the patient is wrongly developing his love aspect. X-rays will no longer be called into use to examine an arthritic joint, but rather research into the patient's mentality to discover the stiffness in his mind.

The prognosis of disease will no longer depend on physical signs and symptoms, but on the ability of the patient to correct his fault and harmonise himself with his Spiritual Life.

The education of the physician will be a deep study of human nature; a great realisation of the pure and perfect: and an understanding of the Divine state of man: and the knowledge of how to assist those who suffer that they may harmonise their conduct with their Spiritual Self, so that they may bring concord and health to the personality.

He will have to be able, from the life and history of the patient, to understand the conflict which is causing disease or disharmony between the body and Soul, and thus enable him to give the necessary advice and treatment for the relief of the sufferer.

He will also have to study Nature and Nature's Laws: be conversant with Her Healing Powers, that he may utilise these for the benefit and advantage of the patient.

The treatment of tomorrow will be essentially to bring four qualities to the patient.

First, peace: secondly, hope: thirdly, joy: and fourthly, faith.

And all the surroundings and attention will be to that end.

To surround the patient with such an atmosphere of health and light as will encourage recovery. At the same time, the errors of the patient, having been diagnosed, will be pointed out, and assistance and encouragement given that they may be conquered.

In addition to this, those beautiful remedies, which have been Divinely enriched with healing powers, will be administered, to open up those channels to admit more of the light of the Soul, that the patient may be flooded with healing virtue.

The action of these remedies is to raise our vibrations and open up our channels for the reception of our Spiritual Self, to flood our natures with the particular virtue we need, and wash out from us the fault which is causing harm. They are able, like beautiful music, or any gloriously uplifting thing which gives us inspiration, to raise our very natures, and bring us nearer to our Souls: and by that very act, to bring us peace, and relieve our sufferings.

They cure, not by attacking disease, but by flooding our bodies with the beautiful vibrations of our Higher Nature, in the presence of which disease melts as snow in the sunshine.

And, finally, how they must change the attitude of the patient towards disease and health.

Gone forever must be the thought that relief may be obtained by the payment of gold or silver. Health, like life, is of Divine origin, and can only be obtained by Divine Means. Money, luxury, travel, may outwardly appear to be able to purchase for us an improvement in our physical being: but these things can never give us true health.

The patient of tomorrow must understand that he, and he alone, can bring himself relief from suffering, though he may obtain advice and help from an elder brother who will assist him in his effort.

Health exists when there is perfect harmony between Soul and mind and body: and this harmony, and this harmony alone, must be attained before cure can be accomplished.

In the future there will be no pride in being ill: on the contrary, people will be as ashamed of sickness as they should be of crime.

And now I want to explain to you two conditions which are probably giving rise to more disease in this country than any other single cause: the great failings of our civilisation — greed and idolatory.

Disease, is, of course, sent to us as a correction. We bring it entirely upon ourselves: it is the result of our own wrong doing and wrong thinking. Can we but correct our faults and live in harmony with the Divine Plan, illness can never assail us.

In this, our civilisation, greed overshadows all. There is greed for wealth, for rank, for position, for worldly honours, for comfort, for popularity: yet it is not of these one would speak, because even they are, in comparison, harmless.

The worst of all is the greed to possess another individual. True, this is so common amongst us that it has come to be looked upon as almost right and proper: yet that does not mitigate the evil: for, to desire possession or influence over another individual or personality, is to usurp the power of our Creator.

How many folk can you number amongst your friends or relations who are free? How many are there who are not bound or influenced or controlled by some other human being? How many are there who could say, that day by day, month by month, and year by year, "I obey only the dictates of my Soul, unmoved by the influence of other people?"

And yet, everyone of us is a free Soul, answerable only to God for our actions, aye, even our very thoughts.

Possibly the greatest lesson of life is to learn freedom. Freedom from circumstances, environment, other personalities, and most of all from ourselves: because until we are free we are unable fully to give and to serve our brother-men.

Remember that whether we suffer disease or hardship: whether we are surrounded by relations or friends who may annoy us: whether we have to live amongst those who rule and dictate to us, who interfere with our plans and hamper our progress, it is of our own making: it is because there is still within us a trace left to bar the freedom of someone: or the absence of courage to claim our own individuality, our birthright.

The moment that we ourselves have given complete liberty to all around us: when we no longer desire to bind and limit: when we no longer expect anything from anyone: when our only thought is to give and give and never to take, that moment shall we find that we are free of all the world: our bonds will fall from us: our chains be broken: and for the first time in our lives shall we know the exquisite joy of perfect liberty. Freed from all human restraint, the willing and joyous servant of our Higher Self alone.

So greatly has the possessive power developed in the West that it is necessitating great disease before people will recognise the error and correct their ways: and according to the severity and type of or domination over another, so must we suffer as long as we continue to usurp a power which does not belong to man.

Absolute freedom is our birthright, and this we can only obtain when we grant that liberty to every living Soul who may come into our lives. For truly we reap as we sow, and truly "as we mete so it shall be measured out to us."

Exactly as we thwart another life, be it young or old, so must that react upon ourselves. If we limit their activities, we may find our bodies limited with stiffness: if, in addition, we cause them pain and suffering, we must be prepared to bear the same, until we have made amends: and there is no disease, even however severe, that may not be needed to check our actions and alter our ways.

To those of you who suffer at the hands of another, take courage; for it means that you have reached that stage of advancement when you are being taught to gain your freedom: and the very pain and suffering which you are bearing is teaching you how to correct your own fault, and as soon as you have realised the fault and put that right, your troubles are over.

The way to set about to do this work is to practise exquisite gentleness: never by thought or word or deed to hurt another. Remember that all people are working out their own salvation; are going through life to learn those lessons for the perfection of their own Soul; and that they must do it for themselves: that they must gain their own experiences: learn the pitfalls of the world, and, of their own effort, find the pathway which leads to the mountain top. The most that we can do is, when we have a little more knowledge and experience than a younger brother, very gently to guide them. If they will listen, well and good: if not, we must patiently wait until they have had further experience to teach them their fault, and then they may come to us again.

We should strive to be so gentle, so quiet, so patiently helpful that we move among our fellow men more as a breath of air or a ray of sunshine: ever ready to help them when they ask: but never forcing them to our own views.

And I want now to tell you of another great hindrance to health, which is very, very common today, and one of the greatest obstacles that physicians encounter in their endeavour to heal. An obstacle which is a form of idolatory. Christ said "Ye cannot serve God and mammon," and yet the service of mammon is one of our greatest stumbling blocks.

There was an angel once, a glorious, magnificent angel, that appeared to St. John, and St. John fell in adoration and worshipped. But the Angel said to him, "See thou do it not, I am thy fellow servant and of thy brethren. Worship God." And yet today, tens of thousands of us worship not God, not even a mighty angel, but a fellow human being. I can assure you that one of the greatest difficulties which has to be overcome is a sufferer's worship of another mortal.

How common is the expression: "I must ask my father, my sister, my husband." What a tragedy. To think that a human Soul, developing his Divine evolution, should stop to ask permission of a fellow traveller. To whom does he imagine that he owes his origin, his being, his life — to a fellow-traveller or to his Creator?

We must understand that we are answerable for our actions, and for our thoughts to God, and to God alone. And that to be influenced, to obey the wishes, or consider the desires of another mortal is idolatory indeed. Its penalty is severe, it binds us with chains, it places us in prisons, it confines our very life; and so it should, and so we justly deserve, if we listen to the dictates of a human being, when our whole self should know but one command — that of our Creator, Who gave us our life and our understanding.

Be certain that the individual who considers above his duty his wife, his child, his father, or his friend, is an idolator, serving mammon and not God.

Remember the words of Christ, "Who is My mother, and who are My brethren," which imply that even all of us, small and insignificant as we may be, are here to serve our brother-men, humanity, the world at large, and never, for the briefest moment, to be under the dictates and commands of another human individual against those motives which we know to be our Soul's commands.

Be captains of your Souls, be masters of your fate (which means let yourselves be ruled and guided entirely, without let or hindrance from person or circumstance, by the Divinity within you), ever living in accordance with the laws of, and answerable only to the God Who gave you your life.

And yet, one more point to bring before your notice. Ever remember the injunction which Christ gave to His disciples, "Resist not evil." Sickness and wrong are not to be conquered by direct fighting, but by replacing them by good. Darkness is removed by light, not by greater darkness: hate by love: cruelty by sympathy and pity: and disease by health.

Our whole object is to realise our faults, and endeavour so to develop the opposing virtue that the fault will disappear from us like snow melts in the sunshine. Don't fight your worries: don't struggle with your disease: don't grapple with your infirmities: rather forget them in concentrating on the development of the virtue you require.

And so now, in summing up, we can see the mighty part that homoeopathy is going to play in the conquest of disease in the future.

Now that we have come to the understanding that disease itself is "like curing like": that it is of our own making: for our correction and for our ultimate good: and that we can avoid it, if we will but learn the lessons needed, and correct our faults before the severer lesson of suffering is necessary. This is the natural continuation of Hahnemann's great work; the sequence of that line of thought which was disclosed to him, leading us a step further towards perfect understanding of disease and health, and is the stage to bridge the gap between where he left us and the dawn of that day when humanity will have reached that state of advancement when it can receive direct the glory of Divine Healing.

The understanding physician, selecting well his remedies from the beneficent plants in nature, those Divinely enriched and blessed, will be enabled to assist his patients to open up those channels which allow greater communion between Soul and body, and thus the development of the virtues needed to wipe away the faults. This brings to mankind the hope of real health combined with mental and spiritual advance.

For the patients, it will be necessary that they are prepared to face the truth, that disease is entirely and only due to faults within themselves, just as the wages of sin is death. They will have to have the desire to correct those faults, to live a better and more useful life, and to realise that healing depends on their own effort, though they may go to the physician for guidance and assistance in their trouble.

Health can be no more obtained by payment of gold than a child can purchase his education: no sum of money can teach the pupil to write, he must learn of himself, guided by an experienced teacher. And so it is with health.

There are the two great commandments: ''Love God and thy neighbour.'' Let us develop our individuality that we may obtain complete freedom to serve the Divinity within ourselves, and that Divinity alone: and give unto all others their absolute freedom, and serve them as much as lies within our power, according to the dictates of our Souls, ever remembering that as our own liberty increases, so grows our freedom and ability to serve our fellow-men.

Thus we have to face the fact that disease is entirely of our own making, and that the only cure is to correct our faults. All true healing aims at assisting the patient to put his Soul and mind and body in harmony. This can only be done by himself, though advice and help by an expert brother may greatly assist him.

As Hahnemann laid down, all healing which is not from within, is harmful, and apparent cure of the body obtained through materialistic methods, obtained only through the action of others, without self-help, may certainly bring physical relief, but harm to our Higher Natures, for the lesson has remained unlearnt, and the fault has not been eradicated.

It is terrible today to think of the amount of artificial and superficial cures obtained through money and wrong methods in medicine; wrong methods because they merely suppress symptoms, give apparent relief, without removing the cause.

Healing must come from within ourselves, by acknowledging and correcting our faults, and harmonising our being with the Divine Plan. And as the Creator, in His mercy, has placed certain Divinely enriched herbs to assist us to our victory, let us seek out these and use them to be best of our ability, to help us climb the mountain of our evolution, until the day when we shall reach the summit of perfection.

Hahnemann had realised the truth of "like curing like," which is in reality disease curing wrong action: that true healing is one stage higher than this: love and all its attributes driving out wrong.

That in correct healing nothing must be used which relieves the patient of his own responsibility: but such means only must be adopted which help him to overcome his faults.

That we now know that certain remedies in the homoeopathic pharmacopoeia have the power to elevate our vibrations, thus bringing more union between our mortal and Spiritual self, and effecting the cure by greater harmony thus produced.

And finally, that it is our work to purify the pharmacopoeia, and to add to it new remedies until it contains only those which are beneficent and uplifting.

Free Thyself

by

EDWARD BACH

M.B., B.S., M.R.C.S., L.R.C.P., D.P.H.

INTRODUCTION

It is impossible to put truth into words. The author of this book has no desire to preach, indeed he very greatly dislikes that method of conveying knowledge. He has tried, in the following pages, to show as clearly and simply as possible the purpose of our lives, the uses of the difficulties that beset us, and the means by which we can regain our health; and, in fact, how each of us may become our own doctor.

Free Thyself

CHAPTER I.

It is as simple as this, the Story of Life.

A SMALL child has decided to paint the picture of a house in time for her mother's birthday. In her little mind the house is already painted; she knows what it is to be like down to the very smallest detail, there remains only to put it on paper.

Out comes the paint-box, the brush and the paint-rag, and full of enthusiasm and happiness she sets to work. Her whole attention and interest is centred on what she is doing — nothing can distract her from the work in hand.

The picture is finished in time for the birthday. To the very best of her ability she has put her idea of a house into form. It is a work of art because it is all her very own, every stroke done out of love for her mother, every window, every door painted in with the conviction that it is meant to be there. Even if it looks like a haystack, it is the most perfect house that has ever been painted: it is a success because the little artist has put her whole heart and soul, her whole being into the doing of it.

This is health, this is success and happiness and true service. Serving through love in perfect freedom in our own way.

So we come down into this world, knowing what picture we have to paint, having already mapped out our path through life, and all that remains for us to do is to put it into material form. We pass along full of joy and interest, concentrating all our attention upon the perfecting of that picture, and to the very best of our ability translating our own thoughts and aims into the physical life of whatever environment we have chosen.

Then, if we follow from start to finish our very own ideals, our very own desires with all the strength we possess, there is no failure, our life has been a tremendous success, a healthy and a happy one.

The same little story of the child-painter will illustrate how, if we allow them, the difficulties of life may interfere with this success and happiness and health, and deter us from our purpose.

The child is busily and happily painting when someone comes along and says, "Why not put a window here, and a door there; and of course the garden path should go this way." The result in the child will be complete loss of interest in the work; she may go on, but is now only putting someone else's ideas on paper: she may become cross, irritated, unhappy, afraid to refuse these suggestions; begin to hate the picture and perhaps tear it up: in fact, according to the type of child so will be the reaction.

The final picture may be a recognisable house, but it is an imperfect one and a failure because it is the interpretation of another's thoughts, not the child's. It is of no use as a birthday present because it may not be done in time, and the mother may have to wait another whole year for her gift.

This is disease, the reaction to interference. This is temporary failure and unhappiness: and this occurs when we allow others to interfere with our purpose in life, and implant in our minds doubt, or fear, or indifference.

CHAPTER II.

Health depends on being in harmony with our souls.

IT is of primary importance that the true meaning of health and of disease should be clearly understood.

Health is our heritage, our right. It is the complete and full union between soul, mind and body; and this is no difficult far-away ideal to attain, but one so easy and natural that many of us have overlooked it.

All earthly things are but the interpretation of things spiritual. The smallest most insignificant occurrence has a Divine purpose behind it.

We each have a Divine mission in this world, and our souls use our minds and bodies as instruments to do this work, so that when all three are working in unison the result is perfect health and perfect happiness.

A Divine mission means no sacrifice, no retiring from the world, no rejecting of the joys of beauty and nature; on the contrary, it means a fuller and greater enjoyment of all things: it means doing the work that we love to do with all our heart and soul, whether it be house-keeping, farming, painting, acting, or serving our fellow-men in shops or houses. And this work, whatever it may be, if we love it above all else, is the definite command of our soul, the work we have to do in this world, and in which alone we can be our true selves, interpreting in an ordinary materialistic way the message of that true self.

We can judge, therefore, by our health and by our happiness, how well we are interpreting this message.

There are all the spiritual attributes in the perfect man; and we come into this world to manifest these one at a time, to perfect and strengthen them so that no experience, no difficulty can weaken or deflect us from the fulfilment of this purpose. We chose the earthly occupation, and the external circumstances that will give us the best opportunities of testing us to the full: we come with the full realisation of our particular work: we come with the unthinkable privilege of knowing that all our battles are won before they are fought, that victory is certain before ever the test arrives, because we know that we are the children of the Creator, and as such are Divine, unconquerable and invincible. With this knowledge life is a joy; hardships and experiences can be looked upon as adventures, for we have but to realise our power, to be true to our Divinity, when these melt away like mist in the sunshine. God did indeed give His children dominion over all things.

Our souls will guide us, if we will only listen, in every circumstance, every difficulty; and the mind and body so directed will pass through life radiating happiness and perfect health, as free from all cares and responsibilities as the small trusting child.

CHAPTER III.

Our souls are perfect, being children of the Creator, and everything they tell us to do is for our good.

HEALTH is, therefore, the true realisation of what we are: we are perfect: we are children of God. There is no striving to gain what we have already attained. We are merely here to manifest in material form the perfection with which we have been endowed from the beginning of all time. Health is listening solely to the commands of our souls; in being trustful as little children; in rejecting intellect (that tree of the knowledge of good and evil) with its reasonings, its 'fors' and 'againsts,' its anticipatory fears: ignoring convention, the trivial ideas and commands of other people, so that we can pass through life untouched, unharmed, free to serve our fellow-men.

We can judge our health by our happiness, and by our happiness we can know that we are obeying the dictates of our souls. It is not necessary to be a monk, a nun, or hide away from the world; the world is for us to enjoy and to serve, and it is only by serving out of love and happiness that we can truly be of use, and do our best work. A thing done from a sense of duty with, perhaps, a feeling of irritation and impatience is of no account at all, it is merely precious time wasted when there might be a brother in real need of our help.

Truth has no need to be analysed, argued about, or wrapped up in many words. It is realised in a flash, it is part of you. It is only about the unessential complicated things of life that we need so much convincing, and that have led to the development of the intellect. The things that count are simple, they are the ones that make you say, "why, that is true, I seem to have known that always," and so is the realisation of the happiness that comes to us when we are in harmony with our spiritual self, and the closer the union the more intense the joy. Think of the radiance one sometimes sees in a bride on her wedding morn; the rapture of a mother with a new-born babe; the ecstasy of an artist completing a masterpiece: such are the moments where there is spiritual union.

Think how wonderful life would be if we lived it all in such joy: and so it is possible when we lose ourselves in our life's work.

CHAPTER IV.

If we follow our own instincts, our own wishes, our own thoughts, our own desires, we should never know anything but joy and health.

NEITHER is it a difficult far-away attainment to hear the voice of our own soul; it has all been made so simple for us if we will but acknowledge it. Simplicity is the keynote of all Creation.

Our soul (the still small voice, God's own voice) speaks to us through our intuition, our instincts, through our desires, ideals, our ordinary likes and dislikes; in whichever way it is easiest for us individually to hear. How else can He speak to us? Our true instincts, desires, likes or dislikes are given us so that we can interpret the spiritual commands of our soul by means of our limited physical perceptions, for it is not possible for many of us yet to be in direct communion with our Higher Self. These commands are meant to be followed implicitly, because the soul alone knows what experiences are necessary for that particular personality. Whatever the command may be, trivial or important, the desire for another cup of tea, or a complete change of the whole of one's life's habits, it should be willingly obeyed. The soul knows that satiation is the one real cure for all that we, in this world, consider as sin and wrong, for until the whole being revolts against a certain act, that fault is not eradicated but simply dormant, just as it is much better and quicker to go on sticking one's fingers into the jam-pot until one is so sick that jam has no further attraction.

Our true desires, the wishes of our true selves, are not to be confused with the wishes and desires of other people so often implanted in our minds, or of conscience, which is another word for the same thing. We must pay no heed to the world's interpretation of our actions. Our own soul alone is responsible for our good, our reputation is in His keeping; we can rest assured that there is only one sin, that of not obeying the dictates of our own Divinity. That is the sin against God and our neighbour. These wishes, intuitions, desires are never selfish; they concern ourselves alone and are always right for us, and bring us health in body and mind.

Disease is the result in the physical body of the resistance of the personality to the guidance of the soul. It is when we turn a deaf ear to the 'still small voice,' and forget the Divinity within us; when we try to force our wishes upon others, or allow their suggestions, thoughts, and commands to influence us.

The more we become free from outside influences, from other personalities, the more our soul can use us to do His work.

It is only when we attempt to control and rule someone else that we are selfish. But the world tries to tell us that it is selfishness to follow our own desires. That is because the world wishes to enslave us, for truly it is only when we can realise and be unhampered in our real selves that we can be used for the good of mankind. It is the great truth of Shakespeare, "To thine own self be true, and it must follow, as the night the day, thou canst not then be false to any man."

The bee, by its very choice of a particular flower for its honey, is the means used to bring it the pollen necessary for the future life of its young plants.

CHAPTER V.

———

It is allowing the interference of other people that stops our listening to the dictates of our soul, and that brings disharmony and disease. The moment the thought of another person enters our minds, it deflects us from our true course.

———

GOD gave us each our birthright, an individuality of our very own: He gave us each our own particular work to do, which only we can do: He gave us each our own particular path to follow with which nothing must interfere. Let us see to it that not only do we allow no interference, but, and even more important, that we in no way whatsoever interfere with any other single human being. In this lies true health, true service, and the fulfilment of our purpose on earth.

Interferences occur in every life, they are part of the Divine Plan, they are necessary so that we can learn to stand up to them: in fact, we can look upon them as really useful opponents, merely there to help us gain in strength, and realise our Divinity and our invincibility. And we can also know that it is only when we allow them to affect us that they gain in importance and tend to check our progress. It rests entirely with us how quickly we progress: whether we allow interference in our Divine mission; whether we accept the manifestation of interference (called disease) and let it limit and injure our bodies; or whether, we, as children of God, use these to establish us the more firmly in our purpose.

The more the apparent difficulties in our path the more we may be certain that our mission is worth while. Florence Nightingale reached her ideal in the face of a nation's opposition: Galileo believed the world was round in spite of the entire world's disbelief, and the ugly ducking became the swan although his whole family scorned him.

We have no right whatever to interfere with the life of any one of God's children. Each of us has our own job, in the doing of which only we have the power and knowledge to bring it to perfection. It is only when we forget this fact, and try and force our work on others, or let them interfere with ours that friction and disharmony occur in our being.

This disharmony, disease, makes itself manifest in the body, for the body merely serves to reflect the workings of the soul; just as the face reflects happiness by smiles, or temper by frowns. And so in bigger things; the body will reflect the true causes of disease (which are such as fear, indecision, doubt, etc.) in the disarrangement of its systems and tissues.

Disease, therefore, is the result of interference: interfering with someone else or allowing ourselves to be interfered with.

CHAPTER VI.

All we have to do is to preserve our personality, to live our own life, to be captain of our own ship, and all will be well.

THERE are great qualities in which all men are gradually perfecting themselves, possibly concentrating upon one or two at a time. They are those which have been manifested in the earthly lives of all the Great Masters who have, from time to time, come into the world to teach us, and help us to see the easy and simple way of overcoming all our difficulties.

These are such as —

LOVE.
SYMPATHY.
PEACE.
STEADFASTNESS.
GENTLENESS.
STRENGTH.
UNDERSTANDING.
TOLERANCE.
WISDOM.
FORGIVENESS.
COURAGE.
JOY.

And it is by perfecting these qualities in ourselves that each one of us is raising the whole world a step nearer to its final unthinkably glorious goal. We realise then that we are seeking no selfish gain of personal merit, but that every single human being, rich or poor, high or low, is of the same importance in the Divine Plan, and is given the same mighty privilege of being a saviour of the world simply by knowing that he is a perfect child of the Creator.

As there are these qualities, these steps to perfection, so there are hindrances, or interferences which serve to strengthen us in our determination to stand firm.

These are the real causes of disease, and are of such as —

RESTRAINT.
FEAR.
RESTLESSNESS.
INDECISION.
INDIFFERENCE.
WEAKNESS.
DOUBT.
OVER-ENTHUSIASM.
IGNORANCE.
IMPATIENCE.
TERROR.
GRIEF.

These, if we allow them, will reflect themselves in the body causing what we call disease. Not understanding the real causes we have attributed disharmony to external influences, germs, cold, heat, and have given names to the results, arthritis, cancer, asthma, etc.: thinking that disease begins in the physical body.

There are then definite groups of mankind, each group performing its own function, that is, manifesting in the material world the particular lesson he has learnt. Each individual in these groups has a definite personality of his own, a definite work to do, and a definite individual way of doing that work. There are also causes of disharmony, which unless we hold to our definite personality and our work, may react upon the body in the form of disease.

Real health is happiness, and a happiness so easy of attainment because it is a happiness in small things; doing the things that we really love to do, being with the people that we truly like. There is no strain, no effort, no striving for the unattainable, health is there for us to accept any time we like. It is to find out and do the work that we are really suited for. So many suppress their real desires and become square pegs in round holes: through the wishes of a parent a son may become a solicitor, a soldier, a business man, when his true desire is to become a carpenter: or through the ambitions of a mother to see her daughter well married, the world may lose another Florence Nightingale. This sense of duty is then a false sense of duty, and a dis-service to the world; it results in unhappiness and, probably, the greater part of a lifetime wasted before the mistake can be rectified.

There was a Master once Who said, ''Know ye not that I must be about My Father's business?'' meaning that He must obey His Divinity and not His earthly parents.

Let us find the one thing in life that attracts us most and do it. Let that one thing be so part of us that it is as natural as breathing; as natural as it is for the bee to collect honey, and the tree to shed its old leaves in the autumn and bring forth new ones in the spring. If we study nature we find that every creature, bird, tree and flower has its definite part to play, its own definite and peculiar work through which it aids and enriches the entire Universe. The very worm, going about its daily job, helps to drain and purify the earth: the earth provides for the nutriment of all green things; and, in turn, vegetation sustains mankind and every living creature, returning in due course to enrich the soil. Their life is one of beauty and usefulness, their work is so natural to them that it is their life.

And our own work, when we find it, so belongs to us, so fits us, that it is effortless, it is easy, it is a joy: we never tire of it, it is our hobby. It brings out in us our true personality, all the talents and capabilities waiting within each one of us to be manifested: in it we are happy and at home; and it is only when we are happy (which is obeying the commands of our soul) that we can do our best work.

We may have already found our right work, then what fun life is! Some from childhood have the knowledge of what they are meant to do, and keep to it throughout their lives: and some know in childhood, but are deterred by contra-suggestions and circumstances, and the discouragement of others. Yet we can all get back to our ideals, and even though we cannot realise them immediately we can go on seeking to do so, then the very seeking will bring us comfort, for our souls are very patient with us. The right desire, the right motive, no matter what the result, is the thing that counts, the real success.

So if you would rather be a farmer than a lawyer; if you would rather be a barber than a bus-driver, or a cook than a greengrocer, change your occupation, be what you want to be: and then you will be happy and well, then you will work with zest, and then you will be doing finer work as a farmer, a barber, a cook, than you could ever achieve in the occupation that never belonged to you.

And then you will be obeying the dictates of your Spiritual Self.

CHAPTER VII.

———

Once we realise our own Divinity the rest is easy.

———

IN the beginning God gave man dominion over all things. Man, the child of the Creator, has a deeper reason for his disharmony than the draught from an open window. Our 'fault lies not in our stars, but in ourselves,' and how full of gratitude and hope can we be when we realise that the cure also lies within ourselves! Remove the disharmony, the fear, the terror, or the indecision, and we regain harmony between soul and mind, and the body is once more perfect in all its parts.

Whatever the disease, the result of this disharmony, we may be quite sure that the cure is well within our powers of accomplishment, for our souls never ask of us more than we can very easily do.

Everyone of us is a healer, because every one of us at heart has a love for something, for our fellow-men, for animals, for nature, for beauty in some form, and we every one of us wish to protect and help it to increase. Everyone of us also has sympathy with those in distress, and naturally so, because we have all been in distress ourselves at some time in our lives. So that not only can we heal ourselves, but we have the great privilege of being able to help others to heal themselves, and the only qualifications necessary are love and sympathy.

We, as children of the Creator, have within us all perfection, and we come into this world merely that we may realise our Divinity; so that all tests and all experiences will leave us untouched, for through that Divine Power all things are possible to us.

CHAPTER VIII.

The healing herbs are those which have been given the power to help us preserve our personality.

J UST as God in His mercy has given us food to eat, so has He placed amongst the herbs of the fields beautiful plants to heal us when we are sick. These are there to extend a helping hand to man in those dark hours of forgetfulness when he loses sight of his Divinity, and allows the cloud of fear or pain to obscure his vision.

Such herbs are —

Chicory	*(Cichorium intybus)*
Mimulus	*(Mimulus luteus)*
Agrimony	*(Agrimonia eupatoria)*
Scleranthus	*(Scleranthus annuus)*
Clematis	*(Clematis vitalba)*
Centaury	*(Erythraea centaurium)*
Gentian	*(Gentiana amarella)*
Vervain	*(Verbena officinalis)*
Cerato	*(Ceratostigma willmottiana)*
Impatiens	*(Impatiens royalei)*
Rock Rose	*(Helianthemum vulgare)*
Water Violet	*(Hottonia palustris)*

Each herb corresponds with one of the qualities, and its purpose is to strengthen that quality so that the personality may rise above the fault that is the particular stumbling block.

The following table will indicate the quality, the fault, and the remedy which aids the personality to dispel that fault.

Failing.		*Herb.*		*Virtue.*
Restraint	......	Chicory	......	Love
Fear	......	Mimulus	......	Sympathy
Restlessness	......	Agrimony	......	Peace

Indecision	......	Scleranthus	......	Steadfastness
Indifference	......	Clematis	......	Gentleness
Weakness	......	Centaury	......	Strength
Doubt	......	Gentian	......	Understanding
Over-enthusiasm		Vervain	......	Tolerance
Ignorance	......	Cerato	......	Wisdom
Impatience	......	Impatiens	......	Forgiveness
Terror	......	Rock Rose	......	Courage
Grief	......	Water Violet	......	Joy

The remedies are endowed with a definite healing power quite apart from faith, neither does their action depend upon the one who administers them, just as a sedative sends a patient to sleep whether given by the nurse or the doctor.

CHAPTER IX.

The real nature of disease.

IN true healing the nature and the name of the physical disease is of no consequence whatever. Disease of the body itself is nothing but the result of the disharmony between soul and mind. It is ·only a symptom of the cause, and as the same cause will manifest itself differently in nearly every individual, seek to remove this cause, and the after results, whatever they may be, will disappear automatically.

We can understand this more clearly by taking as an example the suicide. All suicides do not drown themselves. Some throw themselves from a height, some take poison, but behind it all is despair: help them to overcome their despair and find someone or something to live for, and they are cured permanently: simply taking away the poison will only save them for the time being, they may later make another attempt. Fear also reacts upon people in quite different ways: some will turn pale, some will flush, some become hysterical and some speechless. Explain the fear to them, show them that they are big enough to overcome and face anything, then nothing can frighten them again. The child will not mind the shadows on the wall if he is given the candle and shown how to make them dance up and down.

We have so long blamed the germ, the weather, the food we eat as the causes of disease; but many of us are immune in an influenza epidemic; many love the exhilaration of a cold wind, and many can eat cheese and drink black coffee late at night with no ill effects. Nothing in nature can hurt us when we are happy and in harmony, on the contrary all nature is there for our use and our enjoyment. It is only when we allow doubt and depression, indecision or fear to creep in that we are sensitive to outside influences.

It is, therefore, the real cause behind the disease, which is of the utmost importance; the mental state of the patient himself, not the condition of his body.

Any disease, however serious, however long-standing, will be cured by restoring to the patient happiness, and desire to carry on with his work in life. Very often it is only some slight alteration in his mode of life, some little fixed idea that is making him intolerant of others, some mistaken sense of responsibility that keeps him in slavery when he might be doing such good work.

There are seven beautiful stages in the healing of disease, these are —

> PEACE.
> HOPE.
> JOY.
> FAITH.
> CERTAINTY.
> WISDOM.
> LOVE.

CHAPTER X.

To gain freedom, give freedom.

THE ultimate goal of all mankind is perfection, and to gain this state man must learn to pass through all experiences unaffected; he must encounter all interferences and temptations without being deflected from his course: then he is free of all life's difficulties, hardships and sufferings: he has stored up in his soul the perfect love, wisdom, courage, tolerance and understanding that is the result of knowing and seeing everything, for the perfect master is he who has been through every branch of his trade.

We can make this journey a short joyful adventure if we realise that freedom from bondage is only gained by giving freedom; we are set free if we set others free, for it is only by example we can teach. When we have given freedom to every human being with whom we are in contact; when we have given freedom to every creature, everything around us, then we are free ourselves: when we see that we do not, even in the minutest detail, attempt to dominate, control, or influence the life of another, we shall find that interference has passed out of our own lives, because it is those that we bind who bind us. There was a certain young man who was so bound to his possessions that he could not accept a Divine gift.

And we can free ourselves from the domination of others so easily, firstly by giving them absolute freedom, and secondly, by very gently, very lovingly, refusing to be dominated by them. Lord Nelson was very wise in placing his blind eye to the telescope on one occasion. No force, no resentment, no hatred, and no unkindness is necessary. Our opponents are our friends, they make the game worth while, and we shall all shake hands at the end of the match.

We must not expect others to do what we want, their ideas are the right ideas for them, and though their pathway may lead in a different direction from ours, the goal at the end of the journey is the same for us all. We do find that it is when we want others to 'fall in with our wishes' that we fall out with them.

We are like cargo-ships bound for the different countries of the world, some for Africa, some for Canada, some for Australia, then returning to the same home port. Why follow another ship to Canada when our destination is Australia? It means such a delay.

Again, we perhaps do not realise what small things may bind us, the very things that we wish to hold are the things that are holding us: it may be a house, a garden, a piece of furniture; even they have their right to freedom. Worldly possessions, after all are transient, they give rise to anxiety and worry because inwardly we know of their inevitable and ultimate loss. They are there to be enjoyed and admired and used to their full capacity, but not to gain so much importance that they become chains to bind us.

If we set everybody and everything around us at liberty, we find that in return we are richer in love and possessions than ever we were before, for the love that gives freedom is the great love that binds the closer.

CHAPTER XI.

Healing.

F ROM time immemorial humanity has recognised that our Creator in His love for us has placed herbs in the fields for our healing, just as He has provided the corn and the fruit for our sustenance.

Astrologers, those who have studied the stars, and herbalists, those who have studied the plants, have ever been seeking those remedies which will help us to keep our health and joy.

To find the herb that will help us we must find the object of our life, what we are striving to do, and also understand the difficulties in our path. The difficulties we call faults or failings, but let us not mind these faults and failings, because they are the very proof to us that we are attaining bigger things: our faults should be our encouragements, because they mean that we are aiming high. Let us find for ourselves which of the battles we are particularly fighting, which adversary we are especially trying to overcome, and then take with gratitude and thankfulness that plant which has been sent to help us to victory. We should accept these beautiful herbs of the fields as a sacrament, as our Creator's Divine gift to aid us in our troubles.

In true healing there is no thought whatever of the disease: it is the mental state, the mental difficulty alone, to be considered: it is where we are going wrong in the Divine Plan that matters. This disharmony with our Spiritual Self may produce a hundred different failings in our bodies (for our bodies after all merely reproduce the condition of our minds), but what matters that? If we put our mind right the body will soon be healed. It is as Christ said to us, "Is it easier to say, thy sins be forgiven thee or take up thy bed and walk?"

So again let us clearly understand that our physical illness is of no consequence whatsoever: it is the state of our minds, and that, and that alone, which is of importance. Therefore, ignoring entirely the illness from which we are suffering, we need consider only to which of the following types we belong.

Should any difficulty be found in selecting your own remedy, it will help to ask yourself which of the virtues you most admire in other people; or which of the failings is, in others, your pet aversion, for any fault of which we may still have left a trace and are especially attempting to eradicate, that is the one we most hate to see in other people. It is the way we are encouraged to wipe it out in ourselves.

We are all healers, and with love and sympathy in our natures we are also able to help anyone who really desires health. Seek for the outstanding mental conflict in the patient, give him the remedy that will assist him to overcome that particular fault, and all the encouragement and hope you can, then the healing virtue within him will of itself do all the rest.

Photographs

*Dr. Bach rowing, one of his favourite forms of relaxation.
(Courtesy Bach Centre) date unknown*

*Edward Bach as a young man, circa 1905.
(Courtesy Bach Centre)*

*Edward Bach, circa 1922.
(Courtesy E. Varney)*

151

Victor Bullen
(1887-1975)

"Victor Bullen, friend and partner of Dr. Bach, for over 40 years had dedicated his life to bringing back happiness and health to a great number of people, not only with the Bach Flower Remedies but by his own happiness, kindness, and understanding. Dr. Bach called him 'the soul of honour and integrity' and trusted him to carry on his work in all its simplicity after his own death. This Victor did most faithfully."

Nora Weeks, 1975

(Courtesy Bach Centre)
c.1950

Nora Gray Weeks
(1896-1978)

Nora Gray Weeks witnessed the whole spectrum of Dr. Bach's discoveries first hand — proving herself to be not only his right hand helper, but someone he could rely on to nurture him during the great development of his increasing sensitivity through the latter 4 years of his life. Her dedication and loving respect for the doctor must be recorded as perhaps the back-bone of his endeavour, for without her supportive resilience it can safely be assumed that the doctor's work might have faltered before completion — for he did indeed suffer greatly, both mentally and physically as an integral part of his great discovery. The doctor bequeathed to her the whole responsibility of his work. For over 40 years Nora, with the help of Victor, continued steadfastly to offer the Bach remedies to the world honouring the simplicity and purity of Dr. Bach's vision.

(Courtesy Bach Centre)
c.1923

c.1920

Dr. Edward Bach with his daughter Bobbie
(Courtesy E. Varney)

c.1917

c.1919

The Authentic
Bach Flower Remedies

Because of the extensive use and popularity of the Bach Flower Remedies and Rescue Remedy, similar products have begun to appear on the market. The following will help you to distinguish the authentic Bach remedies and Rescue Remedy from other products and clear up some of the misconceptions surrounding the differences.

The name **Rescue Remedy** is a federally registered trademark, as is **Bach Flower Remedies**, with the latter applying to 38 specific preparations and the unique philosophy and system of their use. All 38 of the Bach Flower Remedies are officially recognized as over-the-counter homoeopathic medicines and are listed as such in the *Supplement to the Eighth Edition of the Homoeopathic Pharmacopeia of the United States.*

The Bach Flower Remedies and Rescue Remedy are prepared at only one location in the world, the Bach Centre in England, where to this day the same wildflower locations originally discovered by Dr. Bach are still used. Similar products prepared anywhere else in the world that claim to be Bach Flower Remedies or Rescue Remedy are not, nor are they proven to be, Bach remedy 'equivalents.'

Some of these newly released products are not made from real flowers at all, but are prepared by radionic methods or other devices said to duplicate or enhance the 'vibration' of real flowers. Some of these other products are made from real flowers, but not from the species used for the actual Bach Flower Remedies.

In addition, there are products on the market that are actually unauthorized dilutions of the authentic Bach remedies and Rescue Remedy. Unfortunately, some of the literature and occasionally the labeling of these products makes reference to Dr. Bach's name. This tends to create the false impression that they are genuine Bach remedies or Rescue Remedy. They are not.

All authentic Bach Flower Remedies, including Rescue Remedy liquid, come bottled in concentrated liquid form. Rescue Remedy also comes in cream form. These officially recognized preparations all meet stringent FDA and homoeopathic labeling and quality-control laws. Unauthorized dilutions (even by retail stores) of the Bach Remedies or Rescue remedy, resold over the counter, often do not meet these stringent requirements. Furthermore, though appearing smaller in size, one ten-milliliter (one-third ounce) bottle of Bach remedy concentrate may produce as many as seventy bottles of these watered-down products. Additionally, these products have a limited shelf life, and cost the end consumer substantially more money than if they purchased the authentic Bach remedy concentrate directly.

Ultimately, what distinguishes the real Bach Flower Remedies, including Rescue Remedy, from similar products is more than just the name *Bach*. The Bach Flower Remedies and Rescue Remedy have been used worldwide for over fifty years and have consistently proven themselves safe, gentle, and effective by countless numbers of physicians, health care professionals, and the general public. To make sure you are getting the genuine Bach Flower Remedies or Rescue Remedy, look for the manufacturer's name and address, The Bach Flower Remedies, Mount Vernon, Sotwell, England, as well as the name *Bach* being depicted in longhand, which is a copy of Dr. Bach's actual signature, appearing on the front or side of every label.

The freedom and right to choose are important to us all; equally important is the information and knowledge needed to choose wisely.

Where to Obtain Rescue Remedy and the Other Bach Flower Remedies

In England, and to enquire about distributors in other parts of the world write:

DR. EDWARD BACH CENTRE
Mount Vernon
Sotwell, Wallingford
Oxon., OX10 0PZ, England

This was the home and workplace of Dr. Edward Bach during the latter years. Today, the Dr. Edward Bach Centre still carries on their hereditary work of helping those in need, educating and advising, and preparing the Mother Tinctures. The responsibility for bottling, distribution and marketing of the Bach Remedies throughout the world is carried out by A. Nelson & Co. Ltd., London, who work closely with and under the supervision of the Bach Centre. Additionally, individual booklets, such as Dr. Bach's *The Twelve Healers* and *Heal Thyself*, as well as other materials related to the work, may be obtained here.

In Germany, Austria, and Switzerland write:

THE GERMAN OFFICE
OF THE BACH CENTRE ENGLAND
c/o M. Scheffer
Himmelstrasse 9
D-22299 Hamburg
Germany

Further and Recommended Reading

NOTE: Copies of the books listed below may be ordered in their individual (pamphlet) form, published by C.W. Daniel. These as well as additional information on where to locate Dr. Bach's books in other languages may be obtained from: **The Bach Centre**, Mount Vernon, Sotwell, Wallingford, Oxon., OX10 OPZ, England.

1. *The Bach Flower Remedies* (three volumes in one) includes *Heal Thyself* by Dr. Edward Bach, *The Twelve Healers and Other Remedies* by Dr. Edward Bach, and *The Bach Remedies Repertory* by Dr. F.J. Wheeler (New Canaan, Connecticut: Keats, 1977). All three volumes originally published by C.W. Daniel, Saffron Walden, Essex, 1931, 1933, and 1952, respectively.[1]
2. *The Medical Discoveries of Edward Bach, Physician* by Nora Weeks (New Canaan, Connecticut: Keats, 1979). Originally published by C.W. Daniel, Saffron Walden, Essex, 1940.
3. *The Handbook of the Bach Flower Remedies* by Philip M. Chancellor (New Canaan, Connecticut: Keats, 1980). Originally published by C.W. Daniel, Saffron Walden, Essex, 1971.
4. *The Guide to the Bach Flower Remedies*[2] by Julian Barnard (C.W. Daniel, Saffron Walden, Essex, 1979).
5. *Introduction to the Benefits of the Bach Flower Remedies* by Jane Evans (C.W. Daniel, Saffron Walden, Essex, 1974).
6. *Dictionary of the Bach Flower Remedies* by T.H. Jones (C.W. Daniel, Saffron Walden, Essex, 1976).

---

1. These separate books as well as all the above are available through The Bach Centre, England.
2. No connection with The Bach Centre.

Contributors Index

Index

Index

ABOUT THE AUTHOR

Over the years, Gregory Vlamis has written numerous articles and organized educational seminars in the field of awareness and natural healing. A tireless worker, he has devoted much of his personal time to assisting non-profit organizations to accomplish their various projects and goals.

In addition to writing *Rescue Remedy: The Healing Power of Bach Flower Rescue Remedy*, Mr. Vlamis spent two years researching throughout the United Kingdom. He interviewed those who knew Dr. Bach and uncovered rare letters, photographs, and other biographical material previously unavailable.

A Tale of Three Cities

A NOVEL

Alexander McCabe

A Tale of Three Cities

Published by Alexander McCabe

Copyright Alexander McCabe 2015

ISBN 978-0-9940447-1-6

CreateSpace Edition

The right of Alexander McCabe to be
identified as the author of this work has been
asserted by him in accordance with the
Copyright, Designs, and Patents Act 1988.

This is a work of fiction and, as such,
any reference to any persons, alive or dead,
is purely coincidental.

The author accepts no responsibility nor
liability for the information contained herein

For Gabriel

The best wee boy in the whole wide world...

"When love is not madness, it is not love"

Pedro Calderon de la Barca

Table of Contents

Prelude

Inverness, Scotland

Thursday 7th January

It was a million-dollar reward. A million dollars certainly isn't what it used to be – and is certainly a lot less when converted into British pounds – but still, it was a nice chunk of change. It was enough to tempt Melissa Chisholm to take a week's vacation from her job as a lowly paid bank cashier with non-existent career prospects and book a flight to New York to claim it.

The article had been spread over two glossy pages of a dated magazine in the dentist's waiting room. One of those dreary magazines that share other's inane tales of their children's triumphs, mundane love trysts, and all family matters in between and sell them back to the public under the banner of 'entertainment'. Those magazines that only seem to exist on the newsagent's shelves and medical waiting areas and, much like Santa and the Easter Bunny, nobody ever seems to question where they actually came from, or know anybody who actually buys them.

The stark headline *'I Beat the Mob.... And Lost EVERYTHING'* was emblazoned with pretend blood dripping off every letter for effect, yet it wasn't this that caught Melissa's attention. Rather, it was the second of the three passport-sized color photographs positioned halfway down the right-hand page. Underneath was the caption *'Kristy Bradley, $1m reward for information leading to her recovery'*. The other two images were of a man named Michael Bradley, her lawyer husband, and one Anthony Di Silva, a New York Mafia boss.

The story was a quick read and Melissa devoured every word. Michael and Kristy Bradley had been college sweethearts who had married soon after graduation. They had relocated to New York so that he could accept a position in a modestly successful law firm and he had made partner in seven fast years. The Big Apple had been similarly generous to Kristy and she had also made partner but in a medical practice where she was a highly respected practitioner. Approaching their 30's, they enjoyed all the trappings of success. Family and friends alike were delighted when they bought a dream house in the suburbs with the intention of starting a family.

A little over a year after their move, Michael was approached to run for local mayor. As a member of the town council – along with every other club that would help elevate his profile – he was well-liked and respected within the community. It took very little persuasion, especially when there was even less competition.

Everything in their world was perfect until it came time for the new tenders to be considered by the council for the community garbage collection. These were contracts that were annually renewable and, even to Michael's untrained eye, the cost seemed excessive. His curiosity was further piqued when only one company bid for the tender. As Mayor, he took it as his personal responsibility to approach other waste management companies to encourage some competition. When not a single company replied to his letters, he took a day off work with the intention of visiting each company personally.

He only needed to see one to understand the problem.

Michael was told that the tender price quoted was exorbitantly high as it was a

Mafia owned and operated company. As such, no other company was stupid enough to bid against them. Not so much bad for business, but rather bad for your health.

It gave Michael the class action case that would make his career.

Within weeks, *Michael Bradley and Associates* – there weren't any as yet but there certainly would be in the future – was established in the study-cum-office of their home. He rounded up enough clients to proceed and the case was duly submitted to the court. The expected threats and intimidation had little effect and he successfully argued at a preliminary hearing that there was a serious risk the company could simply dissolve and declare bankruptcy. The judge ruled in his favor and froze $86 million of the company assets. All parties knew then that this was a case that was never going to see the inside of a courtroom and it just needed a reasonable settlement figure. After exhaustive negotiations that lasted just under a year, the final sum of $34 million was agreed upon and Michael was to enjoy a 30% share from his no win, no fee agreement.

The right side of $10 million.

However, on the day the funds were transferred and cleared into his business account, his wife disappeared and a ransom demand for the full amount was received. The case was too much for the local police to handle and the FBI were called in. After three days, Michael very reluctantly transferred the full $34 million into an account in the Cayman Islands.

His wife was never seen nor heard from again, and the money simply vanished.

The only solace for Michael was that there was enough circumstantial evidence to convict Anthony Di Silva – CEO of ADS Waste Management Services Inc. – for the kidnapping and he was sentenced to 25 years to life. At 62 years of age, it was unlikely he would ever be a free man again.

Melissa finished reading the story and drew her attention back to the photographs and her eyes settled on Kristy Bradley.

"Miss Chisholm?" The receptionist called into the half-filled waiting room. "Miss Chisholm?" The second call quickly followed the first and was now aimed directly at her.

"What…?" She struggled to pull herself from the seedy underbelly of New York and back to the dentist's waiting room in Inverness.

"Miss Chisholm, that's the dentist ready for you now". A perfect white smile followed the words that had been thrown in her direction. The receptionist was a walking advertisement for her boss's work, not that Melissa was paying her the slightest attention. Her six-month checkup was proving anything but routine and she quickly stuffed the magazine into her handbag, all but certain she knew Mrs. Kristy Bradley.

Only that wasn't her name now.

Now she used the name Lady Penelope Munro.

Chapter 1

Auchtershinnan Estate, Invernesshire, Scotland

Tuesday 12th January

I love you.

Three words that are collectively unique to everyone. Powerful and magical. When said at the appropriate time, they have the power to cement a relationship and provide the foundation for it to grow and evolve over two individual lifetimes. Yet, like all good magic, the timing is essential.

I love you.

Three words that are sometimes said all too often and, other times, not often enough. Some people can go a lifetime without ever saying them. For others it is a daily routine, said so often they lose all meaning. Some people say it but never show it, others show it without ever saying it.

I love you.

I have only ever said these words to two other people outwith my family. One was a long-term relationship with my high school girlfriend, and this was the most innocent love I have ever known. Pure in its naivety and true in the sense that I was convinced it would last forever. Then 'life' happened. It got in the way and sullied what we had. Still, I remember it, and her, fondly.

The other was my ex-wife Gemma.

I take an illogical and stupid pride – along with a stubborn satisfaction – in knowing that, in both these relationships, they said 'I love you' first. There was no doubt that I loved them both and I was very happy to instantly reciprocate, but then it was on my terms. In saying these three little words, they had left themselves vulnerable. They had handed me the power over their immediate happiness and to not say it back would have hurt them. Hurt them and shattered their confidence. I had no intention of doing either and neither did I have any cause to. I actually did love them, so saying it sincerely was easy, and they were both delighted and relieved when I did.

It just would never have occurred to me to say it first.

Now, it is different. It has been eight short months since Penny had walked into the pub and stood in front of me in my own *'Super Z'* T-shirt. In my shock and, without saying a word, she had simply bent down and kissed me. Immediately thereafter, she uttered the only words that she would say to me that entire evening: *shall we go?* We held hands as we drove back to my place and made love the whole night. Wonderful, passionate, hungry lovemaking.

'I love you' just didn't seem enough to adequately express how I felt about her.

So, for eight long months, the words have never crossed our lips yet we both know that it is there and growing between us. Of course, we have expressed our love for one another in our respective birthday and Christmas cards. She first, naturally, as my birthday fortunately fell before hers. When it was my turn, I merely reciprocated her exact wording on the humorous card that I gave her. Juvenile as it may have been, it made it less noticeable and so gave less cause for her to question it. Yet now I yearned to say it, to verbalize it, to celebrate it.

To just scream *I LOVE YOU*!

But what if she doesn't say it back?

What if she doesn't feel the same way?

What then for our relationship – would it be over?

I knew, deep down, that this was

illogical. After all, it was her suggestion that I move in with her on the estate. She had given me a 'job' of managing the grounds but, in truth, it was more fun than work and hardly taxing on any of my abilities. That had been less than six months ago and I had loved every single second of my life since then.

Although not nearly as much as I loved her.

So I had waited until today and resolved to myself that this was the perfect time to tell her how I felt. It was an ideal opportunity for me to be romantic, outwith the usual prescribed days of St. Valentine's – it really grips my shit when people say 'St. Valen*time*'s' – birthdays, Christmas, etc. I am all but certain that she has no idea what today represents.

It was exactly a year ago today that we first met.

The ornate card had taken me forever to select. In my quest, I had searched through practically every store in Inverness. So many had been discarded because a single word was wrong. Who would have thought that just *one single word* could make such a huge difference? Yet it did to me. Every last word needed to be just perfect. The winner was housed in a pastel blue envelope and was now carefully taped onto the tall box that was covered in wrapping paper. Beside them, a vase held the overly extravagant flowers.

What better way to say 'I love you' than through the written word? It was the medium of all the great romantics, the poets, the lovers. If it was good enough for Shakespeare, then it is good enough for me. Also, by writing it, this would considerably ease the pressure on Penny to say it back. She could read the card without the need to say *anything* in response. This is not so much the case when it is verbalized. At least, that is what I was thinking when I bought and wrote the card. Now all my irrational fears were coursing back through me in waves. This would be the first time I had ever told her I loved her and now she would not merely have to remember it, she would have the hard copy. Should she not be ready to say it back, then she could simply deflect and talk about the present or the flowers.

Finally, I had taken the liberty of delicately placing the collective arrangement on the very same table in the drawing room where Penny had kept the bottle of single malt that we first shared. Technically, that was the first 'gift' she had ever given me. It was hard to believe that it was just a short year ago when I first visited here as a guest to enjoy a weekend break of solitude. After discovering Gemma's affair, I was here to try and mend my own broken heart, here to escape love.

Instead, love found me.

So, to me, there was no better place. Yet the same disapproving stares still gazed down upon me from every wall. They seemed more akin to a jury than an assembly of her relatives from the dim and distant past. My presence here so offensive that I could almost hear them all spinning in their graves. There was no denying that this room still gave me the creeps, especially after dark, and even more so when I am in here alone. Even the roaring fire hypnotically swaying in the hearth could provide me no comfort. Truth be told, I tried my best to avoid this room. It only ever came alive when Penny was in here with me. She would never know the sacrifice I'd made, and the courage and bravery I'd mustered, to ensure that everything was just perfect for the first time I told her that I love her.

What could be more thoughtful or romantic than that?

There was only one minor problem that was completely unforeseen – Penny. She had left a note to say she would be gone for most of the day but would be back for dinner. There were also instructions for me not to cook as she would bring home takeout.

Yet still there was no sign of her.

It was now dark and it had been nearly two hours since a suitably embarrassed sun had scurried away to hide behind the western end of the glen. Despite its best efforts, it had failed miserably to raise the temperature above freezing. It was creeping past 7pm and I was beginning to fret. I was also ravenous, which didn't help my anxiety. Being a weekday, it could only be presumed that her reasons were work-related and some meeting or another had taken longer than expected. As such, I had known better than to pry; her business matters were her own affair. However, that said, it wasn't like her to be gone so long without at least telling me what was she was doing and an estimated time when she would be home.

Just then, the headlights of a car penetrated the darkness and followed the bend on the drive and settled upon the house. I peered directly at the vehicle in the vain hope of seeing her in the driver's seat but, instead, I only managed to half blind myself and question my own sanity. Did I really expect to see through the full beams and into the car? Sometimes I'm a mystery, even to myself. Not that there was a moment's doubt in my mind of who it would be; it could only be Penny. It was a welcome relief to leave the drawing room and make my way to the front door to see her. It was only upon opening the door did I realize that I was not the only one in the mood for surprises.

Exiting the car with Penny were my parents.

"Oh my, Penny, I knew to expect your home to be impressive but this is quite magnificent." My mum had deftly stepped out from the passenger door immediately behind Penny and stood in wide-eyed awe. As usual, my mother was undeniably correct. The car's approach had triggered a bank of intruder lights that instantly cloaked the house and it proudly basked in its full glory.

"Truly magnificent." Dad dismissively agreed with Mum's assessment without actually looking at the house in all its splendor. He had been too busy trying to escape the confines of the car without dropping the box of takeout that demanded the use of both his hands. It had been no mean feat. Now, stood on the opposite side of the car, he pressed the door closed with his ass and turned to look at her house. His reaction was priceless.

"Well fuck me…. Truly magnificent…"
Mum shot him the death stare but

refrained from chastising him, no doubt due to his further endorsement of her opinion. Penny just chuckled. It was obvious that she reveled in their reaction and allowed them both a moment to feast upon our home.

"Hello darling, I thought it was about time we had your parents to visit." Penny's words brought me crashing back to reality. I presumed that my stunned silence had rendered me invisible as no-one had actually noticed me until this point. She made her way up the stairs and kissed me gently on the cheek. As she did so, she whispered into my ear.

"Oh, and happy anniversary."

"Where do you want this Penny? The smell is working its way around my heart like a wriggly worm and my stomach is beginning to think my throat's been cut." Like most men, my father does not possess much in the way of patience and now had a more pressing desire to see the inside rather than the outside of our humble abode. Although he had been furthest away on the opposite side of the car, he was first in through the door with my mum right behind him. The delicious aroma emanating from his box caught me completely unawares and my bewilderment at these most recent events was complete as I found myself following them inside.

"Straight ahead, the last door on the right. We shall bring in the plates and cutlery." Penny's voice chased them down the corridor. As they followed her instructions and disappeared, she turned to me. "Well?"

"Well? What do you mean 'well'?" I was genuinely confused. Still.

"Well, what do you think? Good surprise?" It had been Penny who had discouraged me from inviting my parents sooner. She hadn't forbidden it, not in the strictest sense of the word anyway, but she had been most reluctant to have them here. They had been so excited when we had actually gotten together as a couple – my mum had actually squealed when I told her. My dad had an altogether more refrained "Go on my son!" and I'd never known them to be so delighted for me.

For us.

Well, not until we told them we were moving in together.

We had been regular visitors to their place and my parents, being 'old school' as it were, had always refrained from inviting themselves to come and see us. When I had broached the subject with Penny, she had always deflected and used excuses like, '*It was easier for us to visit them*' and how '*there was no need to stress your dad with the journey*'. Now, here they were and she had brought them.

What had changed?

"It's an excellent surprise, thank you. I really mean that. I can see that they are so excited to be here, as I knew they would be. This really means a lot to me. So, tell me, what made you change your mind?" I genuinely did want to know, although I really hoped it was because she knew what it meant to me.

"It's not so much that I changed my mind, but rather I felt that it wasn't the right time before. Whereas, now it is." Again, with the deflection. Not that it mattered, they were here now and that was the most important thing. She faced me and softly held both my hands in hers. Her eyes locked onto mine as she asked, "Did you think I would forget our anniversary?" Without giving me any chance to respond, she seemed a little hurt as she continued, "Do you even know what I am talking about?"

"We should eat this dinner before it gets cold." Mum's tone was more an order than a request.

"Goodness me, where are my manners? You are absolutely correct, my apologies. We are coming now." Penny had released one of my hands and led me by the other towards the dining room. As we entered, my eyes were immediately drawn to the wonderful assortment of vibrant colors in their disposable silver trays, a feast for the eyes as well as the body. Undoubtedly, it had been my mum who had set them out as they seemed to be in some semblance of order, the redundant box now contained the discarded lids and was left on the floor beside the sideboard.

The leisurely meal was over all too quickly. One bottle of wine had become three and it was a rather tipsy Penny who had suggested that we leave the dining room for the comfort of the softer chairs in the drawing room. It would seem that my own sobriety was in question as we were halfway there before I realized.

Her present was still there, on the table, beside the fire.

She couldn't miss it. Nobody could.

What was worse is that Penny was walking and talking with my mum in front of me so there was no way I could get there first to hide it. Dad was chattering away at the side of me although, of the two of us, only he knew it was a conversation as I had now lost all interest in what he was saying. "...*it was deeply invasive and all with your mother watching. I don't mind telling you Son, I was more than a little embarrassed...*" I nodded in agreement, the feeling was all too familiar.

As we entered the drawing room, they were already at the fireside. Mum was admiring the flowers and Penny was holding the present and looking directly at me. Her head was angled slightly to the side and her eyes masked two heavy tears that shone and flickered in the firelight. Her look needed no words and it was one that only lovers understand.

You remembered.

I could feel my heart swell inside me and tears came readily to my eyes, yet I couldn't break her stare. My head fell slightly to mirror her own and my left hand found my mouth in a futile attempt to halt the silent words from falling out.

"These are just gorgeous, such a delicate but complimentary bouquet." Mum's remark shattered the silence and broke our moment. "I told you he would remember, Penny." There was as much self-satisfaction as pride in her voice. Still, it could not disguise the sense of relief that she had been correct in her assertion of her own wee boy, yet her delight was still more for Penny. Mum treated her as the daughter she never had and Penny loved her for it. The very fact that Penny had told them about this anniversary, and actually brought them here to celebrate it, demonstrated its obvious importance to her. For that, I was thankful, as it was important to me too – but for a totally different reason.

My reason was altogether more personal and not one to be shared, even with my parents.

"Yes, you did, and he did. Our boy done good." Mum was smiling at the compliment. Penny peeled the envelope from the present and set it aside on the table. Irrationally, I prayed that the card would blow into the fire.

It didn't.

She carefully unwrapped the end of the present and looked inside. Only she could see what was contained therein. She looked up at me with a huge smile on her face.

"Oh, *our boy* did *really* good!"

She tore away the wrapping paper and handed the box to my dad. "Well this looks expensive," he said. He was correct, it was. I had no idea just how rare the bottle that Penny and I had shared until I tried to buy one. Only 6,000 were ever produced and none were available to buy. Not that it would have mattered, as I could never have afforded one anyway. So I had been forced to settle – if 'settle' is the right word – for a bottle of Oban Connoisseur's Choice 20-year-old, a relative snip at £650.

My heart sank as Penny turned her

attention to the card.

"Penny, the card can wait. Why don't we go and get another bottle of wine?" I hoped my desperation wasn't too obvious.

"Nonsense. The very idea! Do you think I have the patience to wait to open the card? Really? I thought you knew me better than that." She chuckled as her finger traced down the seal of the envelope, the all too familiar cracking sound of the glue breaking shattering my ears. "Besides, we should open the whisky. As I said to you last year, it is wasted without good company, and what better company than this?" Her sincerity was unquestionable and my parents were positively beaming at the compliment.

My dad was cradling the bottle as if it were a child.

The card slid out all too easily for my liking. All eyes in the room were now upon her. Carefully, she read the front page. Then, she seemed to read it again.

This was torturous.

As she opened the card up to read what was inside, I could no longer look at her and so permitted my gaze to fall heavily upon the fire. There, awaiting me, were my old friends. Doubt and self-pity. Rarely have I ever been more uncomfortable.

"Penny, are you okay?" Mum's voice immediately drew my attention and I looked at her, then to Penny.

The tears were flowing unashamedly down her face and she was staring right at me.

"I love you too. Absolutely. With all my heart." She was walking towards me with her arms outstretched, no more than four feet away, yet it seemed like an eternity before she was in my arms.

"I love you." It was the first time I'd said it to her out loud and I thought only the four of us had heard me say it.

I had no idea it was five.

Chapter 2

Wednesday 13th January

The glorious winter sunshine streamed in through the half-closed bedroom curtains. The fresh new morning mockingly offering so much promise in the full knowledge that I was in no fit state to accept. Rather, I found my face buried into a pillow that was completely soaked with my own drool. A vain attempt at finding something – *anything* – to cover my eyes from the blinding light had my arm toppling over a bucket that had found a home beside me. Thankfully, it was still empty, although the din it created in no way helped my hangover. Not yet able to summon the strength and courage to fully open my eyes, I quickly tried to piece together last night and the events that had placed me in this most unfortunate predicament.

The memory was proving elusive.

"Penny, what happened last night and why is my head thumping? *Please* make it *stop*." The words tumbled out of my mouth and fought their way clear of my saturated pillow, even I found my whiny tone annoying and irritating. Fortunately, I was the only one. Oh my God, this is worse than I could have imagined. Penny is up and out already, which means that she is fine and so shall enjoy the bragging rights. More abuse coming my way for being a lightweight. Seriously, the girl is a lush whom I have never yet seen drunk. I have a vague recollection of wine and whisky; will I never learn?

Never mix the grape and the grain.

After a long shower, I threw on some clothes and valiantly headed down for breakfast. It could only aid and certainly couldn't hinder my recovery. The voices wafted along the corridor and the laughter quickly followed. I was almost certain that two of those voices belonged to my parents, but that would be impossible.

Oh wait...

Everyone sounds as right as rain, how can it only be me that is suffering? Surely we all drank the same? Time to sort myself out; I cannot lose face in front of Penny and my folks. As confidently as I could muster, and with a fixed smile that would fool nobody, I strode purposefully into the kitchen.

"Still drunk then, Son? Don't you worry, it's a good breakfast that you need. Sit yourself down and I'll sort it for you. If that is okay, Penny?" Mum looked for the approval as an afterthought for she was already lifting down the hanging frying pan.

"Certainly, *mi casa es su casa*." The reply was, as always, light and airy – and in Spanish. My face held my confusion and to save my blushes, Penny whispered discreetly in my ear, "*My house is your house*."

"My castle is your castle, more like." Dad couldn't resist the jibe although it was just too close to the truth and, instead of being funny, just made everyone slightly uncomfortable. Nobody laughed and it hung in the air for way longer than it should. Yet his joke and Penny's nonchalance – combined with my mother's accurate assertion of me still being drunk – only served to wind me up.

"Incidentally, I am not *still* drunk. How could I be *still* drunk when I wasn't drunk in the first place?" I was fooling nobody and everybody knew it. "Although the breakfast would be most welcome, thank you very much." Happy with the illusion of having made my point behind a veil of sarcasm, I made to sit down. However, my mother was not quite ready to let it go and her response halted me in my tracks.

"Not still drunk, Son? Well maybe you want to tell your fingers, for you are one button too high all the way up the left side of your shirt and you might want to zip up your fly while you're at it." A quick check merely confirmed that she was correct – as usual. It really was an annoying trait and one that I had failed to inherit.

"Tea?" A sniggering Penny was trying to change the subject and save my blushes, but my embarrassment was complete.

"I'll take a fruit tea please." My zip had been a far easier fix than my shirt and I was now wrestling with the buttons and fighting the urge to just rip the bloody thing off and go and find a jersey.

"What kind?" *Is she fucking kidding me? What kind?* I knew that Penny was only trying to be helpful but, in reality, she was more trying my patience. I really didn't care what kind, just a cup of *fucking* tea. I shot her a look that I hoped would relay my feelings and end this conversation.
However, she wasn't actually looking at me.

Nobody was.

Sometimes my own immaturity astounds me. This was my family and my partner. The woman who *loves* me. I now know this to be absolutely true because she has told me, all too recently and not yet nearly enough. I doubt she could ever tell me enough. They were teasing me and I was being an idiot by taking it too seriously. Time to relax and just enjoy their company. It was then that I remembered Baruch's quote; it is one that I all too often, and far too easily, forget.

> *"Be who you are and say what you feel, because those who mind don't matter, and those who matter don't mind."*

"Can I have a fruit tea too please? I've never had one before and always fancied trying it. I have read that green tea – is that a fruit tea? – has many medicinal benefits." It had never crossed my mind that my dad had been so deprived of the simple pleasure that is a fruit tea. He would have seen it as a waste of money, no matter how insignificant the sum, on buying a box to try just one. It would have been fine if he liked it, and so justifying the expense, but that was just too much of a gamble for him.

He was old school, every penny was

hard earned and demanded respect. Yet he would buy a box for me if I were to simply ask him to. He was always careful on what he spent on himself, but was generous to the extreme with both Mum and me. Whatever we wanted, we would have. He saw that as his role in life, to provide for his family. To me, that's a 'dad'.

Every kid's hero.

My hero.

One day, I hoped that I would be a 'dad'.

My imagination began to wander and I dared to dream. In my mind's eye, it was so easy to visualize our children playing around this wonderful home, their laughter breathing new life into the old building. The mischief that could be had in such a mysterious old house had me, for the briefest of moments, slightly envious. Such an idyllic childhood awaited any children Penny would have and I could only hope to be part of such an adventure. Of course, to entertain such a notion was folly and all too premature in our relationship, but it was altogether too enticing a prospect that seduced me far too easily. It really is nice to dream.

A sudden pressure on my foot immediately dragged me back to reality.

As she was, in practically everything in

life, Penny had been deliberate, delicate and discreet; soft enough to be painless but strong enough to have the desired effect of drawing my attention. As I was about to protest, the look on her face told me everything I needed to know.

A picture really does paint a thousand words.

When the freshly brewed concoction was placed in front of him, Dad reached for the milk and poured a generous helping into the cup. Penny had seen what he was doing and drew my attention in the only tactful way possible. Rather than laughing, she surreptitiously gestured that I should follow suit, obviously to save his blushes. The things we do for love.

"This green tea is not too bad, Son."

I have no idea how I managed to stifle my gag reflex, for it was completely and utterly revolting.

Chapter 3

Auchtershinnan Estate, Scotland

Wednesday 13th January

It is often all too easy to forget that our parents are actually people, with very real emotions. I had never really thought about it before today but, seeing my father hurtling around the estate on one of the quad bikes, his unbridled joy was as infectious as it was obvious. It seemed like he had reconnected with his inner child. He really was like a kid in a toy shop, this being his first time ever on a quad. For once, it was my turn to warn him of the dangers and, to complete the role reversal, it was his turn to totally ignore me and race away at full speed into the crisp winter morning. Of course, when I was younger, he had regaled me with stories from his own childhood, but I could never really imagine what he was like then. To me, he was always just 'Dad'.

Until today.

The conditions were perfect for quad biking as the temperature hovered around the freezing mark, which served to ensure that the ground was solid. The sun seemed to have a little heat although we were both well wrapped up to face whatever turn the weather may take. Mum had insisted upon supervising us in that regard. Penny hung in the background and actually gave me a second pair of gloves, *'Just in case either of you lose a pair'.*

It's *'easy done'*, apparently.

Had it not been for the fact that I do – with alarming regularity – misplace, lose, or otherwise surrender possession of so many damned pernickety little items like car and house keys, wallet, clothes or practically anything that is entrusted to my care, then I would be justifiably upset. As it was, I was thankful for her caring foresight, especially after I realized that I had accidentally left my first pair of gloves in Andy's workshop when Dad and I stopped off to have a chat and a coffee halfway through his daring escapades. I was almost hoarse from screaming to those spots where he had so recently been and so the respite had been most welcome.

Andy's workshop is a converted part of

the old stables and really has every imaginable tool for the professional handyman. Well, it seemed that way to my untrained eye. He is most often to be found tinkering around there on some project or another and he seems to be most adept at finding work to do around the place. He really is quite capable and can turn his hand to fix most problems and, as such, is a very trusted member of staff. To Penny, however, the staff are viewed and treated more like family.

It is yet another endearing quality of hers.

The wood-burning stove in the corner of the workshop seems to always have a full pot of coffee on the metal plate that sits to the side of its small chimney stack. Thankfully, today was no different. No sooner had we pulled the quads inside the doors and turned their engines off than Andy immediately downed tools and headed for the steaming pot. As always, anyone within his immediate vicinity or, indeed, eyeshot, is obligated to enjoy a coffee and shoot the breeze for as long as he determines.

There is absolutely no doubt that this is his domain.

Mugs of various sizes, colors, and cleanliness are littered around but all within easy reach of the pot, and so in some semblance of order. The filth and grime that grace the inside of each cup merely add an authenticity to the experience. Penny had once been so bold as to offer replacements; she simply did not understand. New, or even clean, cups would have somehow demeaned and emasculated us. We are men. As such, our stories, fables, and tales are to be found in, around, or – in those most desperate of occasions – at the very bottom of goblets such as these. They hide from the memory and await to be rediscovered in the very filth and grime that she suggested replacing.

The very idea!

These wondrous chalices are men's mental equivalent of the iCloud.

I'm all but certain that this area – at best, it could be very charitably described as a 'general recreational station' – would be instantly condemned and forever shut down by any half-competent health and safety officer. For comfort, two old high backed armchairs adorned either side of the stove and faced the main doors of the shed where the quads now sat.

Never were there thrones more regal than these.

The steam headed heavenward as the silky black liquid was shared among the first three cups that came to hand. I knew better than to even ask for extravagances such as milk or sugar, and my dad soon also understood as he accepted Andy's offering with a simple "thanks" and a respectful nod. Their unspoken bonds of friendship were cemented as they each instinctively took their respective seats in what, to me at least, seemed to be the perfect coronation. It was disturbingly fitting that I was left to stand.

After all, I was – in practically every respect – the 'common' element.

"Get your coffee while it's hot, Son." Dad's suggestion was more of an instruction and I was momentarily embarrassed by my father's comfort in Andy's domain. Yet, from the smile on his face, it was apparent that the King was more than happy to share his realm. It was actually quite heartwarming and made me inexplicably proud, watching these two men forging this new friendship. In playing the part of dutiful son, and burning my lips in the process, it became apparent that I'd also, inadvertently, became surplus to their requirements. In the few seconds that it took for me to regain my composure, and the feeling in my lips, these two elder statesmen had shamelessly exploited my silence and were now chatting away like I wasn't even here.

It was truly magical.

I found myself a seat on the workbench and settled down to relish every single second of the wonderful stories that I knew were going to follow. I was certain that there would be some I would already know and these would be even better as I could anticipate the ending and, for the most part, Andy's predictable reaction; genuine or polite laughter. In these circumstances, one was always as good as the other. This being due to the fact that I was far more familiar with my father's stories and that, on those occasions when it was just us, Andy had proven himself as more of a listener than a talker. As a man who always enjoys the sound of his own voice, this always suited me just fine, yet now it was my turn to be surprised.

"...they are definitely practical but also great fun. I have driven a few fast cars in my time but nothing beats tearing down the glen on the quad on a beautiful summer's day". As my dad sat nodding in agreement at Andy's assertion, I tried to imagine him doing *anything* fast. He had certainly not demonstrated any such inclinations as long as I had known him. Mind you, that wasn't exactly a long time but, still, you get a general feel and understanding of someone. Admittedly, these can sometimes be well off the mark. As he continued talking, it was becoming more and more apparent that this was one of those times.

"At least I can enjoy the freedom and speed here on the estate without attracting any unwelcome attention from the law. Not that I haven't had my fun with that too." To the untrained eye, it would seem that he lifted his cup for a quick sip of coffee and dramatic effect but, to me, I knew he was actually searching for a tale appropriate for this occasion. The mischievous look that the cup left as he set it aside signaled his success.

"The first Gulf War officially started in early August 1990 but we were in there beforehand, carrying out reconnaissance and ensuring everything went smoothly on the actual day we invaded." As a statement, everything he said made perfect sense and I could already see that my dad was enthralled. Yet all it did was raise more questions than answers for me. Andy was in the military? I had no idea, not even an inkling, and yet I realized that I had never actually asked what he had done for a career. Ignorantly, I had presumed that he had worked on the estate his whole life.

When will I ever learn about stereotypes?

Who were the *we* he was talking about? It was only logical to think that this would mean Special Forces – SAS, SBS, etc.... – yet my head just couldn't get there to picture him as one of those. Those guys were the elite, the cream, and lethal weapons. These guys were *deadly*. I just could not imagine Andy here as one of them.

"So, it was late June and I was running late for work. Coincidentally, there had also been a briefing that the IRA had announced that they were stepping up their military action on the mainland. As part of the threat, they had stated that all military personnel should consider themselves as a target. As such, we were advised to be more vigilant with our own security. The usual stuff – check for car bombs before every trip, be more aware of our surroundings, watch for suspicious activity, that sort of thing."

So he *was* in the military. The questions raced through my mind, as there was so much I wanted to know, but they would have to wait. He was in the middle of his story and I could not risk scaring him from telling it.

Dad would never forgive me.

"So, there was me, late for work and hurtling along the motorway pushing 100 miles an hour when I spot the unmarked police car on top of a bridge. The cop in the passenger seat is pointing a speed gun directly at my car. In the moment that I notice, the car takes off and it's obvious that they are coming for me. So what else could I do? I sped up!"

He threw himself back in his seat in triumph as if we should know how the story ends and that his actions were completely logical. They weren't and I was relieved to see the look of confusion on Dad's face that betrayed the fact that he didn't understand either. Andy enjoyed the silence long enough to ensure our ignorance made us feel uncomfortable, and then he continued.

"Well they were on my tail in no time and they had those silly blue lights that they house in the front grill, flashing for all they're worth. I hogged the overtaking lane until I saw the next service station, when I cut right across the three lanes and took the exit. I knew that there was a police office in this particular services and I came screeching to a halt right at the front door. I could practically see the LCD display of the radio station that the duty officer was listening to on the front desk!"

As he chuckled away at his own weak joke, I caught Dad's eye and I knew we were thinking the same thing. Was this guy an idiot?

"As the unmarked police car came to a halt behind me, I'm already out of the driver's seat and screaming *'HELP...HELP!'* in the general direction of the police office. The duty officer came racing out at the same time that the two cops jumped out of their car. That is when the fun began..."

Began? He really was an idiot and I was regretting having introduced this halfwit to my father. Yet he sat there in a respectful silence, sipping his coffee, and allowing Andy to finish his story.

"So, safe in the knowledge that the duty officer was a witness, I turned my attention to the two cops who were making their way towards me and brandishing handcuffs. *'What the actual FUCK do you think you are FUCKING doing? Are you two FUCKING idiots?'"* The shock on their faces was a picture and they actually stopped in their tracks.

I was loving every second of it.

Before they could respond, I took the lead. "So, you guys already know who I am, right?"

It was passenger plod that answered. "You are Andrew Jamieson. You live at..." Now he had given me all the information I needed, so I cut him off.

"It doesn't matter a *fuck* where I live. You *know* that I am military. You also know that there is a heightened alert for IRA activity on the mainland. You *should* also be aware that someone in my position is on stand-by for worldwide operations at a moment's notice?

The driver nodded. He was the one with the sergeant's markings and obviously the brains of the outfit. Some brains." He chuckled to himself as he said this and took another quick shot of coffee.

The end of the story must have still been in the cup.

"Yet, you two *fucking idiots* think it's wise to sit in an unmarked car, atop a motorway bridge, and point a gun at *ME?!* Even that is forgivable, I understand you have a job to do, but then you chase me and – even when you know who and what I am – you *STILL* think it best to pursue me!

Complete fucking idiots!

'But you were speeding...' Passenger plod still thought it best to try and justify their position. The look the driver shot him told him to shut up, now.

'Yes, I *was* speeding. I am being scrambled for an operation. Not that it's any of your business, and it's certainly above your pay grade. Now, what name do I tell my commanding officer is the person responsible for me being late and the reason why there is a plane being held up on a runway, fully fuelled and loaded with my mates and ready to go, all just waiting on ME?'

Rather than getting a ticket, I got a police escort to the base!"

He had set both my dad and I up perfectly. Andy was far from an idiot; this man was a genius!

Andy knew as well as I that there were only two working quads on the estate so it was a fruitless endeavor asking him to join us on our adventures. However, Dad asked him anyway. He politely declined and so Dad insisted that he at least join us for dinner. This was an offer he couldn't refuse and so we left him to his tinkering as we chased the last of the sun around the grounds.

The promise of more stories in the dusk made the chasing that little bit sweeter and the quads seem that little bit faster.

Chapter 4

Glasgow, Scotland

Wednesday 13th January

The aircraft thundered along the runway and took off into the night sky, as all its occupants seemed to settle into their usual inflight routines. It was quite easy for the flight attendants to discern the nature of each individual's trip. Mostly, it was for pleasure although there were a few familiar business faces within the mix. Those were never smiley happy faces, especially when they were turning right instead of left upon entering the plane.

The cabin crew had been pre-warned of a stag and hen group on the flight and was thankful to their colleagues at the check-in desk who had managed to seat them separately. That made their job this evening a whole lot easier. It was obvious that both parties had started drinking early and it seemed that the girls were actually more boisterous than the boys. Experience told them that they would need to be extra vigilant around the bathrooms for the duration of the flight. The 'mile high club' always seems to attract new members although they are not always welcome.

Nobody had noticed the single passenger sat in 3A.

Initially, the window provided a false and completely illogical comfort for Melissa Chisholm. She had the irrational belief that seeing the outside world, seeing normality, would somehow ensure her safety. As the wheels left the tarmac and the plane hurtled upwards into the void, she watched her normality disappear right in front of her eyes.

It was terrifying.

No longer merely staring out the window, she was transfixed and desperately searching for any hint of familiarity upon the dark surface below. The plane's ascension into the clouds simply added to her distress, albeit momentarily, until it happened. The clouds, so often the natural barrier to the night sky, obscuring the stars, obscuring her dreams, now spread invitingly underneath like a magnificent carpet. Beyond them, the clear night sky welcomed her to the heavens. It was majestic, beautifully mesmerizing yet wholly intimidating.

The Heavens – where the Gods resided.

The Heavens – that place where her hopes and dreams were to be found.

The Heavens – home now to her family.

As she gazed out into the wondrous universe, it seemed that each star shone brighter than the last. Her eyes searched among them, desperately seeking the faces of her beloved parents. Yet, she would happily settle for even the merest glimpse of her cherished grandparents. It had been a lifetime since she had felt so close to them all, almost among them, but not quite. Still they eluded her. The tears came all too easily and scalded her cheeks. Unconsciously, she wiped them away in one flowing action with her sleeve, her eyes never leaving the portal and she was completely oblivious to the rest of her travelling companions.

Lost in her own world, but caught in theirs.

Yet no longer was she seeing the heavens. Rather now she was staring deep into her past, dredging through well-worn memories and sadistically embracing the sorrow and devastation that it invariably brought. Sadness was now a very common, although most often, unwelcome guest to Melissa and she knew the very day that it had come into her life – *Thursday April 4th, 1996.*

It was only a few days after her 18th birthday. She knew it was her 'coming of age' and naively believed that she was fully prepared for all life could throw at her. Unfortunately, her grandmother had agreed with her; how could they know that they were both wrong?

So very, very wrong.

It would prove to be a mistake that the old woman would deeply regret for the rest of her life. Melissa was all she had left of her own family after her husband had succumbed to cancer when he was only 32. She had loved him, faults and all, and felt cheated from a lifetime of happiness. In the years that followed, she had shunned the offers of companionship from other men and settled uncomfortably into widowhood. It was only to herself would she admit that she enjoyed the martyrdom. Such a gentle old lady. The very epitome of the perfect grandmother – loving, patient, understanding and kind. She had long yearned to tell Melissa the truth about the accident that left her an orphan and robbed her of other grandparents. She knew that her only grandchild had a right to know, but knowing how sensitive a soul she was had always been a cause for pause. It was her role to protect her, to safeguard her innocence, to ensure she had a childhood; a childhood that she had provided, as best she could.

Whenever Melissa broached the subject about her parents, it always seemed to catch her off guard. It just never seemed to be the right time. This was not to be a casual conversation; it was more serious than that. It would have disrespected those that lost their lives that night and that was all she had left to offer them.

Her respect.

Melissa could remember everything about the conversation and now replayed it over in her head as her eyes danced among the stars. The fragrance of her birthday bouquet from almost twenty years ago instantly replaced the stale air from inside the cabin. Her grandmother wearing her favorite blouse and apron, sitting aside her on the patterned sofa. As a child, she believed that it was a magic apron, for it seemed that her nana – as she affectionately called her – had everything she ever wanted or asked for within its mysterious pockets. Sitting on the old teak coffee table that her grandfather had bought as an anniversary present a lifetime ago, was a tattered and worn folder that she had never seen before. Her nana had said nothing as she handed it to her. Not because she didn't want to, but because she simply couldn't.

Her own grief, still so raw and overwhelming, silenced her.

Melissa opened the file. *'HORRIFIC'* was the headline on the front page of an old newspaper and was the first thing she saw. It was designed to be sensational and overly dramatic but, for once, the headline was quite redundant. Her eyes were quickly drawn to the accompanying photograph, a grainy black and white image of a mangled mess that she took a few seconds to realize was once a car. The subheadings were factual bullet points for ease of reading.

- *Four dead*
- *Child, 4, fights for life*
- *Police appeal for witnesses*

"Nana? But, this would mea…? *I was there? I was in the car?*" Melissa searched the photograph, trying to recognize something – *anything* – that she may find familiar. A tentative hand found her shoulder and gave it a reassuring squeeze. It didn't work. "How did I survive when they didn't? I should be dead." It was said without thinking and it served as a lesson to her that has stayed with her forever since.

So often it is the thoughtless statements

that carry the most truth, but hurt the deepest.

Her grandmother's anger overwhelmed her own grief and the voice she found was one Melissa had never heard before. "You listen here to me young lady, don't you ever say that to me again. *Ever!* I have shown you this to give you understanding, to let you know the truth. Not, and I repeat, NOT so you can dwell upon it. What happened, happened. Yes, it was a tragedy and, yes, you lost most of your family. However, I am your family. I love you. I always have and I always will. This is to give you closure. Closure so that you may grow and see a future from knowing your past. It is *not* to drag you back there. There are bigger questions in life than death. Certainly, for you, there are bigger questions that really matter, like who you are going to be. Not should you *be* at all. I, like you, suffered great loss that day and you owe it to them, and to me, to make us proud of you. Believe me when I say that you do make me proud, every single day."

Her anger subsided as she ended her tirade, but she was suddenly too exhausted, too embarrassed, to face her granddaughter. This was not how she had expected this conversation to develop, yet it was her own reaction that had surprised her the most.

What had she expected? The old woman was just too tired to answer her own question. Seeing it all again herself, after all these years, brought back a fresh sense of loss. Made it real all over again. Exposed her own raw emotions. Hers was an instant embarrassment from her own selfishness; her own grief had simply overwhelmed her and had left her unprepared for Melissa's questions.

She tried to hide her thoughts and shame deep in the heart of the fire in the hope that Melissa wouldn't search for them there.

Yet Melissa hadn't actually noticed her grandmother's discomfort. Rather, to her, it was all too obvious that to read any more was to risk further upsetting her nana with another thoughtless statement. As such, she simply couldn't trust herself to read the contents of the folder in her presence. Instead, she reached over and hugged her, kissing her on the side of the head. "I love you, Nana." The old woman gently patted the hand on her shoulder, but said nothing. In the silence, Melissa closed the folder and stood, taking it to her bedroom.

She left her nana staring deep into the fire.

Over the intervening years, she had found the guilt of surviving often more powerful than her grandmother's words of wisdom. The doctors had told her that this was 'natural' and 'to be expected'. Normal almost. However, it seemed that every single doctor had felt the need to give her a medical diagnosis that required further treatment and pills. Always some radical new pill or another. Her medical records now showed her to be a sufferer of 'depression', whilst others liked to mix it up and state that she also exhibited signs of 'bipolar disorder'.

Melissa would never understand why these 'learned' medical professionals – she used the term advisedly – who commanded such reverence, and with all their education, could not simply accept that her painfully faint memory of her parents and grandparents, and their tragic loss, just made her sad. Who wouldn't be sad at having such a tragic experience reside within you but that you simply cannot remember? How did they not realize that it was this very lack of the memory that made her sad? She really didn't need such strong prescription medications to further erase an already forgotten memory and artificially stimulate her into feeling happy.

She was just sad.

Sad that she had no memory of the accident, no recollection of those last fatal moments. Sad for the loss of her family. Sad for the loss of memories that would never be created. Sad for the profound loss of a familial support structure that everyone else seems to take for granted.

Such realization left no scope for happiness.

Yet still their questions came at her. *No, she had never thought of suicide.* Such thoughts only ever entered her head when they asked them. She dismissed them before they had even finished the question. She, more than most, knew just how precious life was. Even more so now, as she gazed out into the beautiful universe.

Death is too permanent and it's eternal.

Life is too fragile and it's for living. This was her time for living, and she was determined to enjoy every last second of it.

It took a second tap on her hand, this time more a slap than the first genuine tap, to shake the memory of her nana and draw her attention to the passenger in the seat beside her. As she turned, she saw that it was actually the air stewardess who was demanding her attention. "I'm sorry madam, would you like a drink?" Scrambling with her thoughts, she knew that was exactly what she needed.

"Can I have a gin and tonic please? I'm so sorry, but I need to get my purse from the overhead locker as my money is there." As a first time flyer, she had no idea that there was a complimentary drinks service on this transatlantic flight. She felt completely foolish and embarrassed by her own ignorance when she was told, although she knew there really was no need to be. She just wanted to seem more chic and knowledgeable, but all she had done was to further undermine her own low confidence and self-worth.

It was a hard habit to break.

"Thank you." As the drink was handed to her, she realized that gin wasn't her usual tipple. Indeed, she had actually never tried it before. She found it somewhat odd that she should be trying it now. *Mother's ruin.* Her nana's voice was ringing in her head; it was nice to have familiar company.

As she took her first sip, it all felt so appropriate.

Chapter 5

Harrison, New York

Thursday 14th January

"Turn left. Your final destination is sixty yards on the lef..." Melissa quickly silenced her new found 'friend' before she could complete her command. The tinny voice had been her constant companion since she picked up the small Honda from the rental lot at JFK airport. From there, the voice had successfully managed to coax and coerce Melissa to her hotel in the city center with the utmost patience; even tolerating the odd wrong turn here and there. Although 'tolerating' might have been too strong a word for it as she could have sworn there was a sense of despair and frustration with her last two mistaken turns. It felt as if an argument could ensue at any given moment. It didn't help anyone when she began

answering the machine back. Mistakes or otherwise, when they arrived at the hotel, there was definite tension in the car – and not in the usual sexy way.

A decent night's sleep had done them the power of good and they both started the new day afresh and friends again.

On their journey from the hotel, Melissa realized that she was completely reliant upon an impersonal and faceless female voice that she had no choice but to implicitly trust. Being beholden to anyone – or any *thing* – made her deeply uncomfortable and gave rise, once again, to her own issues of trust and to question herself on what she was actually doing here. At last count, there had been at least three occasions when she had almost pulled over to change the destination back to the hotel and then for the airport.

Almost.

As it was, she had silenced her travelling companion a mere fifty yards from her chosen location in the irrational fear that someone might hear her colleague and realize why they were here. It was the accompanying *"shhhhhhhh...."* that was said out loud as she did so that worried her most. She immediately recognized the house and pulled up just short on the opposite side of the street, leaving the engine running as a precaution. For her own peace of mind, and to remove any element of doubt, she dug into the side pocket of her purse and pulled out all the relevant papers that she had. She quickly sifted passed the magazine article that had led her to this point and found what she was looking for; the still images of the house in front of her, printed using Google's Street View.

Technology was wonderful when it was your friend.

She checked the time – 4:38pm. Her limited research had uncovered that *Michael Bradley and Associates* had folded shortly after his wife's disappearance, when he almost went bankrupt. The only reason he hadn't was the fact that his clients, every single last one of them, had refused to push for their share of the settlement after they discovered what had happened. Outwardly, he had expressed gratitude and had gone to each and every home to personally explain what had happened and say 'thank you' for their continued trust and support. He also took that opportunity to explain that he wouldn't be seeking re-election. They had all understood and responded with kindness and sincerity and wished him all the best for the future. The usual things that people say when there is nothing else to be said. However, he had seen the pity in every single one of their eyes.

And he hated them for it.

His old law firm had been magnanimous enough to accept him back as a junior partner. A demotion but, still, a job. There were the usual whispers around the water cooler, but there were no looks of pity to be had here. Rather, the looks were smug and self-serving. He had been brought down a peg or two and, to his mind, every last one of his colleagues and associates were reveling in his fall from grace.

He hated Anthony Di Silva for that.

Melissa noticed that there were no other cars parked on the quiet suburban street. Not that this was a street, it was the epitome of an avenue. It actually looked like a Christmas card and the appeal to young suburbanite families was immediately obvious. At this time of year, the sun only works the short shifts and so had checked out over an hour previously. The ornate street lights were of the old Victorian design and so shaped to have the bulbs appear like candles inside teardrop-shaped glass protectors, all whilst providing maximum visibility. Beautiful as they were, she noticed that her car was parked directly under such a lamp. She quickly reversed to the dark spot that was equidistant between two of the lights – to ensure maximum protection and maintain her cover – and switched off the engine.

Thankfully, the new batch of snowflakes were as big as she had ever seen and soon covered the road that had been clear when she arrived. It had the fortuitous side effect of also covering the car and so making it look less conspicuous. However, this meant that the car windows were also being covered and so ensuring that her view of the house and street was now becoming obstructed.

Damn it.

Her frustration mixed with impatience as she zipped up her jacket and pulled the hood down as far as it would go; she didn't want or need anyone to see her face. *It's now or never.* She grabbed the sealed envelope from the passenger seat and after casting a fleeting glance in either direction to confirm that the street was still empty, quickly made her way out of the car. Scanning from under the faux fur that lined the hood, practically every house that she could see – all two of them – were in darkness. The others were hiding behind hedges, fences and thick trees. For some, it was a mixture of all three; the young family suburbanites around here obviously like their privacy.

Or they have something to hide.

Not that this was of any concern to her.

She made her way directly to Michael's house and then silently cursed herself before she was even halfway there. Quickening her step, she tried to remain calm but could already hear her tinny friend's voice berating her lack navigational 'skills' and ignorance to the most basic of American laws – jaywalking. Such an offence does not exist in the UK, but that wouldn't help her here. How would she explain the contents of the envelope to any police officer who was to arrest her for such a petty misdemeanor? She knew she couldn't, certainly not without jeopardizing her claim to the million-dollar reward.

That would be catastrophic.

With a renewed determination, Melissa hastily passed the letter box at the end of the driveway and headed for the front door of the porch; she hoped that this would be unlocked. It was. Through the mesh and glass, she could see exactly what she was looking for. In a matter of seconds, she had been in and out of Michael's home and was now making her way back to her car. Without the envelope. This time, she walked to the top of the street and safely crossed at the lights. Once back in the car, she settled into the driver's seat and turned on the engine. She dared a quick sweep of the window wipers to clear the windscreen. If she was detected now, she could safely drive off. Although her own breath was misting up the windows and she suddenly realized how cold she was, and there was absolutely no need for that. Not now anyway. She found the heating controls with her right hand and turned the temperature dial fully to the right, only stopping when there was resistance. Her left hand had the easier task of locating the button for the heated seat and a comforting warmth soon crept all over her legs and back. In the relative safety and comfort of the now warm car, she allowed her head to follow her eyes as she scanned and explored for any movement in the deserted street.

Just then, from a side street a little further down on her right, a set of lights emerged from behind one of the many hedgerows. The car that possessed them labored to the junction and stopped. It toiled through the fresh snow as it slowly turned away in the opposite direction. As she watched the tail lights head into the distance, her attention was drawn to the two people on foot that had now materialized from the same junction.

Melissa quickly killed the engine and slid down the warm seat to alternate between peering over and through the steering wheel.

Even from this distance, and through the snowfall, she could just about make out the long woolen coats and flat caps sported by both individuals. As they stood chatting for the briefest of moments, neither one paid any attention to the unusual car parked on their normally deserted street. As the shorter man turned to continue his pursuit of the now long gone car, the other jaywalked his way directly towards the sorry house she knew to be owned by the Bradley's. Ignoring the post box, he made his way through the porch and unlocked the door. Before it closed behind him, every window she could see on the main level suddenly basked in a soft welcoming light.

After a mere ten minutes – to her, a lifetime – she took a deep breath and exhaled. It felt like her chest cavity would implode as the air raced to escape from her tense body and she immediately berated herself for breathing so loudly, it was deafening; there would be plenty of time to breathe later. Once again, the snow had almost covered the windscreen and she took the gamble to clear it, not that she had a choice. Enjoying the newly cleared view, her eyes instantly searched every corner and chased every shadow in the house. Simultaneously, she slipped her hand into her pocket and removed the new burner phone. It had been her only purchase in New York so far and this was its only number. Already programmed as #1 on speed dial, it was ringing in a matter of seconds.

Answer machine.

> *"Hi, this is Michael…and I am Kristy…and we are the Bradley's. Neither one of us is home right now so, please, leave your name, number and any message after the beep. Thank you and have a great day!"*

As she struggled to find the right words to say, her eyes never left the house. He was no longer to be seen and, illogically, she now worried that he knew she was here and was on his way out for her. Just as she was about to hang up, he came into view. His coat had been discarded along with any tie that he might have been wearing. His shirt was loose at the neck, definitely one but maybe two buttons undone; she really couldn't be sure from this distance. What was certain was that it was obviously a brandy glass that now graced his right hand and it was practically full. She guessed it wasn't apple juice.

Melissa started the car as she began to talk.

"Mr. Bradley, you don't know me and you really have no reason to. However, I believe that your wife is alive and well. Furthermore, I believe that I know where she is. Naturally, I expect you receive crank calls regarding this matter every day but the difference with me is, I can supply you with proof. I have left an envelope underneath the doormat in your porch with a photograph of your wife as she is now. There are also some instructions there, should you wish to know more from me. I cannot stress strongly enough, Mr. Bradley, that I do NOT want to have any contact with the police. All I want is to help you find your wife"

...and the million-dollar reward.

She hung up with the sentence still in her head. It would have been ignorant and uncouth to have actually said it out loud as this was his life she was playing with. As such, the money would have no real value anyway. Not to him. Not when compared to the lost love and support of his wife. In any event, they both knew what she wanted anyway. Her eyes never left him as she terminated the call and he hadn't moved at all throughout. There was no way she could leave now and risk him seeing her. From deep in the driver's seat, she watched as he took a long, slow pull on his drink. When he leveled the glass in his hand, she could see half its contents were gone.

At last, he stood.

Still, she watched.

Michael Bradley drained his glass and set it down beside the chair. He disappeared for a second and Melissa scrambled unsuccessfully to get the car in gear and make her escape, when his front door opened. Immediately she took her foot off the brake for fear he would see the reflection of the car's tail lights. There was no need to worry as he never paid her any attention.

She was used to that from all men and so found it oddly comforting.

Michael reached down and came back up with her envelope in his hands, wasting no time in immediately opening it and removing the contents. She had deliberately placed the grainy picture of Penny as the very first page.

Suddenly, to Melissa, everything seemed to happen in slow motion. She watched as his hand found his mouth in a futile attempt to muffle the scream that crept out and into the street. Although confident that only she heard it, there was no time to check as she now had more pressing concerns.

Michael had collapsed.

The envelope and its two single-page contents had been sent skywards and were floating peacefully towards where his body now lay.

He was completely still.

Oh, my God, I've killed him. What do I do? The thoughts raced through her head. She could go directly to him and try to help but, if he recovers, how does she explain herself? It would be pretty obvious that hers was the latest voice lingering on his answer machine, there was no hiding the accent. As she contemplated calling 911, she saw him move. Only slightly, but it was definite movement. He lay in the light of the still opened front door and he raised his head enough that she could see the tears reflecting from his cheeks. He struggled to his feet as he tried to compose himself, gathering the contents of the envelope and looking at Kristy's image once more at the top of the pile as he stumbled back into their home.

Before the door was fully closed, Melissa's old friend was impatiently barking out instructions to take them back to their hotel.

Chapter 6

Harrison, New York

Thursday 14th January

Michael Bradley had no idea that he was being watched and that his collapse had been witnessed. As he closed the door on the world in the house they had shared, he was also completely oblivious to the compact Honda that was slowly making its way out of his street and heading back into the city. Not that he would have cared, for his mind was racing over the implications of this new information. He held the image of his wife in his hands, and once again carried her over the threshold, unconsciously squeezing tighter on the bottom of the page and crumpling her neck – not for the first time.

The bitch. She IS alive. I fucking knew it. Now where the fuck is MY money?

His eyes never left hers as he made his

way to his chair. He knew these eyes, and there was no doubt that they belonged to his bitch wife. Even now, she was staring back at him without any fear; once again mocking him, taunting him.

Would she never learn?

The beatings had been fierce and brutal. He would use anything that came to hand – lamps, crockery, tennis racket, anything that would just *get the job done*. There had been that one very memorable occasion when he had broken his favorite baseball bat over her back. The smile found its way easily onto his face as he recalled each savage blow; it had been worth the loss. Still, she stood up for more. The realization chased away the smile just as quickly as it had appeared.

Never once – not once – had she backed down in the face of his beatings and simply accepted his conditioning. Over and over he had told her that he was following the teachings of scripture. The teachings of the Holy Bible. Yet still she continued to defy him. To defy the very word of God. *Stupid bitch.* Did she not realize that he would have simply stopped if she had only accepted her role as *his* wife? Then he would have known that he had broken her. Women were, after all, just like pets. Didn't she realize that? He needed to have her house-trained.

Trained in the ways of *his* house.

His God fearing house.

He had to admit, she had her uses. She was a decent earner who kept the house clean; not that he gave her much of an option. She also polished up quite nicely when he needed a 'wife' for those all too frequent social events and random gatherings. Although she often spoilt those occasions by actually engaging in conversations with others. She just didn't know what he knew, that *nobody* gave a fuck or was the least bit interested in her opinion? She was, however, great in the sack. A proper fucking whore in the bedroom; not that he gave her much choice about that either.

His hand found the growing bulge in his pants and he slowly started to rub himself as the memories came flooding back.

Some of those chicken-hearted liberals – the tree huggers and advocates for women's rights, assholes every one who needed to grow some balls and teach women their place – would no doubt call it 'rape', but he knew better. She had wanted it, always did. Sometimes she just didn't know it. Those were the best times. After all, his ripping off her lingerie, clothes, whatever she happened to be wearing, only gave her good reason to go out and buy more.

It was the very definition of win/win.

Not that the panties that she wore towards the end could ever be described as 'sexy'. Kristy had succumbed to one too many arguments over who she was wearing the kinky underwear for when she went to work. He never understood that she simply felt better wearing nice underwear. It was about the only thing left that she had that belonged to *her*. Something that made her feel like the beautiful, desirable, sexy woman that she once was.

In a time before she ever knew Michael Bradley.

The *real* Michael Bradley.

The constant arguments with the irregular, but all too frequent, beatings had worn her down and she had succumbed to his will. For the most part. She learned to play along until she could decide what to do, how to escape. He had ensured that any friends she had were now a distant memory and they had cancelled so many family engagements that the invites simply dried up. It had been easier that way.

Michael sat in his master's chair and scoured every corner of the picture, desperately searching for clues, but none were forthcoming. Still his hand held the image tightly by the neck. His free hand hit the play button on the answer machine. Their pre-recorded message bellowed through the old house. Merely hearing her voice caused him to punch her face on the page.

He was bitterly disappointed not to see blood.

> *"...any contact with the police. All I want is to help you find your wife."*

The message was all but over before he realized that he hadn't heard it. His anger was familiar and soothing, like an old friend, and allowed him to fantasize on the many beatings he would give Kristy when he found her. *Not long now.* All that was required was to meet this new bitch and keep her sweet until he got all the information he needed. A simple charm offensive. Of course there would be no cops, he didn't need the hassle of a free Anthony Di Silva chasing him. Plus, he could enjoy the full settlement without having to pay the patronizing assholes, those who played their roles as clients whilst masquerading as friends, a single cent.

God had answered his prayers with this new voice on his answer machine, one that was truly heaven sent.

As he pressed the play button again, he picked up a pen to take notes on the pad he kept by the telephone. He had no idea that the notes he was about to take had already been taken elsewhere. The man took off his headphones and reread what he had just written. Not that there was any need, the words were already committed to memory. He picked up his cell phone and dialed. In a matter of seconds, a curt voice replied, *"What do you want?"*

"I need to talk with the Boss. Now."

Chapter 7

Fallsburg, New York State

Thursday 14th January

Every inch of the exposed brick walls was covered with deep red velvet drapes that emanated from a central point in the ceiling and gave the room a surprisingly warm and cozy feel. Silk sheets with gold braid struggled to contain a luxurious duvet and the matching pillowcases had an equally unenviable task. The ensemble was so resplendent that it would easily adorn the most regal of homes.

Except that this was a single bed and the room was no larger than one would expect from a broom cupboard in such palatial abodes.

A beautifully ornate antique bureau fit snugly into the opposite corner and ran directly parallel to the ostentatious bed. Its matching chair had red leather panels on the seat and back that were held tightly in place by brass studs that were both practical and aesthetically pleasing. A similar panel was to be found on the writing surface of the desk although it was no longer used for such a purpose. Instead, a keyboard nestled neatly under a large computer screen that doubled as a television.

A plush rug gave warmth and protection from the cold concrete flooring underneath and conveniently meandered to hug every corner of the room.

Curiously, all the other rooms within this building had a single panel of frosted glass to only provide a source of light, not so for the luxury of external viewing. This room was the exception. Here it had been swapped out and replaced with a triple glazed, and fully transparent, window. All other illumination was adequately provided by two lamps; one, a table lamp that sat next to the computer monitor, and the other, a floor lamp that loomed discreetly over the head of the bed to allow for night-time reading.

Not that there were any books here to read.

For the past three years, Anthony Di Silva had called this room home. It was in the Isolation Wing of the Sullivan Maximum

Security Prison, although he had done nothing to merit being removed from the general population. Well, not according to his prison record. As far as it was concerned, he was the model convict. However, it was a constant struggle for the ever-menacing Anthony to maintain his position as head of one of the most powerful Mafia families ever assembled in the USA. Yet, his 'request' for this private accommodation and its trappings had been favorably met by a warden who had managed to simultaneously ensure his own family's safety whilst also becoming a multi-millionaire overnight.

Anthony's genius was reflected in the fact that only he knew how large his empire actually was. Over the years, he had exercised caution and patience to strategically build it up by combining and manipulating individual factions of criminal activity without ever allowing those involved know that he was the head of their respective groups. As such *nobody* knew that he was at the top of the pyramid. Instead, he portrayed himself as a lieutenant who was always answerable to others. It was seen as the ultimate act of disloyalty to question who his superiors were. People had died for less. He even spread rumor and conjecture himself to ensure and protect his ruse and this had also proven, on occasion, to fortuitously flush out potential threats.

It had all worked so perfectly, until Michael Bradley had become the Mayor of Harrison.

ADS Waste Management Services Inc. was the only legitimate jewel in Anthony's business empire, and a relatively small enterprise by comparison. He had installed himself as CEO to provide a legal income and so satisfy the IRS and the US government of his independent wealth. This allowed him the liberty to live the life of luxury without too many questions and, more importantly, a respectability that afforded top lawyers to fend off any interference and unwanted attention.

Until three years ago.

On reflection, he knew he had gotten greedy and complacent. He should have tendered a more reasonable figure for the garbage collection contract, but hindsight is always 20/20. What he should have done was paid off Michael Bradley. That would have been far cheaper than what it eventually did cost him in terms of reputation, liberty and cash.

He should have paid him off then had him disappear.

Instead the 'untouchable' Anthony Di Silva was now languishing in prison for the first time in his life and, in all probability, for the rest of his life. His bank account $34 million lighter, Michael Bradley still alive but penniless, and Kristy Bradley still missing with him being held accountable for her kidnap.

Worst of all – and for once – he was completely innocent.

Chapter 8

Manhattan, New York City

Friday 15th January

The dreamcatcher had been a gift from a friend for Melissa's 17th birthday and had adorned every single bedroom she had slept in since. As the morning sun streamed in the hotel window, she knew that there were neither good nor bad dreams to be found caught in its net, for she had not slept at all that night. Instead, she had simply lain in the fetal position and stared through its intricate web and out into the night's sky, watching the stars whilst constantly wondering what she had gotten herself into.

All in the name of adventure.

Is that what this was? Was it an adventure? The feelings that coursed through her body were certainly founded upon the sincerest of intentions but somehow, instinctively, they just didn't seem right. They didn't seem, or feel, well… *adventurous*. Over and over she had thought about leaving, to abandon this noble quest and return home to the mundane normality that was her life. Yet curiosity held her firmly in its grasp and simply would not let her go. She tried to convince herself that she knew what she was doing and that, after all, fortune favored the brave. Embrace the fear and enjoy the 'adrenaline rush', for surely that's what these feelings were called. After her all-night deliberations, Melissa concluded that this would be one of those episodes in her life that she could one day reflect upon with such fondness and affection that it convinced her to carry on.

Sadly, it would never be true.

It was just before 6am that the concierge gave her the alarm call that she had requested. A long shower to wash away the lingering negative thoughts followed before dressing and heading for the subway station. Breakfast could wait, as could her normal travelling companion who she left to sleep on as she took the train north and out of the city. The carriage was relatively empty due to the early hour and the fact that practically every commuter seemed to be heading in the opposite direction. It was just after 7am when she found her stop.

To even the most casual observer, her next action was most curious.

Alighting the train on the west side, Melissa ignored the other handful of passengers making their way for the exits and promptly headed over the bridge and took a seat at the furthest end of the east platform. There she sat under her umbrella, hiding from the fortuitous fresh flurry of snow, and watched five trains come and go back into the city before she saw who she was waiting for.

Michael Bradley looked like hell.

Even from this distance, it was obvious that he had enjoyed more than the single glass of whatever alcohol she had watched him drink in two hurried gulps the previous evening. If she were a betting woman, she would lay good money that she wasn't the only one who hadn't had a minute's sleep since their last encounter. Although, admittedly, she was the only one of them that actually knew that they had an encounter.

He was a pitiful sight and, if it was his intention that she feel sorry for him at their meeting, she found it was working.

As the next train pulled in, she watched as he took the first carriage and took the seat closest to the front. In her mind, this was perfectly understandable for this was as near as he could be to the city. To their meeting. To his wife. Following his lead, she stepped forward and managed to squeeze herself into the packed caboose. She never recognized the irony of her own actions. In the rear, it was standing room only all the way back to the city. As it got busier with each passing stop, it became a constant battle to peer through the crowds in a futile attempt to see if Michael got off at any of the stations in between. She believed that he had no such intentions as this, after all, was probably his only real opportunity to find his wife and surely he would never gamble with that.

Who would?

Grand Central Station is quite a magnificent building although, once again, Melissa had no time to admire nor enjoy it. Rather, as was the story of her life, she followed the masses as they hastily shuffled for the exits. Alone in the crowd, she bid adieu to her rude and unappreciative audience – it seemed that nobody realized that this was the performance of her life – and headed along the main concourse towards the Biltmore Passage. She had not seen Michael since Harrison but she knew where he would be. The instructions on the second sheet of paper had been plain and simple to avoid any risk of confusion.

Tomorrow, 9:30am,
Starbucks at Grand Central
Station. Take a seat outside,
alone. I'll find you. Any sign
of the police and I'm gone.

The police. She had been so caught up in her own web of intrigue and deceit that she had completely forgotten about them. It was only after a second person had unceremoniously crashed into her – and a second person to *not* apologize – did Melissa realize that she had come to a complete halt as she frantically twisted her head in all directions looking for the tell tale signs of being followed or watched.

Not that she had any clue what those 'tell tale' signs actually were.

She had naively thought that this was the ideal location at the perfect time as there would be safety in numbers and so she would easily spot any police presence. She now knew this to be wrong. They were professionals and she could be described, at the very best, as an amateur. Even then, it would be a most generous description. As the morning light flooded through the windows and illuminated all in its wake, it brought with it another realization that she had also not yet previously considered. She had seen enough crime shows from the

States to know that, by not contacting the police but rather contacting Michael directly herself, she could now be considered… now, what did they call it…?

An accessory after the fact.

This was serious. Really serious. That would be jail time. She couldn't handle jail, that was one certainty she absolutely knew to be true. Such certainties were all too rare at this moment and yet this one provided practically no comfort. Yet if there were police, the fact that she had been standing rooted to the spot for what seemed like an eternity would only be drawing their attention.

In blissful ignorance to her plight, the vast majority of her posse were slowly making their escape onto 42nd Street. How she desperately wished to join them but it was too late now, it had gone too far and her own curiosity too piqued for her to simply walk away.

It simply provided yet another reason to hate herself.

As the Starbucks logo came into view, she allowed herself the briefest of smiles at the irony. Over and over in her mind she had envisioned this moment of triumph, where she returns a life to this broken man. Yet here she was in defeat and resigned to her fate. How fitting that it was the Siren – that teasing and taunting minx who lured many a man to his demise – who would preside over these proceedings.

Sitting directly underneath her seductive smile and flowing locks, was Michael.

Chapter 9

Friday 15th January

Michael Bradley had never believed that Anthony Di Silva was responsible for his wife's disappearance. However, the asshole being jailed for the crime had been the only silver lining to his onerous cloud. Di Silva, the Mafia Don? Some Don! *He'll know better than to ever again mess with a Bradley.* The thought had him almost admiring Kristy. *Almost.* Under his table, he stole another look at the folded picture slipped from his pocket and just knew it was her. Surely it's her? It must be her. If it is, then she is free. Certainly free enough to contact him, which she hasn't done.

Freer still to spend the cash.

His cash.

The idea of recovering the money was

almost as delicious a thought to Michael as that of making Kristy pay for stealing it from him in the first place. Oh, and how she would pay. She was still his wife and so still belonged to him; she always would. As much his property as the dusty pile of rubble that they called 'home'. So long as she drew breath, that would always be the case. Not that death would relinquish her commitment to him, for he fully intended to reclaim her in the afterlife. It was, after all, what they swore to one another in front of their friends and family. *And before God.* He had ensured that they had used the traditional wedding vows; to love, honor, and obey. His focus had been more on the obey than the love and honor, although he had been faithful to her. He held constant suspicions that she couldn't say the same – especially now that he knew she had been running all around the world, spending his money.

Yes, for that humiliation, she would definitely pay.

Obviously, she thought she could simply leave. Just walk away from him and their marriage. Did she really think he wouldn't find her? Did she really believe he would just let her go? He *loved* her. He had vowed to love her in this life. And the next. She was, after all, almost the perfect wife. *Again, almost.* Time and time again, over and over, he had tried to teach her the error of her ways, taking the time to show her where she was going wrong. How she was displeasing him. After all, that is what loving husbands do. It was unsurprising that she did not yet understand that. It was as if all his efforts, all the beatings, were somehow pointless.

It merely confirmed his belief that she had always been stupid.

Had he not proved this to her? It seemed like she would just never learn. He had even been considerate enough to positively reinforce the point at those social occasions they had been forced to endure during his mayoral election campaign. How many times had he recognized that she had, year on year, grades that were better than his? Thus ensuring that her first degree was better than his second-class honors. Yet this only served to prove his point – medicine is far easier to learn than the law. Everybody knew that. This is why you practice medicine, but wrestle and fight with the law. That had been his killer punch line that everyone else had laughed at, except her.

Never once did she laugh.

She was that stupid she couldn't see the joke cleverly concealed within the serious statement. Her failure to simply stay at home and wait until he returned in triumph, and with the fresh ink still wet on the check, had only served to further prove her stupidity. If she had, he wouldn't be sat here waiting on yet *another* stupid bitch; his world was just full of them. They would be on a beach somewhere sipping a mojito with Kristy fussing over him as her champion, such was his generosity of spirit. Yet the greedy whore wanted it all for herself had up and vanished with his dreams.

And his cash.

Oh, how she would pay. So many times. Over and over.

His first order of business would be to buy a new favorite bat. These exciting new thoughts had rendered sleep impossible, although that was no bad thing and certainly not unusual these days. Instead, his imaginings of revenge and lavish spending had swum with his nightly bottle of scotch. For once, he had returned to oblivion as the celebrated king rather than his usual station as that of the clown.

Soon, very soon, he would no longer be a subject of anyone's pity.

Chapter 10

Grand Central Station, New York

Friday 15th January

Melissa found herself hiding behind one of the many obstructive pillars that all too frequently spring up in the most inopportune locations with the sole purpose of ensuring the safety of those patrons of the station. Quite literally, they were keeping the world from collapsing in on her yet that was exactly what she felt was happening. Unlike every other, this one was actually useful as she took a moment to compose herself and think through her next move. As she took advantage of the column for both cover and support, she fixed her gaze upon Michael and felt all of her maternal emotions swell within her.

He looked so helpless.

How could her intentions be seen as

anything other than noble to aid this man? She had seen his reaction to seeing his wife's picture. So overwhelmed with that sense of love and loss, he had collapsed. Here she had the very real opportunity to help him reclaim his life – reclaim his wife – and no matter what, she immediately resolved to help him do exactly that. If that meant questioning by the police, so be it. If it meant betraying the bank's client confidentiality, so be it. If it cost her job, so be it; it could hardly have ever been described as a career anyway. Here she had the power to help repair this broken man and reconcile him with his wife, and all for the sake of bending a few rules. It would all be worth the risk, both personally and professionally. Even if it did cost her the mundane job that she'd had for the past twenty plus years – *had it been that long? Where had the time gone?* – then it would be well worth it. Definitely worth it. She could live with the consequences of her decision, and with her conscience, as it had been a decision made with the most honorable of intentions.

Besides, she fully intended to quit with the reward money anyway.

Nervously rocking gently on her feet, she had a final sweeping glance all around. Deeply inhaling through her nose until it felt like her lungs would explode, she held her breath for a few seconds. Melissa needed the cavity space to house both her courage and bravery. She exhaled slowly as she caught her stride on the final rock forward and made her way directly towards the world's most famous coffee shop.

This also seemed to be the world's busiest coffee shop.

She had seen the constant queue from her vantage point and thought that she had timed her approach perfectly. However, as she set off, there seemed to be fresh faces appearing from every direction, all being seduced into the lair of the silent Siren. The formerly slender line was now rather robust and altogether too healthy for her comfort or liking. It snaked out of the store and directly in front of Michael.

There was no choice but to quickly find a place at the end of it.

Now standing less than two feet from him, Melissa turned her back to ensure that her face did not betray her. She rummaged in her pockets for her new phone; she desperately needed to look busy and inconspicuous. Not that the sweat was helping, she could feel her blouse sticking to her underneath her jacket. *How many ways are there to be uncomfortable?* She wrestled with the thought as she pretended to be reading the news, when she suddenly became aware of the voice behind her.

"...yes, right out the door." The indignation was apparent in the loud sigh that followed. *"I know, right? It's not as if this coffee is actually good, right? Not that any of these people would know the difference between good or bad coffee."* It was not lost on Melissa that this was said by a woman who was actually stood at the end of a not insignificant queue, waiting for a fresh beverage that she was already complaining about. *"Yeah, I know, get over yourself already Starbucks."* As she laughed at her own joke, Melissa fought every urge to turn around and stare at the woman. She knew of the New York 'attitude', everybody does, and it was an attitude that the Scots share; straightforward and no nonsense.

This wasn't it, this was just rude.

It proved to be a long five minutes before Melissa was finally asked for her order. She could only admire the beleaguered barista whom she had watched working so hard, all whilst listening to the mouth behind her. Although 'endured' would have been a more accurate description. In that time, she had managed to concoct a quite spectacular range of complaints; it was difficult not to admire her ability to find fault in everything. What was most surprising to Melissa was the fact that the invisible party to these proceedings had continued to maintain the conversation.

She knew she would have hung up long ago and quickly deleted this contact from her phone – and her life.

"Can I have a cup of tea, please?" Melissa had been so preoccupied with both Michael and the 'noise' from behind her, that she had paid no heed to the menu and so ordered the first thing that came to mind.

"What kind of tea can I get for you today? We have…" As the patient young man politely smiled through his recital of the Starbucks menu of teas, Melissa found that she was now the subject of The Voice's consternation. In the same snide tone that was all too familiar to her now, she actually seemed to be louder than usual. Obviously looking for a receptive audience of more than one.

"Well, is that not just perfect? We have been standing here for an age and this woman in front of me. Before you ask, yes, directly in front of me, hasn't even bothered to decide what she wants… I know, right. It is just ignorant, isn't it? Some people have no class…"

Any embarrassment Melissa thought she could hide found its way to her face; it was beaming. Shining so brightly that she was certain, should there be a power cut at that very moment, she could lead them all safely out without so much as a stubbed toe. Quickly, she ordered the English breakfast tea. As he prepared her drink, the young man called over his shoulder to ask if she would like room for milk or cream. Unfortunately, she couldn't quite make out what he said. The continued gripes coming from The Voice ensured that's all she could hear.

"I'm sorry?" Melissa said as her drink was placed on the counter in front of her. Before the barista could respond, The Voice took over.

"Now she is 'sorry'. She must be Canadian! Although she is not as sorry as I am to be standing behind her…" As she laughed at her own jokes, she looked to see if anyone else was joining her.

Nobody was.

Maybe it was the stress of her situation, maybe it was the fact that she hated bullies, maybe it was everything, maybe it was none of that. Maybe it was something completely different. Maybe it would take years of therapy to uncover. Whatever it was, Melissa knew it was something she would never care to understand. She just knew that this woman had pushed her too far.

Much too far.

She turned as The Voice continued talking. *"Yes, Canadian! I know, I thought it was a good one too!"* The laughter started again. Melissa swiftly grabbed the phone from the woman's left hand and, before The Voice could protest, she dropped it into the steaming paper cup of English breakfast tea that had just enough room for milk or cream. As the mouth tried to formulate the words, it seemed to Melissa that the whole coffee shop started to holler and cheer. After a few seconds, the man immediately behind The Voice shouted over the noise to the barista.

"I'd like to pay for another cup of whatever that lady ordered please." Melissa saw that he was pointing directly at her. The Voice saw it too and she fled with her hands vainly attempting to stem the flow of tears that were now ploughing through her mascara.

As Melissa drew her eyes back from watching her leave, she saw that Michael was staring directly at her.

Chapter 11

Friday 15th January

Melissa felt her blood run cold. Her body began to ache as it realized what her brain hadn't – she had stopped breathing. She was transfixed, frozen to the spot, and completely oblivious to anything and everything that was going on around her. Everything in her world had, quite literally, stopped.

All the while, Michael held her gaze.

Suddenly their eye contact was broken by the man who had ordered her a fresh cup of tea. He had stepped directly in front of her and was looking for the attention that she was giving to Michael. Although his presence and wants were not immediately apparent to Melissa, whose eyes were still looking through one stranger to another.

Only when the man spoke did she realize that he was actually there. In what seemed like the first time in forever, she exhaled. Her eyes refocused onto the man with the ready smile and kind eyes whose expression told Melissa that he was seeking an answer to a question. As she had no idea what he had asked, her mouth quickly spat out *"what?"* at him. The word came out far louder than intended and she was instantly certain that Michael must have heard it. For the second time in as many minutes, her body screamed for air.

Surely he will recognize my voice from his answer machine.

"I was just saying, that was absolutely brilliant what you did there. You made my day, and most everyone else's in here I'm sure." He could have no idea just how much she was going to make one of these particular patron's day, but she weakly smiled in the hope that he would let her go soon. She was beginning to feel very self-conscious and somewhat jealous of the wisdom that The Voice had exercised in immediately fleeing the scene.

How she now wished she had followed her.

"I know I just bought you a cup of tea but, well, I was wondering if you would maybe like to grab a cup of tea sometime? I mean, well, obviously, like some *other* time." *Wait, what? Has this guy just asked me out?* Melissa felt like she had been punched in the stomach and stepped back to really look at the man. She guessed he was around her age and seemed fairly normal, so why on earth would he be asking her out? Actually, a closer inspection told her that he was cute.

Very cute.

So many words tumbled around her head, but she simply could not catch any to throw out. No bad thing as she was still worried that Michael had already determined who she was from the single word she had said. She knew how illogical that was, but logic was in short supply at the minute. As she panted and fought for words and breath through her embarrassment at this man's forwardness – *am I actually flustered?* – he seized the moment and slipped his business card into her jacket pocket.

"Please, think about it. You have gumption and are a real beauty. How could I resist such a great combination? You can call me *anytime…*" As she continued to struggle to find any words of sense or consequence, he deftly turned on his heel and followed his coffee cup out of the store and disappeared among the new masses that were heading in all directions. With the new confidence and impenetrability that only comes from being asked out, she turned her attention back to Michael. Suddenly she felt beautiful, attractive, chic, and sexy; it was time to work more of her magic.

Michael was gone.

Chapter 12

Starbucks, Grand Central Station, New York

Friday 15th January

Melissa found the seat that Michael had all too recently vacated and sat down. It was still warm. She immediately understood why he chose this spot as it had the perfect view of everyone entering the shop. What she did not understand, however, was why he had left. Just as she pondered that very thought there was a tap on her left shoulder.

"I'm sorry, but this seat is taken." There were three other vacant chairs around the table and Melissa was not in a tolerant mood. As she turned and lifted her head, fully prepared for another tussle with the natives, her mouth instantly dropped to the floor.

"Michael." It was whispered as a statement of fact rather than a question.

"You…?" Michael struggled to align the person in his seat with the all too familiar voice that now lived in his home. He knew he had to quickly regain his composure if his charm offensive was to work. He did, after all, need this woman; although 'need' might be a little strong. He never had, nor never would, 'need' any woman – far less this one. He took a seat directly opposite Melissa. "So, do you really know where my wife is?"

"I thought you'd gone?" Melissa ignored his question and tried to take control.

"I went to use the restroom. My nerves just got the best of me, I suppose." A smile accompanied his joke and she recognized the happy face from the photograph in the article. As a lawyer, he knew enough basic psychology to know that smiles were meant to disarm and put others at ease. This particular nugget of information had served him well throughout his career and, from the way her shoulders shifted and settled, he was certain he had the desired effect.

Advantage to the Master.

"Ah, the *restroom*." Melissa said this more to herself as she confirmed that what he had said was true. She looked beyond where he had stood and saw the signs for the toilets in the back of the shop. 'Restroom' was just another quaint Americanism to which she was not yet accustomed. That would take some time and time had been in short supply since she had arrived in the country.

She relinquished his seat and spun into one opposite; as she did so, Melissa had another quick scan of her surroundings. Satisfied that they weren't the subject of any untoward attention, she sank low and deep into the hard chair and attempted to answer his question. However, as she went to speak, her tongue was to be found firmly stuck on the roof of her mouth. Realizing that she was parched, she leant over the table to reclaim her tea and took a sip.

Michael's patience was wearing thin and he suppressed the very real urge to slap and shake every answer from her; right here, right now.

Melissa was completely oblivious to his anxiety, she had enough of her own. Taking just a minute to finally compose herself, she placed the disposable cup back on the table and she searched for some courage in the eyes of the Siren. Holding her gaze, she took a deep breath and she started to talk. "Yes, I believe I know where your wife is. I can only imagine what you have been throu…"

It all happened so quickly, but she saw it in slow motion.

The man stumbled into her peripheral vision and then collapsed, falling into Michael before tumbling onto the tiled floor. The steaming fresh cup of coffee was quickly sacrificed in order to free his hands to break his fall. The plastic lid came to rest under their table as the majority of the scalding hot liquid found Michael's crotch. Under normal circumstances, she would have thought this quite funny.

These circumstances were anything but normal.

Melissa jumped up and stepped over to the men to ensure he was okay, instinctively trying to help him back to his feet. It was only in doing so that she became aware of his rather unique aroma; a quick look at his attire merely confirmed that this was obviously a man without much means. His long herringbone overcoat discreetly concealed most of the wear and tear, but it could not mask it all.

Certainly not at this proximity.

Before his feet found the floor, she saw the holes in both soles and the burst stitching along the inside seam of the right shoe. Dark trousers admirably masked the heavy stains and, for the most part, hid under the once expensive coat. The exposure of the lower legs ensured that they were now a very different color to the material above the knee. The weather had taken care of that. It seemed, to Melissa at least, that through this coat he endeavored to maintain an outwardly appearance of respectability. Any dignity and integrity that he had left were safely secured within it. Yet, in falling so spectacularly, his sense of pride disappeared faster than the contents of his cup – a beverage most likely bought with every penny he possessed. That very realization found Melissa's hands searching for her purse. She was about to ask if she could buy him a replacement, but was to be denied the opportunity.

"You fucking IDIOT!"

Michael first grabbed then pushed the helpless man in disgust. Thoroughly embarrassed, he offered no resistance but merely whimpered and cowered as he struggled to stand; his feet were in more flight than fight mode. With Michael's help, he fell for a second time and yet continued to apologize profusely – he must have said *"sorry"* more than six times already – desperate to be anywhere but here. This was a man used to living in the shadows, used to being ignored, and who was obviously deeply uncomfortable at being the sole object of Michael's attention. He meekly pointed to the spot where someone had spilled their drink before him and he tried to explain that he had simply slipped and fell because of it.

It wasn't his fault.

Melissa could take no more of the debacle and quietly excused herself. "I'm going to use the *restroom*." She whispered this to nobody in particular whilst tentatively using her index finger to indicate towards the general direction of the toilets. As she headed off to hide for a few minutes, she glanced over her shoulder to see Michael pick the man up by his collar and throw him back out onto the main concourse. Thankfully, another man stepped forward from an adjacent table in a rather vain but altogether bold attempt at calming Michael down. As the herringbone coat quickly scurried away and disappeared into relative safety of the crowd, she could see the stranger had his arm around Michael's shoulder and was talking quietly into his right ear. Michael's continued disgust was apparent as he grabbed the man's arm and threw it back at him. The would-be peacemaker threw both hands up in surrender and backed away, both his palms now facing Michael in a final attempt to calm him down and show he meant no harm. It was an exercise of futility and the man, now realizing as much, quickly found the seat he had so recently vacated.

To give Michael some extra cooling off time, Melissa thought it wise that her five-minute bathroom break should now be ten.

Chapter 13

Auchtershinnan Estate, Inverness, Scotland

Friday 15th January

For reasons best known to himself, and best left alone, Andy had been unable to make the standing dinner invite for the past two nights. Indeed, he had only accepted this lunch invitation at Penny insistence; she promised 'severe' repercussions if he embarrassed her again by cancelling.

Nobody knew what they would be but were even less inclined to find out.

Yet, here it was, the luncheon in full flow, and here he was, reveling in his role as head of the table. The irony was not lost on me that this would have been the very same table, in the very same room, that the servants would have dined at in yesteryear.

Although merely noticing made me feel like a complete asshole.

The stories and jokes were rolling thick and fast with each one seemingly funnier than the last. Thankfully my fear of Andy being too crude for Penny and, to a lesser extent, my mum, proved to be quite unfounded.

"Z, I meant to ask you earlier, I have been laboring for a few days over a final clue in a prize crossword and the deadline for entries is looming. It really is tormenting me and I hate to concede defeat, but I'd hate to miss out on the money more, so could you help me?" Andy's request took me completely by surprise. He'd never asked for my help before.

Ever.

"Sure, what's the clue?" All attention fell upon me and I was desperate to be the hero.

"It's *'Post office carnage'*. It really has me stumped."

"Post office carnage?" I repeated more to myself than to anyone else, confirming the clue and buying me some time to think. Nothing immediately came to mind and I needed more information. "How many letters?"

"Bloody hundreds!"

Everybody knew that they were laughing at me and I was laughing with them. Childishly, I felt foolish for being so gullible. It was Mum who spoke first after the laughter had died down.

"Something very similar actually did happen to me a few years ago. I was one clue away from entering a prize crossword for a brand new car. I later discovered that the word I had been missing was *Armageddon*. I was really quite upset that I missed out but, you know…" She paused just long enough for effect.

"It wasn't the end of the world!"

Good old Mum. She'd saved my blushes by moving the conversation on, and with a joke of her own – and a good joke at that. I had no idea she could be so funny.

"Do you know who invented the crossword? Not that I'm certain that 'invented' is the right word. Does one 'invent' the crossword? Maybe design or construct is more accurate?" Penny was now in a full-on discussion with herself.

"No idea, who was it?" I tried to bring her back, but was wary of being caught out again. As they say, *fool me once…*

"Arthur Wynne. He was actually British, but is widely credited with 'inventing' the modern day crossword puzzle when it was first published in the *New York World* newspaper. This is the very same newspaper that is believed to lend its name to the baseball World Series. As such, it is not a world event in the accepted sense that its participants come from all over the world, but rather that the newspaper is an original sponsor. A belief that is unverified, incidentally. Anyway, what is most interesting is Arthur Wynne's final resting place. *Although I am still not convinced that he actually 'invented' the crossword...*" Once again, she had drifted off to grapple with the thought.

After a few moments of awkward silence, I was about to ask when Dad beat me to it. "Well?"

"Well, what?" Penny seemed genuinely surprised to find the question directed at her.

"What was interesting about Arthur Wynne's final resting place?" Dad was asking what we were all thinking. The smile lit up her face before the words left her mouth.

"Oh, just that he is buried three across and four down!" Penny savored the moment before turning to Mum. "Shall we?"

"We shall." Mum got up and started for the door that Penny was now holding open; they shared a look of mischief. The bond between them was growing ever stronger and it pleased me no end. Although, at times like these, it was altogether more unsettling.

Certainly for me at least.

"What are you two up to?" Another

question that I would no doubt come to regret asking.

"We are going to watch the box set of Downton Abbey that Penny bought me for Christmas." Mum loved the series, but was far happier with the actual gift, and who it had come from. They were already chuckling away in the corridor as Penny's voice wafted back into the kitchen.

"Or 'the good old days' as I like to call it!"

Chapter 14

Starbucks, Grand Central Station, New York

Friday 15th January

Melissa mustered all her bravado to exit
the restroom and walked with a steely grit
and determination along the dank and dirty
corridor to head back into the fray. At least,
that is how she perceived herself in her own
head; the reality was far less flattering. Her
back was firmly stuck to the far wall of the
small passageway as she took small side
steps to shuffle along and peek out. All in an
effort to ensure everything was peaceful,
maybe even normal.

Not that any of this was normal.

When she saw Michael, she froze.
Through yet another new crowd that had
gathered in her brief absence, Melissa saw
him in an animated discussion with one of
New York's finest boys in blue. Between

them both, she recognized the all too familiar features that she thought were gone forever.

It was the face that belonged to The Voice.

Since disappearing from the shop without her phone, and having been so publicly humiliated in front of people she would never know, she had obviously decided it best to return and claim the moral victory in front of even more people that she didn't know. This new crowd of people undoubtedly cared even less than the first, if that were at all possible.

Melissa watched their body language and tried to lip read what was being said. Unsurprisingly, The Voice was fully utilizing its face along with her arms that were being thrown in all directions as if conducting a symphony to this overtly theatrical performance. Naturally, she was the wronged party and demanded satisfaction; not only for the loss of phone, but also for loss of face.

Never for loss of voice.

It was now Michael's turn to play peacemaker and she could tell he was doing an admirable job. At least, it seemed to be the case from this distance for the policeman looked completely disinterested.

Then it happened.

All three parties focused their attentions towards the restrooms. Thankfully, Melissa was obscured by a few fake plants and the queue that now snaked along the counter and its display case, and back down towards the front entrance that doubled as an exit. Panic gripped her as she took one large side step back along the corridor to completely hide from the unwanted attention.

What was happening?

This was supposed to be her moment of triumph, when she reunited lost love and rekindled romance. Where had it all gone wrong? Her meticulous plan, the foolproof idea that covered every eventuality, the protection of a public place; it had brought her to this, and now she was trapped. Her dreams were literally dying in front of her and she was powerless to save them. Suddenly struggling for air, she was suffocating. She needed to breathe. She needed to escape. She needed time. They would be here any minute and there was nowhere to hide. The Voice would have her moment of glory at Melissa's expense.

That could never happen.

As she headed back down the corridor towards the array of doors that all provided temporary relief to the Siren's patrons, she opted for the only other door. One that offered a permanent reprieve. One that had a tired 'Fire Exit' sign painted upon it. Heading along yet another dank and dirty passageway, Melissa followed the brightly illuminated signs. Under a minute later, she slipped inconspicuously onto the sidewalk of Park Avenue and just kept walking. Heading off in search of a crowd in which to get lost.

The policeman, Michael, and The Voice made their way back from their fruitless search of the restrooms with a new topic to discuss – *where was she?* The Voice was seething at missing her moment of glory whilst the cop never had any interest in the petty squabble anyway. The disappearing perpetrator had given him the perfect excuse to wash his hands of the whole sorry affair and get back to work. In truth, having experienced The Voice first hand, he completely understood Melissa's actions and empathized with her predicament. There had been countless times when he'd wanted to do the exact same thing. He could only hope that The Voice would learn from her own mistakes and arrogance, but he knew better. Sadly, the mean streets of New York City were filled with such self-inflated egos with no respect for anyone or anything – including the police. Until they were needed. Like now.

He knew Michael and his ilk to be just

as bad.

It came as no shock that his opening words of *"Good morning, Sir"* to Michael were met by *"I'm a lawyer, so I'd urge caution Officer; I know my rights."* Everybody seemed to 'know their rights' these days, especially in this city. At least once every day he considered how TV shows like *Law and Order* and their ilk had a lot to answer for. Through gritted teeth, the lawman insincerely thanked Michael for his 'assistance', such as it was, and disappeared himself into the terminal with The Voice's protestations literally ringing in his ears.

Evidently, she was far from happy with this unacceptable outcome.

Michael reclaimed his seat and stared intently at the restrooms for Melissa to materialize. They had searched every stall, but she had simply vanished. *Just like someone else I know.* He had been so close, so very close, to discovering where was his bitch wife. The anger swelled within him as he realized the irony.

He had, quite literally, just seen his best efforts disappear into the toilet?

Yet Melissa's escape had not gone completely unnoticed. The man who would be peacemaker, whose arm Michael had so rudely and readily rejected, had surreptitiously watched and listened intently to all of their conversation. Every last word. Sitting with his laptop, he quickly searched the New York Department of Buildings online and checked the schematics of the coffee shop. He lifted his phone and sent a text that was both short and to the point.

Fire Exit Park Avenue
halfway down.

As Melissa ambled north, the man in the herringbone coat sent his reply.

Got her, following now.

Chapter 15

Friday 15th January

It had only taken a few idle twists and turns for Melissa to land on Madison Avenue. As she walked along in pace with everyone and yet no-one in particular, she could not help but feel the city holding her close, making her feel safe again. It was warm and comforting, like an old friend. She half-expected to meet people she recognized on these streets. People that she knew so much about but had never met. People that resided here among these familiar buildings, stores, and landmarks, but yet lived happily in her television back in Scotland.

It was reassuringly odd.

She had no idea how long she had been wandering nor, indeed, what the time was when she came to a halt at the entrance of the Empire State Building. Rather bizarrely, she had happened upon one of the world's most truly iconic structures by complete accident as she had never thought to simply look up during her aimless sauntering.

'Ostrich Syndrome' her nana called it. The old woman hated Melissa's tendency to always have her head down, especially when walking. She could hear her now, *"Head UP, keep your back STRAIGHT, walk PROUD!"*

It felt good to smile again.

Now, faced with the same famous entrance that so many had seen before her, she generously allowed herself a moment of sheer indulgence as she feasted upon the splendor of the building. The art deco design, so distinct and recognizable, was even more impressive in the flesh. Its seductive lines drew her eyes upwards, only to disappoint as they disappeared into the winter sky. She found another smile as the old adage sprung to mind – *always leave 'em wanting more.*

As she stood there in the snow, completely oblivious to the cold, the man in the herringbone coat stepped into a nearby doorway. Unfolding a crumpled piece of cardboard with the words 'Help the Homeless' scribbled on the side, he held the sign in one hand with an empty Styrofoam cup in the other. His battered and well-worn shoes had been replaced with new hiking boots that he drove into the snow to maintain his cover.

His eyes never left Melissa.

She toyed with the idea of playing tourist and enjoying the magnificence of New York from the observation deck, but decided against it. That was something to be enjoyed with someone special; a lover, a partner, a friend. Hopefully, she will have all three one day; and hopefully they will all be the same person. It was a long-held dream, but wasn't this the very city where dreams came true? She hadn't realized that her eyes had closed – *when did that happen?* – and as they opened she had to blink rapidly to clear away a few heavy tears. She pulled her scarf up over her nose and the hood of her jacket down to hide her face. Taking the cell phone from her pocket, she chose the satnav app and quickly punched in the name of her hotel. According to its calculations, she was a 14 minute walk away.

She was there in 11.

As the day slipped away in the city that never sleeps, she sat alone in her room and contemplated her next move. Her opinion of Michael had changed rather dramatically and she wondered if she really wanted to help him at all now. There were a few days

left of her trip – so time was on her side –
but she desperately needed to sleep.
Although when she tried, her own demons
kept her awake. To alleviate the boredom,
and to hear some friendly voices, she had
turned on the TV and absentmindedly
flicked through the channels. Foolishly, she
stumbled across *Jeopardy* and thought it
wise to pit her wits against the contestants.
She stubbornly engaged for far longer than
was good for her, as it was so American-
centric that it only served to make her feel
even more stupid than she already did.

Maybe food would help.

Looking out of her bedroom window,
she saw the neon lights of the small pizzeria
directly opposite the hotel. It looked clean
enough, and something quick and easy was
all she wanted; the diet could wait until she
got home. This was, after all, her vacation –
such as it was. She managed to leave the
hotel, order two slices of pepperoni, and be
back in her room before the adverts had
finished on 'Final Jeopardy'.

She couldn't decide if it was her who
was fast or if the adverts were slow.

Placing the wrapped pizza slices on the
sideboard, she was in the midst of taking her
jacket off when there was a knock at her
door. She froze. A mild panic hit her as she
immediately thought of Michael. Had he

found her? She struggled to assemble her wits as the voice behind the door said "*Room service*". Obviously a mistake. As she chided herself for being so silly and melodramatic, she finally slid off her jacket and threw it onto the chair as she made her way to open the door.

It happened so fast that she simply had no time to react.

As she pulled down the door handle, a force from behind the door pushed hard against her. Caught completely unaware, she stumbled backwards and hit the sideboard, causing her to twist and fall face first onto the bed. Before she could turn, a man jumped onto her back and pinned her down. He held her from behind as his strong hand suddenly clamped firmly but gently over her mouth. He whispered softly into her ear, *"I shall let you go if you promise to keep quiet, can you do that for me?"*

The shock hit her as she saw the other man lift her discarded jacket from the chair and hang it up in the empty closet. He returned to the seat and took a moment to brush it down with the black leather gloves he held in his hand. Finally, he sat. Lazily crossing his legs, he brushed yet more imaginary fluff from his immaculate trousers before allowing his eyes to settle upon Melissa. He gave an idle nod to his companion and, once again, the man asked if she would be quiet so he could let her go. Only, this time, he said "please". Melissa doubted she could scream if she wanted to, such was her fear; for the first time in her entire life, she was genuinely terrified.

She closed her eyes to focus, and subtly nodded.

Although still holding her tight, he slowly released his firm grip and took his hand away. As promised, she said nothing but managed to open her eyes to look directly at the man sitting in her chair. She recognized this man. He was the peacemaker who had tried to calm down Michael in Starbucks. *Why is he here? What could he possibly want with me?*

Melissa realized that the other man had released her and she was now alone on the bed. Although she didn't feel any less threatened as he was now stood menacingly behind her with the only noise in the room coming from the TV; the closing music of *Jeopardy* filling the void. It was an irony that none of them could appreciate.

The man in the chair was the first to speak. "My companion and I have reason to believe that you know where we might find Kristy Bradley. We would like you to share this information with us. *Please.*"

This had just gotten very serious, very

fast. Now Melissa just wanted to go home. Home to where it was safe. *Why am I here? What have I done?* She struggled to compose herself and was about to deny everything when he continued.

"Trust me, we mean you no harm. If we had, we could have done so already. Many times. At Starbucks, in the Fire Exit at Grand Central Station, Park Avenue, Madison Avenue, outside the Empire State Building; anywhere at all today, really. So, please, believe me when I say that we really do mean you no harm. We just want to know where Mrs. Bradley is?" The peacemaker utilized the same smile that Michael had done earlier, but his was far more convincing to her.

Genuine, almost.

"You have been following me?" As she realized the implications of what he said, Melissa quickly scrambled up the bed until she felt her back pressed hard into the headboard. She then pulled her knees tight under her chin and wrapped her arms tightly around her legs. Her eyes darted between both men. She thought she recognized the second man too – *but from where?*

"We have an interest in Mrs. Bradley that is of no consequence to you, Melissa." *He knows my name?* "However, as I am sure you can appreciate, that interest now extends to include you. So, *please* can you tell us where she is and we shall be immediately gone from here, and from your life, forever." The man's soft tone was as charismatic as it was sinister, the smile never left his face and she could not help but believe he was sincere.

"I really have no idea what you are talking about. Who is *Kirsty* Bradley?" Melissa deliberately gave the wrong name and tried to speak with an authority and sincerity that fooled nobody. Yet she somehow felt that she was in control. It was strangely exciting to be needed, even in this most perilous of situations, and the very real danger she felt only added to the appeal. As she stared straight into the eyes behind the smile, she felt herself becoming strangely aroused.

"Come now, Melissa." For the second time, The Smile used her name although, this time, it was said slowly and deliberately to emphasize the fact that he knew it – and made her believe that this was not all he knew about her. Similarly, he said Penny's real name slowly for effect, "Kristy Bradley is nothing to you. Just tell me where she is and we can be on our way. You can then *safely* enjoy your next few days in our great city before heading home and back to normality." Again, with the emphasis.

As she was about to deny all knowledge for a second time, more from a blend of sheer stubbornness and stupidity than fear, the other man spoke.

"Is *her* location worth *your* life?" There was no disarming smile to be found on this face nor subtlety in his tone, it was one completely devoid of either charm or charisma. It was full of undisguised menace and in stealing a brief look into his eyes, she saw nothing. He left her cold and her newly found bravado abandoned her. She also recognized the voice, although the last time she heard it, it was wrapped in a herringbone coat and full of apologies.

Yet she was the one who was now sorry.

Her mind raced, scrambling for alternatives, but she already knew there were none. These were serious men, no longer just anecdotes from a glossy magazine. The threat on her life felt very real and, if she was wrong about Penny being Kristy, then they would simply leave her alone. She knew she wasn't wrong, but the idea that she could be provided some doubt and was the only sliver of solace to be had in this situation.

"Miss Chisholm, please forgive my associate's bluntness." The Smile had been constant throughout, but the eyes had flashed a warning to his companion. He got the message and found something interesting to look at through the window. There had been no need to threaten her, it was implied from their very presence here in her hotel room. In any case, he already knew she was scared for her life – her actions and subsequent escape from Starbucks had proven that. They all knew that she would tell them what they needed to know, there was no need for threats nor intimidation. He could see that this girl was in way over her head and was desperate to get out and back home, and the last thing they needed was her reporting this to the police; they could all do without the routine of that particular charade. What was it his old English teacher used to say?

Softly softly catchee monkey.

"My friend is just as keen, as I am, to talk to Mrs. Bradley. She has information that could greatly help us. So, please, just tell us where she is…" He moved forward in his seat and perched on the end of the chair. His elbows resting on his knees and his thumbs rolling impatiently around each other, his other fingers interlocked as if being restrained. She could only imagine the damage those hands had done. The smile disappeared and he held her gaze with menacing eyes.

"...Now." It was an order more than a question.

Melissa's eyes were locked onto his as she sent a silent prayer up to all the God's for protection. Surely this wasn't how it would end, in a cheap hotel room in the city of her dreams? She knew that was no longer in her control and compliance was her only option.

"You understand that I have no actual proof that it is her? It's only that she looks remarkably similar." She could tell from his exasperated look that he really didn't care for the explanation, but she was now worried that she was wrong. If she was, would they come back looking for revenge from her for wasting their time? Yet what other options were there? She told them what she knew. "She lives on the Auchtershinnan Estate near Inverness in Scotland. Except now, she uses the name Penelope Munro."

The smile was back. He nodded towards the door, indicating a silent instruction to his acquaintance that was immediately obeyed. Opening it, the man looked up and down the corridor and threw the word "clear" in the general direction of The Smile. He kept his seat for a few seconds, still holding her gaze, but peering deep into her soul.

"Thank you." His soft soothing tone had

returned.

The fear had never left, but now her imagination ran riot. She was of no further use to them, they had all the information they needed. As he stood, she closed her eyes tight and buried her head deep into her knees, waiting for the inevitable. She heard his footsteps and strained to hear the weapon of choice; probably a gun – *wasn't that the favorite?* She wondered if the silencer was already fitted or if it being attached to the barrel of the gun would be the second last thing she ever heard. Maybe he would just use a pillow, she knew from TV and films that this was just as effective. As the door clicked closed, an instinctive tension gripped her tightly in preparation. Quickly wrapping her arms around her legs and pulling them tightly to her, she prayed it would be quick. Nothing. All she could hear was her own heartbeat thumping in her ears and, over this, the soft comforting tones of Sam Elliott extolling the virtues of a Dodge Ram. Not that she had any idea of what a Dodge Ram actually was, but none of them had bothered to switch off the television during this whole charade.

Enough already.

Melissa had just about as much as she could take. If this was how it was, then so be it. She was no match for these two men, even without the guns. Yet she did still have her pride and self-respect. Not very much, but enough. The bravado was back and she would not go down without a fight. She threw her arms wide and jumped in one fluid motion from the bed towards the door. That was the last place she had known The Smile to be. As she grabbed at thin air, hoping to connect with hair, face, and skin – maybe even rip the smile itself – she hit the sideboard and landed in a heap upon the floor.

They were gone.

She stood all too quickly and her knees, still shaking from the mix of fear and adrenaline, offered no support and she crumpled back onto the floor. Her lunge from the bed had brought the door within reach, so she scrambled onto her knees to engage the dead bolt. Pain from her collision with the sideboard coursed through her and she looked at her left arm and saw blood. Although, on closer inspection, it didn't quite feel like blood.

This blood had a slice of warm pepperoni attached.

Beside her, lying face down on the bedroom floor, were the two slices of pizza that were to be dinner. The absurdity of the situation hit her and the laughter came easily. How would she ever explain this back home; *who could, or would, ever believe me?* Soon she was laughing so hard her shoulders shook and she threw her head back, struggling for a breath. Realizing the irony only made her laugh even more, but all too soon she was sobbing deeply from sheer relief.

Relief to be alive.

Yet all of *her* actions, those actions she had taken to ensure that love won through, had placed a stranger in danger. A very real danger. Her motivations, objectives, hopes, and dreams for the happy ever after for both Michael and Kristy – Kirsty? Penny? Whoever she was – had proven to be as much of a fairy tale as Snow White, Cinderella, and Rapunzel. Only this time, there would be no Prince Charming.

Then it hit her. Maybe, just maybe, this could have the happy ending after all.

Michael…

Chapter 16

New York City

Saturday 16th January

It had been almost five hours since Melissa had collapsed onto the grimy floor of the hotel bedroom and surrendered herself to an exhaustion that so easily robbed her of all consciousness. For a few delicious moments, the fog of drowsiness kindly obscured the nightmare of the reality in which she was waking up. Natural instincts of self-preservation ensured that her body remained perfectly still and her eyes firmly closed although she had no idea why. Then her last memory instantly refreshed in her mind; the empty room that sleep had taken her from had, inexplicably and inconsiderately, returned her here.

Was she still alone?

Under normal circumstances, she would

wallow in her slumber and find every corner of her bed; always with the childish belief and vain hope that natural beauty is to be found through sleep. As a single woman who had never enjoyed a real relationship, it was easier to blame her looks than her personality, attitude, or any number of other legitimate reasons why she repelled men. The irony of it was that her overwhelming fear of further abandonment starkly highlighted her issues of finding the happiness she greatly desired. This ensured every potential relationship was always doomed to fail. There had been a few suitors who had found this rather endearing, but their enthusiasm had all too soon waned in the face of her dogged determination to be miserable. Allowing herself to trust would have ensured the contentment that she desperately craved. So she had convinced herself that the very least she could do would be to help Penny and Michael rekindle the love that she could never find.

It had all been such a noble and gallant quest that was now lying in tatters beside her; not that she dared to look. She reasoned that it was better to play dead than waking to find that the two men had returned to make it a reality. The absurdity of the situation was all too apparent to her – *if that was their intention, they could have killed me already*

– but there was no need to take the risk.

Her all too recent past was blocking her present with the very real possibility of ending her future.

The questions spun around in her mind as she mustered all of her other senses to scan her surroundings. Surely the men had no cause to return? She had, after all, complied with their demands – actually, it was just a single demand but still, it was enough – and told them all she knew. Well, *almost* all she knew. In an instant, another multitude of reasons for their return flooded her mind, leaving no room for the possibility that they wouldn't.

The television was still blaring with a fresh wave of the same tired old adverts. She became aware of the unmistakable rhythm of a headboard battering against the wall adjacent to hers, it had a woman's voice who was in the throes of positively adulating "God". In equally close proximity, but from across the hall, another voice yelled in ironic frustration, *"Would you shut the FUCK UP ALREADY!"*

"Yes….
yes…*YES*…*YEEES*…*YEEEEEESSSSSSSS*…
" It was apparent that God was now surplus to her requirements, and the positive response to the question happily coincided with yet another thump of the headboard

against the wall. The lack of reply from the complainer could be explained, in part, by the very obvious fact that they were nearing the end. A few seconds later, and with one final cry for the Almighty, the woman fell mute and the headboard ceased bullying the wall.

It was only then that Melissa became aware of the fact that the television, rather miraculously, had managed to find an actual program. The presenter kindly informed her that it was 2am as she introduced yet another rerun of *Jerry Springer*. Her fog of drowsiness had now completely lifted and was replaced with a measured calmness that ensured she was ready for anything. Whatever fate was waiting for her behind the curtain that was her eyelids needed to be seen and dealt with.

But only on her own terms.

She pulled herself up into a seated position and, wrapping her arms tightly around her knees, pushed the small of her back into the hitherto offending wall of sex. Taking a final deep breath, she slowly opened her eyes as the air escaped from her lungs and readied herself to process the onslaught of images that was the vision before her.

She found she was alone, although now sharing a completely oblivious audience with Jerry.

She ignored them as her attention was drawn to her dreamcatcher that was hanging redundantly on the window. The flashing neon lights from the street below seemed to be pulling her into it and, for the briefest of moments, she was certain there was an actual dream to be found there. Staring through its very core, she clearly saw what she had to do.

She had to act.

The power cable for the television was first. The socket was at her right hand and the cacophonous rabble was immediately silenced with one swift yank of the cord. She quickly wondered how many others had wished they could pull the plug on shows such as these and kill them just as easily. It was car crash television that passed for entertainment and she hated it. She hated herself more for having, on occasion, enjoyed it. Occasions that were simply much too frequent. Not that now was the right time to berate herself for such a realization, now was more a time for action rather than words.

Well, different action.

Positive action.

Hers was a reluctant admission that, on reflection, this valiant quest had been completely foolish and undeniably dangerous. Adrenaline coursed through her veins as she formulated the new strategy to ensure her own safety that maybe – *just maybe* – could still find a happy ending for this noble crusade. Foolish, she may well have been and wounded by her own naivety, but Melissa was definitely not stupid and she quickly pulled a new plan together.

"Are you certain you wish to check out Miss Chisholm?" The hotel's night manager took another slow and elaborate look at the oversized clock that hung behind him. It showed 2:21am, although he knew from cross-referencing with his computer that it was a minute fast. He pointed to the wall, "It is, after all, the middle of the night and your reservation is until Monday. As you will appreciate, there is no question of a refund at this late stage." Melissa also noted that there was no question as to why she wanted to leave nor if she had actually enjoyed her stay. It was obvious that he didn't actually care either way, on both questions, and was merely exhausting the formalities before bidding yet another customer adieu. After all, to him, this was only a job that he had taken until something better came along; that had been almost 14 long years ago. She, like everyone else, would never know how he felt betrayed by fate and abandoned by the God whose house he visited every week, praying for that eternally elusive career opportunity. The fact that he hadn't actually sought nor applied for any other positions throughout those 14 years was completely lost on him.

"Yes, I'm sure, thank you." Melissa complied with the ritualistic formalities as she handed back her room key card and turned towards the underground car park. All her belongings had been swiftly packed into the small overnight bag that now trundled sheepishly at her heels. She knew that checking out merely minimized the opportunity for her unwelcome guests to drop by again.

The hire car was her safest option.

She parked her hotel-room-on-wheels in the very same spot from where she had observed Michael the previous night. *Oh what a difference a day makes.* The wry thought rattled around in her head. She turned the heat on full and left the engine running, having already checked to see when the sun would rise – 7:17am according to the all knowing Google – and so set the alarm on her phone for ten minutes beforehand. She didn't want to run the risk of Michael, or anyone else, catching her here. Yet this is exactly where she felt safest and, rather inexplicably, closest to home.

It was just after 3am and a single lamp

was the only source of light from Michael's home. It shone like a lighthouse with a similar warning for all to steer clear. The only other visible piece of furniture was the high backed chair, but that faced into the home and so it was impossible to determine if he was in it. Obviously, this had been by design rather than default. Even from her obscure vantage point, it was evident that there hadn't been many guests of late. The fact of the matter was, other than Michael, the last person to walk through this house had been Penny.

She had barely done so with her life.

Melissa stole a quick glance in all three mirrors and, satisfied the street was deserted, once again exited the car to tentatively make her way towards the light. The wind was biting and the snow fell lightly upon her, but she was oblivious to both, her eyes scanning and searching through every corner of the window. Within a few short steps, she could see the figure in the chair. A final careful and deliberate step clarified that it was Michael, slumped within its embrace and sound asleep.

He looked so peaceful and serene.

It was a look that was deceptive and one that he didn't wear well. What she couldn't see was the empty bottle of scotch that he had purchased on his return home from their earlier encounter. Its simple task was to provide consolation whilst obliterating the very memory of their doomed meeting. Self-pity was an easy and extremely loyal companion to Michael Bradley and he took every opportunity to welcome its company. Her curiosity satisfied, she quickly made her way back to the car and settled down into the driver's seat. Sleep would be impossible but, by making herself comfortable, she would at least give it a fighting chance.

A car slowly entered the street behind her and its headlights filled the cabin of her temporary dwelling. Paranoia gripped her, and she struggled to stay low in her seat whilst desperately trying to see into a mirror – any mirror – but none were obliging. *Just relax.* She closed her eyes and took a second to think. It was just as she reasoned that it was simply a neighbor heading home that the car pulled in directly behind her. She fought the idea that she had once again been found by her two most recent friends and replaced it with the more logical explanation that it was a date being dropped back home. *Shit!* Melissa quietly berated herself for having left the engine running as she carefully reached for the key and switched off the ignition. In this weather, nobody could fail to see the industrial sized stacks of smoke heading for the skies and drawing unwanted attention. All in a selfish effort to keep herself warm.

As the cold quickly penetrated the car, she was suddenly sweating.

The red and blue lights immediately mixed with the bright white headlights and Melissa froze. Although they only flashed briefly, the lights were enough to ensure panic gripped her and she was struggling to breathe when the police officer tapped the window. Recognizing her distress, he disregarded the usual protocols and opened the driver's door. *"Ma'am, please, just relax. Take deep breaths…. that's right, deep breaths…. you're doing fine ma'am, just relax…."* In a few short minutes, Melissa managed to regain some semblance of composure; although to her, it had felt like a lifetime.

"Ma'am, are you okay?"

"Ye…" Her tongue was dry and refused to work. She quickly located a bottle of water that was on the passenger seat and took a sip, "Yes, thank you officer, I am now. Thank you." She immediately felt stupid for saying thank you twice to the very man who had caused her such distress in the first place.

"Good. Okay then. So, ma'am, can you please tell me what you are doing here?"

"Well…yes, well, you see…" Lies

could not be found, with her brain only seeming to permit a variant of the truth. Mustering her most confident tone, she tried to take control of her situation. "I'm here to see Michael Bradley, although it seems that I have overestimated my travel time and so arrived here far too early. Or far too late, depending on your outlook." She smiled faintly at her poor attempt at humor whilst pointing in the direction of the house. "I realized that this is a most ungodly hour to be disturbing him and so was intending to simply stay here until morning."

"Is he expecting you?" The officer gave no indication whether he believed her or not.

"Of course." The lie came all too easily and just as quickly trapped her.

"Well it seems that Mr. Bradley's excitement for your imminent arrival has caused him to wait up for you." The policeman exemplified the famous New York sarcasm, "So why don't I escort you over *the mean street* and save you an uncomfortable wait." It was an order more than a question. Melissa followed the direction of the officer's arm although she already knew who was waiting beyond its reach – Michael. The light show must have roused him. She cursed her own stupidity at actually being here. She could've, and should've, gone anywhere else other than here. *Anywhere* else would've been less conspicuous. *Anywhere* else would've been safer.

A dark silhouette filled the front door with the head pointing in their direction; she couldn't see his face, but knew it was him. It wasn't until after he flicked on the porch light did she see that he wasn't looking at them. Michael Bradley was staring directly at her. The cop saw it too. The mischievous eyes and malevolent grin was a look that the officer recognized and made him instantly fear for her safety. With 24 years of service, he had only moved out to the suburbs to appease his wife who wanted to ensure that he was alive to enjoy his impending retirement. At least he'd thought it recent and failed to register that it was almost 5 years ago. Although it had been a while, he'd seen this very same look many times before and experience told him that she was in danger.

Grave danger.

Everyone in the neighborhood knew of Michael Bradley, and the story of his missing wife was already legendary. There had been the usual rumors after she had disappeared, including some preposterous and slanderous accusations from her work colleagues that he had beat on her. The cop knew better than to believe the idle gossip.

Primarily because Michael had always been
nothing but pleasant and courteous through
their limited dealings; one could say almost
cordial. That was a hugely endearing quality
in this particular town. Indeed, when he
heard the story of his wife's kidnapping, he
had actually felt sorry for the poor schmuck.
To think, on the very day that he won his
greatest ever victory with riches beyond the
wildest dreams of any beat cop, his wife –
and all that money – vanished? All he could
give him was pity, and he had happily done
so.

Until now.

Now, as Michael was making his way
towards them, he could actually see the
menace that others had suggested. It was
chilling. He suddenly held a very real fear
for Melissa's safety and, as it said on his
patrol car, he was duty bound to *'protect
and serve'*.

Yet, instead of protecting Melissa, he
had served her up to Michael.

He needed to act, and act fast. "Ma'am,
it may be better for you to find a local hotel
for the evening and come back fresh
tomorrow? I'm sure you are tired after your
long journey and I can escort you to a nice
place right near here in town. I know the
guys there, they will do me a deal fo…."

"Nonsense. There is absolutely no need

for that officer, she can stay right here with me. I have, after all… *been expecting her*." Michael interrupted as he approached the car; lies had always come easily to him and so he was far more convincing in his execution. Yet the sinister tone was unmistakable and came with a fresh smile that had also been perfected through years of practice. It was one unique to every politician and designed to engage and disarm. However, in this instance, it made Melissa's blood run cold and a new panic immediately gripped her. She was afraid and desperately wanting to accept the offer of help, but the fear and anxiety had rendered her speechless. Her internal screams were deafening as her eyes filled and silently pleaded with those of the portly man in uniform – but still no words would come.

"Well, then, as long as you are sure everything is okay here?" The officer raised his eyebrows and implored her to respond. *Say something. Please. Anything? Anything at all?* Nothing. They all knew that this was a charade, but he could only stand back and watch. Melissa exited the car and, for the second time that night, trudged slowly towards Michael's house.

"Sure, we're sure Officer, and thank you so much for your *vigilance*." It was now his turn to be on the receiving end of the sarcasm.

He didn't much care for it.

Melissa took a long time to make the short walk from her car to Michael's house. With each step seemingly slower than the last, it was a constant fight to not simply turn and run back to the safety and security of the waiting policeman's car. He, in turn, could only observe and wonder if he was watching another missing person disappear in front of his eyes.

Never had he felt so desperate. So impotent. So helpless.

Unable to understand her own actions, Melissa's decision was aided by Michael's firm hand in the small of her back that carefully guided her every step through the porch and ushered her into his home. It was only removed once she had crossed the threshold, and only then, so it could be further utilized to wave back into the street. *"Thank you again, Officer. Have a good night."* The politician that resided within him had emerged through his drunken haze with a voice that was sanctimonious, cheery, and light.

The patrolman was unimpressed and stood motionless. *"I never voted for you anyway, asshole."* His breath was visible in the cold and it drifted down the street, taking his words away from politician's earshot –

he instantly wished he had said them louder. He watched as Michael stepped backwards into the house, holding his face against the edge of the door as he slowly closed it, his eyes firmly fixed on the officer who fearlessly held his gaze. Michael gave the man a sly wink and a malevolent smile before slipping effortlessly behind the panel of wood. It would be all of 27 minutes later before the policeman very reluctantly left his position to answer an emergency call that proved anything but urgent. Neither Michael nor Melissa would ever know that he would return another twice during his shift and then another once on his way home.

He would never see either of them again.

As Michael closed the door and turned to enter his home, he found that Melissa was facing him, but had actually been looking through the portal towards her would be protector. He had her exactly where he wanted her, here in his home. Now was not the time to allow her to slip through his grasp for a second time; certainly not before eliciting all she knew. A moment of lucidity graced his drunken consciousness as he realized that sobriety was demanded. Sober Michael was charming, engaging, delightful. Sober Michael was also able to fully appreciate and assimilate what she had to tell him and he needed to savor every last detail. But sober Michael needed time to make his greatest appearance.

And drunk Michael realized that it was very late.

"Welcome to my home, such as it is. Please forgive the mess, but the maid only cleans every other Monday." Even the most fleeting glance around the place was enough to determine that there was no maid. "May I take your coat?" Once again, he utilized the professional smile that had served him so well throughout his career. A smile he frequently borrowed from sober Michael. It provided neither the intended solace nor exuded the confidence that it was designed to elicit. *It's a jacket.* She corrected him in her head as she slipped it off and watched him hang it on an empty peg by the door.

"You must be exhausted and yet we have so much to discuss. Please, allow me to offer you a bed in one of the spare rooms and we can pick this up in the morning?" It was a mistaken belief on his part that it was the charm and charisma that secured her acceptance of his offer. In truth, it had been the fact that he had slurred every single word he'd uttered and so she knew that there was no point in talking with him in this condition. Sleep was the only solution and it would be most welcome and, she could only hope, it would easily find her.

They climbed the staircase in silence, the only noise being the temperamental floorboards venting their anger at being disturbed, echoing throughout the old house. Michael offered a spare room that locked from the inside in the hope of soliciting and building some trust. However, if it did, it would be more by default than design. In point of fact, it was more to ensure that she didn't escape into the night. The lock was so loud, and with the room being directly opposite his own, meant that he could sleep with a reasonable confidence that he would quickly discover and halt any such effort on her part.

"Goodnight." Melissa closed the door and immediately slid the heavy lock into place.

He followed the wry smile into his own bedroom, the inside of which he hadn't seen in months.

Chapter 17

Fallsburg, New York State

Saturday 16th January

The Neversink river originates in the Catskill mountains and meanders down and through a valley that shares its curious, yet wondrously oxymoronic, name. On a gentle slope to the east, and behind an evergreen carpet of trees, lies the Sullivan Correctional Facility. Its picturesque location is home to some of America's most heinous criminals who have committed some of the country's ugliest crimes.

And one man who was not guilty.

It would stretch even the wildest imagination to ever consider Anthony Di Silva as 'innocent', for in the realm that is the seedy core of the Big Apple – where law enforcement shares an uncomfortable bed with career criminals – he was the undisputed King. Yet nobody had actually known it. His empire was involved in every aspect of illegal enterprise and he enjoyed a healthy slice of all returns, irrespective of the profitability of the ventures. He was known simply as *'The Accountant'*, as all the dirty money in the city was laundered through him; everyone believing that he was acting for, and answerable to, a higher authority. As such, he was able to garner a wealth of information from those who saw him as a peer rather than a boss.

To the casual observer, he was a law-abiding businessman who owned a very successful waste management company. Those who had observed a little closer had found that the annual turnover was far in excess of the company's capabilities. Then, there were those foolish few whose observations had given rise to actually question this commercial disparity had a nasty habit of mysteriously leaving town – never to be heard from again. It was ironic that just such a disappearance had resulted in him now enjoying the hospitality of the federal government. A disappearance that he genuinely knew nothing about, and not for the lack of effort, yet Kristy Bradley had simply vanished with his cash.

The only thing she had left was enough circumstantial evidence to convict him.

The subsequent investigation had convinced the District Attorney of two things, beyond any measure of doubt. The first was that Anthony Di Silva was the biggest mob boss the city or, indeed, the country had ever known; even bigger than Lucky Luciano. The second was that he was absolutely innocent of any involvement in Kristy Bradley's kidnapping and ransom.

Ironically, in his eyes, the first had proven the second.

Anthony's undoubted genius was in ensuring nobody knew his true role as the head of the criminal under-bellied snake. He was absolutely meticulous in every aspect of his business life, both legitimate and not-so-legitimate. As such, he would never have risked himself to such exposure for the sake of a paltry $34 million. And, from what they now knew, there was no doubt that this was indeed a paltry sum to Anthony. Kidnapping Kristy Bradley was simply too crude a move from such a sophisticated operator. His composure at interview, combined with his genuine surprise at the events, and sheer incredulity that he was even considered a suspect, only reaffirmed the D.A.'s belief of his innocence. Yet he also knew that the mastermind behind her disappearance was equally smart and had ensured that Anthony was the only viable suspect.

They had left the D.A. with no option but to press charges against Anthony.

Not that he wanted any other option. This presented the perfect opportunity to reveal Anthony's true identity and role within the criminal fraternity so that, even if he was found not guilty, his future – or lack thereof – was secured. Either way, New York would be a safer city just by virtue of the case being presented to 12 of its finest citizens. There was no doubt that his actions in bringing such a case were ethically questionable, he could just as easily dismiss it and let Anthony crawl back under his rock, but to do so would be to allow the criminal to win. Justice doesn't, and shouldn't, work that way. Besides, he wouldn't be the first to use the full scope of the law to ensure the safety of the public. Elliot Ness had set the precedent all those years ago with a certain tax evader, one Alphonse Gabriel Capone. The fact that his case against Anthony – win or lose – would attract international media coverage and elevate his own profile, catapulting his career into the stratosphere, was only a secondary consideration. At least, that's what he kept telling himself.

On the first day of the trial, the D.A. had perfected his look of being suitably surprised as he exited the car and pushed his way through the media frenzy that had encamped on the steps of the courthouse. He threw out more than a few of the obligatory, "No comment" statements for effect. In truth, it was said so that he could later hear his own voice on television; and his proud Mum too. Not that he was actually surprised by the presence of the media, for he had called practically every single editor in the state to ensure as much publicity as possible. When Anthony's defense attorney had requested that the media be excluded from proceedings – *"it would only be detrimental to my client and could possibly influence, inadvertently of course, the integrity of the jury, Your Honor"* – it presented the D.A. with the perfect opportunity that he had hoped for.

Actually, he had prayed for.

"Your Honor, if it pleases the court, I must object. This trial is in the public interest and, as such, the public has a right to know about the character, persona, business, and criminal practices of the defendant, as exercised in the very same city we all share. This can only be assured by allowing the broad spectrum of media outlets to report as they see fit.

However..."

The D.A. paused for dramatic effect, casting his eyes towards the table that housed the defense team; four lawyers, two on each side, with Anthony sat in the middle. The man himself was wearing thick, dark-framed glasses with an ill-fitting grey shirt and an old blue kipper tie that was at least four decades out of date; a knitted dark brown cardigan completed the ensemble. Having been in Anthony's home and seen his wardrobe, and his impeccable image in the framed photographs, the D.A. knew that this was a ruse to appear like a harmless and dithering old man.

Like an everyday grandfather.

An everyday grandfather that they knew, but couldn't actually prove, was guilty of murder, racketeering, extortion, drug dealing, and any amount of other criminal activities that generated serious revenue of which he, befittingly, took the King's share.

The D.A. recognized, and secretly admired, Anthony's attempt to look both frail and outdated, yet warm and homely – insignificant almost – to evoke the empathy of the jury. It was just another stroke of genius to be expected from such a calculating man who leaves nothing to chance. That was evident in the expensive suits that surrounded him and who, ironically, made him seem more like an eccentric billionaire than bewildered old man.

"*However*, Mr. District Attorney?"

"Ah, yes, 'however'…" This was his moment and he intended to savor every second. His was an unprecedented request, but one with which he had taken every precaution to ensure was an easy decision for the judge.

"Your Honor, as my learned colleague for the defense rightly states, given the status of their client – we aim to prove that Mr. Di Silva is the head of the biggest criminal family ever assembled in, not only New York, but the whole of these great United States of America – this does, indeed, give rise to questions of integrity regarding the jury."

"*Objection!* Your Honor, Mr. Di Silv…" The defense lawyer fought to escape his seat as he shouted in the direction of the bench, fully prepared to defend his client against the expected accusations.

"Overruled. It was clearly stated that this is the intention of the D.A., not a statement of fact Mr. Cooper. You can make your arguments during the trial, but not now." The expensive suit with the corresponding name once again slipped back into its seat. "I'm sure that the District Attorney will soon enough get to a point or, more hopefully, a question?"

"Thank you, Your Honor. Of course. I would kindly ask, sharing the same concerns as my colleagues on the opposite bench, that the jury be sequestered and, for their own safety, be bound over together each night at a hotel close by that I have commandeered for the duration of this trial.

Furthermore, if it would please the court, I would kindly ask that the jury be protected by a team of 40 seasoned police officers, each with a minimum of 20 years of service, on 8 hour rotations per juror. The 4 extras would be used as cover for any unforeseen eventualities.

Finally, I would stress that my office believes Mr. Di Silva to be so dangerous and manipulative, with such scant regard for the law, that I would kindly request that the jurors be prohibited, under threat of contempt of court, from discussing the case – even with each other – until the deliberation phase. Each meal to be eaten together, with their respective chaperone to be seated between them to ensure that there is no actual physical contact."

As he closed, the D.A. continued to stand and stare straight ahead in a vain attempt to find the confidence that he had earlier; it was at that moment that his mother's voice entered his head – *'it'll be where you last had it'*. By that reasoning, his confidence must still be in the shower that he had less than two hours previously. Suddenly, his body screamed for air and he realized that he had unconsciously held his breath as he waited for the judge's decision.

The defense team contained their objection, in part because of the so recent rebuke from their last one, but mostly because the D.A.'s request was so preposterous and so unprecedented as to border on the ridiculous. As such, their objection would be moot and could only antagonize the judge, so they remained seated in smug silence.

"You already have the hotel. What about the 40 officers?" The judge ignored the defense table and was staring straight at the D.A.

"Yes, Your Honor. Just waiting for the word, Your Honor." The words escaped the D.A. in a single sharp breath. *Was the judge actually going to go for it and grant this?*

"So ordered. Anything else?" The judge could see the anticipated scramble on the defense bench as they huddled to formulate a coherent objection, and was quick to cut off any exhaustive legal discussion. "Excellent, then we are adjourned."

"Obj…Your Honor, I must object. *Your Honor…?!*"

The judge was already making her way

to chambers.

So set the tone for the rest of the trial. As it progressed, it became increasingly apparent to Anthony that the attorney he should have hired was the very man prosecuting him. The D.A. was so convincing that he even had Anthony questioning his own guilt, and so it was hardly unexpected when the jury returned their verdict of guilty in under an hour.

He was only surprised it took them that long.

At his age, touching sixty, Anthony knew that the sentence of 25 years to life meant he would never again be a free man. At least not one who could enjoy that liberty, for he already suffered from the pains of arthritis and those other ailments that time unfailingly delivers. It was ironic that his being in prison had actually saved his life, as the details of his business dealings – as described in court by the D.A. – ensured that he could never safely walk the streets of his beloved city any more. The contracts on his life were many, each more lucrative than the last, and they were all valid until the day he would eventually succumb and shuffle off his mortal coil. He knew how seriously they would be taken and how many wished to be the one to take him down.

He had ordered too many similar contracts in his time to believe any different.

It had been over three years since he had arrived in the Neversink valley and he – and his money – had been warmly welcomed by the warden. Following his instructions, the warden already had the very best cell preselected for him in solitary confinement. The frosted and reinforced sheet of transparent plastic that masqueraded as a window had been replaced by a triple glazed pane of clear glass that allowed him the luxury of viewing out into the forest of trees that surrounded the oval facility. On a good day, like today, he could catch a glimpse of some of the wildlife. He so admired the eagles and hawks that patrolled their area, sometimes he saw them with prey in their talons.

Those were extra special days.

They were apex predators, graceful, and elegant. If the reincarnation teachings of Buddhism are correct, it's as one of those magnificent creatures that he would wish to be in the next life. The moose were more infrequent in their visitations, but whenever he saw one, a smile always found his face. He had only ever seen them on television before and, to see them for real, was to wonder how they managed to maintain their balance. Such gangly creatures that were just funny. God must have a sense of humor. He heard the bears more than saw them and he knew from chats with the guards that they were a threat that they took very seriously.

Oh, to be a bear.

As he peered out of his window in search of the peace and contentment that all the power and money had never brought, or bought, there was a gentle knock on his door.

"Tony, you have visitors." Billy was a brute of a man, but had the softest tones he had ever heard. Soothing almost. For as soft as his voice was, his brain was equally sharp. Anthony knew, from professional experience, that this was a lethal combination. Every time they spoke, he always thought of how he could have used Billy within his organization. Of course, that would have demanded some lessons in manners. The first being that it was only friends and family that Anthony allowed to call him 'Tony'.

Those who had mistakenly done so found that there was a distinct lack of a second chance to make amends.

The guard stepped back to allow the two men to enter the confined space. Anthony liked that there was no room for guest seats and so they were forced to stand as he sat in the only chair in the corner, with his back to the wall and facing the door.

Old habits die hard.

Anthony took a sip from his tea and replaced the cup onto its matching saucer; just because he was incarcerated didn't mean he had to live like a barbarian. Pursing his lips menacingly and narrowing his eyes, he adopted his game face – it was show time. He could never be seen to be weak, even in these most telling of circumstances where appearances were *everything*. He knew how easily it was to sense weakness. Showing such weakness, in his chosen profession, found you quickly dead.

The early morning visit was unscheduled and had been organized at very short notice. As were his orders, and following the appropriate protocols, there had been no clues as to the reasons for the meeting. However, given the urgency and timing, Anthony knew that it must be important, so he had reluctantly agreed.

He raised his head in silence and saw the same two men that Melissa prayed she would never see again. Nodding to the one who had checked his charming smile at the gate – there was no need for it here – it was the order to talk.

"Tony, we found her. Kristy Bradley is alive and living in Scotland."

Chapter 18

Auchtershinnan Estate, Invernesshire, Scotland

Saturday 16th January

There is no doubt that the Auchtershinnan house – *I still think it's a castle, but Andy assures me I'm wrong* – is truly magnificent. Nestled in the very heart of the glen, the gentle slopes seek to protect it from the elements and provide a stunning backdrop that always seems to be ever changing, and yet forever unique. As with most houses of its ilk, they struggle to ever be homes as they are from a bygone era where servants lived to service every whim and want of the owning family and their friends. Now, the servants have long gone and the family has shrunk to just Penny, and so the fact that it feels like home to me is perhaps the greatest compliment I could possibly pay to her. One thing is for certain, I never could *repay* her.

Ever.

For everything.

Undoubtedly, my favorite room within the castle is the library. It has an old wood-burning fireplace that provides as much romance as it does warmth, with a selection of deep pile sheepskin rugs that lie invitingly in front of it. Long into dateless and timeless nights have we made love there and quietly talked deep into the small hours, as only lovers can, with the firelight dancing freely around us as if passionately celebrating with us.

Yet, in all our conversations, never once has the subject of money come up.

It is undoubtedly emasculating to know that she has a wealth with which I could never compete. The traditional, if somewhat sexist, role of breadwinner is one which shall never be afforded to me within our relationship. It is a harsh reality and an uncomfortable fact that I believed, over time, would become more palatable.

I was wrong.

There is part of me that is secretly quite pleased that I still yearn to provide for her, and so for us, but there is no denying that it still hurts me to know that she will never have this reliance, that dependence, upon me. From the outset of our relationship, I always knew this would be the case and have tried to learn to accept it. However, it was another uncomfortable lesson to discover that there is a huge difference between *acceptance* and *agreement*.

Apt, then, that it should be in this very room that I discovered the serenity prayer. Well, the first three lines of it anyway and, after all, isn't that the most important part? Certainly it is for me. I chanced upon an article by a recovering alcoholic who disclosed that this prayer is part of the Alcoholics Anonymous recovery programme. More than once have I recited these thirty words in the hope of appeasing my own discomfort and save myself from ruining our otherwise perfect relationship. So often, in fact, that I now know it by heart.

> *O God, give us the serenity to*
> *accept what cannot be*
> *changed,*
> *The courage to change what*
> *can be changed,*
> *And the wisdom to know the*
> *one from the other.*

Although I appreciate that my own particular plea is not of any real importance compared to practically every other person who uses this prayer in asking for the strength and guidance of the Almighty but, as they say, 'ask and you have half a chance'. As I contemplated my dilemma whilst staring out the window and through the rain, I found myself so lost in thought that I never heard the door opening.

"You okay?" My mother asked as she took the seat opposite me.

"Uh hmm." I more hummed than spoke and gave her a weak smile that literally didn't have the strength to break my lips and show teeth.

"Ah…." She gave a single nod of her head and threw her eyes down the glen and I was instantly terrified that she would see my thoughts there.

"What?" My question was too harsh and hasty and so betrayed my very real fear of exposure.

"Why do you think it is that every son the world over believes that they can hide the truth from their mothers?" Her maternal tone was soft and soothing whilst her gaze was left to roam in the glen. "I carried you for nine months, gave birth to you, I watched you grow. I can tell your every mood from just your look or demeanor, and so I also know when to push and when to back off. Like now. Now I know it's a time to push." As she said this, her head gently drew from the outside and inclined towards me, and it felt like she stared straight into my very soul.

"So, tell me, what is troubling you?"

Safe in the knowledge that she was the one person in the world to whom I never needed to provide any explanation for my reason or rationale, I blurted out my thoughts en masse and in no particular order. It was only in reciting the serenity prayer to her did I start to feel uncomfortable and rather embarrassed. Actually, I felt downright stupid, hearing out loud what was bothering me made it seem even more ludicrous than it actually was. There were people in the world with very *real* problems and I wasn't one of them. I could only hope that she would just ignore me and let my words disappear into the ether. If I was really lucky, she would simply stand and leave. As my gentle rant came to a close, I glanced sheepishly in her general direction and caught her in my periphery. Her face, ever beautiful, was being lovingly caressed by the firelight that seemed to shine brighter against the darkness of the blustery day. Not that she noticed, her being in deep concentration with lips pursed and her twinkling eyes, once more, cast back down into the glen. The intermittent crackling of the fire was the only interruption to the rain tapping rhythmically against the tall windows.

After a few seconds that felt like an age, she spoke with a mother's voice, full of wisdom and understanding, that fell lovingly around me and held me close.

"Well it seems to me that you have a choice. You can either continue to fight this instinct, a perfectly natural instinct and one that is both chivalrous and admirable; or you accept it, safe in the knowledge that you can and will never change it. Penny is what she is, and all this…" she paused to throw her right hand in an aimless spin around the room, but I knew that she meant the whole estate, "…all this is what she has, and what she grew up with. She was born into money and now – at the cost of her parents, an exceptional price to pay from one so young – she has inherited that money." As only mothers can, she made my problem sound so redundant and pointless, yet also comforting me in a way that made my redundant feeling of helplessness inevitable; almost noble.

In the silence, I returned to scan the glen in a new search for my old problem.

"If I were you…" Experience dictated that, whenever Mum starts any sentence with these words, it is far more than a simple suggestion. Not always have I followed her advice and on those occasions, almost always, I have come to regret it. In my mum's case, I am forced to begrudgingly admit that age certainly does bring wisdom. "…I would focus more on making *her* happy than making *you* happy. The traditional gender roles have all but disappeared over the last generation or so and equality is almost upon us, and it'll definitely be here soon. It is simply the will and way of the modern world. Women are, more and more, becoming the main breadwinners in the household and so the idea that this is still the role of the man, or that the role of staying home and looking after the family solely belongs to the woman, is now a nonsense.

However…"

We were both facing out the window, but it was only as I caught her reflection did I see that she was looking directly at me. She obviously had more to add but, for some reason, wouldn't simply throw this thought out with the mere hope that it would penetrate my consciousness. No, this was a pearl of wisdom to be conveyed directly upon her son. I shifted in the seat to shake off my discomfort, and turned to face my mum.

"Zacchaeus." My full Sunday name? This was about to get serious. "Just two days ago, both you and Penny openly declared your love for one another. That is a beautiful, wonderful, and magical moment in any relationship. Yet that brings with it very real, but now different, responsibilities. Not those antiquated and primitive ideals of yesteryear. You are a very capable young man who has found love with an exceptional young woman. The secret to any strong relationship is to *pick your battles*. There will be disagreements, but not all are worth fighting. This is one of them. It's one you will never win, so why fight it? Your role now is to simply be her partner, to be there for her, and to make her happy. In many ways, that is a far greater challenge than merely handing over a paycheck at the end of a week. Now you don't have that concern, it's one less thing to worry about, not another thing to worry about. That gives you even more time to ensure her happiness as that is all you have to focus upon."

The lesson was obviously over as she stood and silently walked away. Mum's words were still sinking in as she made her way out of the room. I was ravenously devouring everything that she'd said and considering their implications when a final thought was tossed back into the room as she closed the door to ensure it couldn't escape.

"So, start now. *Today...*"

Alone with Mum's thoughts, it took me an enjoyable hour before an idea came to me. By happy coincidence, the library also happened to be the best place in the house for internet connection. In opening the laptop in this lonely room in the middle of a remote glen, so far removed from civilization, I invited all of the avarice that the world had to offer into my home. Amongst all this natural beauty and amidst the written works of the masters, it felt exactly what it was, artificial and seedy. Yet it was a necessary evil that only required a long ten minutes of my time.

As the page confirming my purchase flashed up before me, there was a light knock on the door that was already slowly opening. "I thought you'd be in here, is everything okay?" Penny's kind face held such a soft and beautiful smile as it emerged from the smallest gap among the shelves of books. When closed, it really is almost impossible to tell where the door actually is. It is yet another reason to adore this room.

"Yeah, I'm fine thanks. Actually, even better now you're here. You?"

"I am now that I know you're okay", yet she didn't seem fine. Cautiously entering the room, she closed the door as slowly as she had opened it; turning the knob with her right hand and pushing with her left, only releasing when she knew it would lock in place without the usual *click*. She stood for a moment, still facing the wall. It was as if she were trying to compose herself. I was mesmerized by her curious actions and watched as her shoulders rose as she took a deep breath and, as they fell, she turned and slowly made her way towards me. Her usual confidence was missing and her head was down as she took the same seat so recently vacated by my mum. Something was definitely wrong and the only times I had ever seen this sort of behavior before was…the realization hit me and my blood ran cold. I tried to compose myself, but could feel the all too familiar lump in my throat and my eyes welling.

Surely not?

Was this it, was I about to lose her?

She took another deep breath and, as she exhaled, it seemed to push her head back to face me. Our eyes locked although I could barely see her. "I just spoke with your mum. I think we need to talk…"

Fuck! Mum? I knew I shouldn't have said anything. I would've figured it out on my own. Eventually.

I tried to save us both the heartache of a long, drawn out breakup conversation. They were never easy, no matter what side of it you were on; the heartbreaker or heartbroken. "It seems to me like we don't. I have been here before Penny, I know when it's over, so I can save you the speech and let's just cut to the end. It should be easier for us both. Certainly easier for me." The adrenaline coursed through my body and I just wanted to run as far away from this situation as possible. To leave my emotional vulnerability, that weakness, my shame, here in this seat. I wanted to scream, to shift this building hurt, to ease this fresh pain, to...

Her unwanted interruption proved to be a welcome distraction to my nomadic thoughts.

"My darling, I'm so sorry, but you misunderstand. Your mum explained everything to me and I get it, truly I do. But now you also need to understand. *I love you.* I want us to be together and, to me, money is simply an issue that is a problem for others. *We* have it. Together. *We* can use it as we want. To enjoy *our life together*. That is, after all, what money is for. Did you not once tell me, before we became a couple, that money cannot buy experience and that is what it should be used for? So let's use it that way. I want a life with *you*. I want to experience all the joys of life with *you*. Please, don't let something as fickle and worthless as money come between us.

Please..."

Without another word, I simply handed her the laptop. Through her own tears she quickly read the open page.

"Florence?"

"Yeah. I thought we could begin *our* new life of fun and adventure there. Only for a week but, hey, it's a start. Although, being honest, I thought you were dumping me so I was actually crying about the thought of losing my cash for this trip. You see, there are no refunds!" The joke was weak and in poor taste, but it was all I could think of at that particular moment.

She placed the computer on the chair as she stood, her eyes never leaving mine, with her arms held out towards me, inviting me in. Leaving my own chair to meet her, I slipped my arms around her and we tightly embraced. Closing my eyes to savor the moment, I could feel her soft fingers caressing my back. Her tantalizing fragrance, the finest scent I have ever known. Her soft kisses upon my neck.

It was divine.

Slowly my hands traced around her back to her waist. In one effortless movement, I lifted her slender frame until she was able to look straight into my eyes and I saw her soul – it was full of love. A love that was ours to share. Our lips brushed together, gentle and tender at first, but then with an overwhelming passion the likes of which I have never before experienced. The moment took us and soon we were making love that was as frantic as it was intense; and over all too soon. Lying on the soft rugs, I could see the embers were in desperate need of company and the readily welcomed the new log as she spoke.

"Florence will be so romantic at this time of year. Not too hot, but nice and warm. I could use a little heat."

Little did I know what real heat was coming our way.

Chapter 19

Inverness Airport, Dalcross, Scotland

Saturday 16th January

The Gulfstream landed under the cover of darkness and, following the tower's instructions, taxied to the only private hangar in the airport. At least, that's where the pilot thought she was going. In truth, it was more of an educated guess on her part for, other than the main terminal, there was no obvious structure that she could see to house aircraft of any size – certainly not one as prestigious as hers. She had expertly guided the plane towards the small outbuilding where she saw the other few private planes that had been abandoned, and drew to a halt. Slipping off the headphones and freeing herself from the confines of the seatbelt, she took a moment to sit back in her chair and heave a sigh of relief; that was not her easiest landing. The conditions were beyond treacherous with an aggressive crosswind from the Moray Firth only adding to the excitement.

Not that they were completely unexpected.

They had been in constant contact with the tower over the previous ninety minutes and she had been consistently advised that they should divert to Glasgow or Aberdeen. The initially cool and confident voice from the airport quickly evolved into one of frustration and panic that fought through the static to all but beg and plead with her to land elsewhere. In desperation, they even suggested the airport at Wick. *Anywhere else but Inverness*. This voice was eventually replaced by one claiming to belong to the airport manager who informed her that the handful of expected commercial flights had all either diverted or had cancelled and rescheduled for tomorrow. He spoke with an authority that his colleague had lacked, ordered them not to land, and that the airport was closed until further notice.

She now knew why.

Their warnings had not been exaggerated, although they were completely ignored, and it was testimony to her flying skills that her passengers remained oblivious to just how difficult and dangerous the landing was. Either that or they simply didn't care. She had summoned the lead passenger – there were only two, but it was obvious who was in charge – to the cockpit after the first advisory. Never before had her authority been questioned and she had been under the mistaken belief that this would merely be a straightforward discussion to agree the new destination. She was immediately corrected and left in no doubt that they would only be landing at Inverness.

"In pieces if needs be."

The statement was as sinister as it was sincere and had left her both shocked and shaken. He hadn't meant it that way. Rather, his intent was to relay the importance and time-sensitive nature of their business; from one professional to another. Although the mirrored aviator glasses covered most of her face, her reaction betrayed an obvious fear and trepidation and so he quickly changed tack. The smile he never left home without was immediately employed, along with a promise to double her already substantial fee, if she would just land at their designated airport of preference without any further discussion. It was, after all, what they had agreed. She tried to compose herself and deflect the responsibility.

"I'm afraid that I simply don't have the

authority to make that decision. Unfortunately, it's just not my call to make. I shall need to contact the company president to…"

"Bullshit Amelia, *YOU* are the company president. You are also the company owner, inheriting it from your father some, what, six years ago now maybe?" He paused for her reaction, but she had been stunned into silence. Her mouth agape, he took it as his cue to continue. "It would seem that flying runs in your family and I'm guessing you were named after a certain Ms. Earhart? I certainly hope you don't meet the same fate." Another pause for her to enjoy his joke. He thought he was being charming, quirky, and sincere, but it certainly didn't come across that way. Now she was genuinely afraid, and not from the flying. "He even named the company after you though, right? Americo Air. AMelia ERIn COchrane – the initials of daddy's little girl. Sweet. So, do we have a deal, Madam President?"

Who is this guy and how the hell does he know so much about me?

She took an illogical satisfaction in the fact that he hadn't known that her father had been disappointed that they had an extra 'E' at the end of their surname. Throughout his life he had always maintained that

Jacqueline Cochran was the finer aviator. As such, their surname was a close enough match for him to name his daughter after Amelia Earhart, thus ensuring the best of both worlds. It was one of the few compromises he ever made.

It was a happy coincidence that her mother just happened to hate the name Jacqueline.

One of the few things Amelia Cochrane's passenger didn't seem to know was that she needed the money, so his doubling of her fee was enough incentive. There really had been no need for the heavy-handed tactics. The 'fleet' her dad left her had consisted of three old, battered, and bruised island hoppers that came with equally antiquated pilots. Their respect for her died with her father and so she had gambled on herself and discarded both the planes and their attitudes, and threw every cent she had into the Gulfstream. She thought it would help elevate the profile and clientele of the company, but all it did was left her working three times as hard for way less than three times the money.

"Well, *Amelia*, do we have a deal?"

Knowing there was no real choice – not that she wanted one – she had accepted his lucrative new offer.

Suddenly, a light caught her attention as

a door violently swung open and brought her crashing back to reality. A disheveled young man came rushing from the building, fighting with the paddles in his hand to pull on a bright orange jumpsuit with its reflective markings, not quite ready to direct the plane to a suitable spot. It took him two full steps into the wild wind and driving rain before he realized her landing lights were static. As he gathered his thoughts and wondered what to do next, a gust of wind blew into his overalls and inflated them, and he instantly looked like the Michelin man. Although he couldn't see into the cockpit, she still politely covered her smile. Ignoring his own predicament, he swiftly peered around and readily accepted that she was already in the perfect spot. He used his spare hand to throw his thumb up in her general direction as his sign of approval and raced back to the hangar to escape the turbulent elements.

She barely caught herself returning his gesture in the direction of the closing door.

Just then, a car with all lights blazing through the rain came racing around the side of the hangar and pulled alongside the plane. *Oh here we go, the welcoming committee.* Her hands quickly found her head as she desperately tried to shake free all the tension and frustration by running her fingers through her hair. She needed to relax, to prepare herself in readiness of the wavy finger lecture that was no doubt coming her way. Amelia knew it could be far worse, depending on how much of an asshole he wanted to be. As she instantly imagined all of the possible consequences, she pulled her hair tightly back from her face and harnessed it into a ponytail. She fixed her captain's hat firmly in place in the forlorn hope that it would relay her authority and demand respect.

If that failed, she had brought the 'sexy charm offensive' with her, just in case.

"Sir? Sir? I'm sorry, but you mustn't…. *SIR*?" The air stewardesses, Tiffani, had been Amelia's best friend since childhood. She knew of the earlier discussion with The Smile and it scared her too. However, now was the time to be brave and play ignorant to protect her friend. yet her courageous attempts at being authoritative were roundly ignored as the same head that housed The Smile peeked into the cockpit for a second time and gave her quite the start. "Remember, you go nowhere. Stay right here and be ready to move when we get back. There will be an extra passenger for the return. We don't expect to be too long, a few hours maybe, give or take."

"Thank you for flying Americo Air

today gentlemen, we hope you enjoy your time here in sunny *Scotchland*." Tiffani's joke was deliberately weak – she determined that they didn't deserve any of her better ones – and was intended to break the tension; as well as deflect the passengers' attention from the tumultuous landing and dreadful weather. As usual, it was perfectly timed and said just before opening the door as she knew all too well what pandemonium awaited. Experience dictated that the elements were fully prepared to assault their tranquil and vacuous sanctuary and, so too it would seem, an irate airport manager who had charged straight onto the aircraft before its steps touched the tarmac.

"Where is the captain?" The brusque Scottish brogue determined the question was more a demand. Timidly, Tiffani made to point in the general direction of the front of the plane, but was interrupted.

"I believe that a fine is due, will this suffice?" The Smile stepped forward and held out a wad of $100's. Tiffani reckoned the pile was at least an inch thick; never in her life had she seen so much cash. The glint in the airport manager's eyes suggested this was a first for him too. Taking the bundle, he thumbed through to ensure that Benjamin Franklin was the only consistent face.

"That seems to be about right." He had

no idea how much money this equated to in British Pounds, but he was certain it was enough. It also bought a new attitude, one that was altogether more hospitable. "Welcome to Scotland! Now, is there anything else you need to make your stay more enjoyable?"

"We need to hire a car with a GPS. Is there anywhere we can do that?" The Smile was back to his disarming and charming self.

"For how long?" The airport manager held the bundle tightly in his pocket and sensed it came with companions. These were his kind of clients, big on the money and small on the questions.

"No more than a few hours or so. We have a pressing engagement here and need to be back Stateside ASAP."

"Well, as you know, the airport is now closed and all the staff have gone, including those at the rental desk. However, this is my own car that I *could lend you* for such a short duration." Tentatively, his right hand held up one of his chins as his left arm snaked underneath the corresponding elbow, yet it was still barely able to provide adequate support. His head indicated towards the still running and nearly new BMW. In his haste, he had left the driver's door open and every light on. "Of course, I would have to use one of the other vehicles lying about for the evening…"

No-one was in any doubt of how much of an inconvenience that would be.

"Maybe this will help to ease your suffering." There was no question, just an understanding as another bundle made its way into the airport manager's other pocket. This one was about half as thick as the first, but still more than enough to buy the car outright.

"Certainly. Oh, and please, don't bother filling it up when you return it, this will amply cover that expense." He tapped his lighter pocket.

The two men disappeared down the stairs and into the car, leaving the airport manager believing that he had been both lenient and generous.

Chapter 20

Inverness Airport, Dalcross, Scotland

Saturday 16th January

The BMW slowly rounded the corner of the hanger and was scarcely out of sight when it came to an abrupt halt. Its headlights played with the rain and bounced off the shiny wet concrete that stretched all the way out to the airport's frail perimeter fence. Ahead in the distance, the reflection of an 'exit' sign that mockingly pointed towards the automatic barrier, and beyond which lay the main road.

And Kristy Bradley.

"What the fuck are you doing?" The Smile employed a tone that was a deliberately intimidating mix of confusion, anger, and frustration.

"I don't know where we're going." He knew all too well what the man with The

Smile was capable of, but he also knew he was the man with the plan.

"You know as well as I do that we are going to the Auchtershinnan Estate, now *MOVE!*" Patience with his ever-present companion was wearing thin.

The 'exit' sign's goading wasn't helping.

"Yes, I know *that*, but *how* do we get there?" The question was obviously rhetorical as the driver, seemingly oblivious to his colleague's discomfort and the taunting signpost, was clumsily stabbing randomly at the touchscreen system in the vain hope of stumbling across the GPS. He only succeeded in turning on the radio.

At full volume.

They were both so startled that they threw themselves back in their seats, instinctively scrambling inside their coats for the weapons that were in the discarded backpack on the rear seat. Quickly realizing what had happened, The Smile composed himself and reached for the power off button – just before Bon Jovi could finish his declaration that they were *"...only halfway there..."*

He already knew they were living on a prayer.

"For fuck's sake, don't worry about that now, just get us outta here. The last thing we need is anymore unwanted attention." The very thought sent a shiver down his spine. A few seconds passed and still they hadn't moved. The Smile turned to face the driver, who was now staring straight ahead with both hands gripped tightly on the wheel, at the perfect 10 and 2 position. "Well, what are you waiting for now? Would you fucking *MOVE!*" It seemed that he was alone with his concerns about being caught. Yet, in the ambient red night light of the car's cabin, he noticed a bead of sweat slip down his driver's left temple before being quickly swept away by his sleeve.

"Well...um, well... maybe it's best if *you* drive while I sort the navigation? That way, we will be moving *and* going in the right direction. Two birds with one stone, if you know what I mean?" He stole a quick look at his passenger hoping to find his friend, The Smile.

"What are you talking about? Would you just drive already!" He instantly knew the problem, his companion had never driven on the left and was understandably nervous. Given the weather, probably scared too.

The Smile certainly couldn't admit that he had never driven on the left either.

One thing he had learnt from Tony was to always look and seem strong. Make decisions and stick by them. They may weaken you but never give off that impression, and certainly never – *never* – acknowledge it. This was a time to be strong. He could, however, be understanding. Compassionate almost.

"Look, just take your time, but let's get outta here. There's the exit up there…" He almost flipped the bird to the gleaming sign, but refrained, instead turning his finger to point in the direction of the barrier. "Just get us outta here and we can figure it out as we go. This ain't like the city, where all the roads are straight and on a grid, so be careful. I didn't see a whole lotta street lights either when we were flying in, so we are literally holding our cocks in the dark here. So, as I say, just take your time…"

The car was moving before he had finished his pep talk.

They had been on the road for twenty minutes before The Smile conceded defeat and ordered him to pull over. The 'driver' had successfully meandered through the storm, and erratically along a deserted country road, only to ensure that they were out of sight of the airport, but not quite its proximity. They had been fortunate to stay on the tarmac, although all attempts of maintaining the legal side – as agreed with all the other vehicles – had been quickly abandoned. Turning onto the arterial route for Inverness, the straighter road was altogether more forgiving, with the center line almost always where it should be. It was then that The Smile had been able to relax somewhat, albeit temporarily.

It came from nowhere.

The high hedgerows that had suddenly appeared on either side acted like soft buffers that protected the car from the howling wind and driving rain. They also helped hone the driver's focus as they blocked all that lay in the darkness behind them; quite literally providing tunnel vision. Yet the full beams could only penetrate two hundred yards or so before being swallowed up and disappearing into the murky depths of the night. His head was pressed so far forward that his chin was almost touching the steering wheel; his eyes straining deep beyond the capabilities of the headlights in the forlorn hope of finding that happy balance between speed and haste.

How he wished this night were over and they were heading for home.

As he allowed himself a moment to enjoy the thought, he hadn't noticed that the hedgerows had come to an abrupt halt. *And so had the road.* It was only as the tarmac veered sharply to the left did he realize he was going too fast. His foot quickly shot for the brake as he wrestled with the steering wheel, fighting to keep the car off the grass. It was in the very second when he thought he had everything back under control that he saw it.

Straight ahead, in the middle of the road, there was a roundabout.

Reverting to instinct, and fighting a new fight to maintain control of the vehicle, he drifted onto the other carriageway and drove more through the roundabout than around it. He exited from the opposite entrance and was continuing to drive on the right when The Smile's voice broke his concentration. *"I think I better drive."* He found a layby and brought the car to a complete halt – still on the opposite carriageway – and, in one fluid motion, shut off the engine, unbuckled his seatbelt, threw the door open, and jumped out. The wind and rain immediately accosted him as he used both hands to wipe his face; the precipitation mixing freely with the perspiration.

Never had he been so relieved.

The driver had been so preoccupied with his own distress that he hadn't noticed that The Smile had also jumped out from the car and promptly threw up. He took a bottle of water from his pocket and rinsed out his mouth. He emptied the rest of its contents to clear the evidence. Another sign of weakness to be eradicated. A stick of gum helped rid the offensive taste that his stomach contents had left on their exit. He walked around the car and slipped in behind the wheel.

"Okay, now can we get going already?"

The question was moot, lost as it was among the din from the elements and the numerous squeals of distress from the BMW – *seatbelt... ignition... lights... doors open...* each had a unique signature alarm that, akin to a spoilt child, were each demanding immediate attention. To complete the assault, corresponding warning lights were flashing and illuminating the dashboard like a Christmas tree. As his oblivious companion happily jumped into the passenger seat and closed the door, one alarm was silenced. Restarting the car and securing their seatbelts was finally enough to appease the vehicle. After swiftly adjusting the seat and mirrors, The Smile took a quick look around and saw that the road was still deserted, and then cautiously eased the car over the white lines and back into the legal lane.

They drove in silence until they made the outskirts of Inverness. Speed had been conceded for safety, and time had passed ever slowly. Although, thankfully, the storm had abated and so now they could better see the road. Yet the improved conditions had also enticed out other cars; an unwelcome development that had only ensured the elevated stress levels of The Smile were firmly maintained. His passenger hadn't seemed to notice, far less care. He was just happy not to be driving.

The small and ornate *Welcome to Inverness* sign stood proud and pathetic underneath a monolithic monstrosity that was more intimidating than informative. Just beyond, a second dreaded roundabout. Erring on the side of caution, The Smile summoned all of his powers of concentration to ensure he didn't fail as spectacularly as his passenger. That would make him weak and, in his companion's eyes, almost an equal.

That would never be acceptable.

On the roundabout, a single post stood in its center and held six lights that shone down from on high onto the circular mound of grass; the illumination intended to both protect and highlight its existence to all motorists. Nestling underneath, piles of mud that – from spring until autumn – were strategically carved flowerbeds that held elaborate and resplendent displays of plants and flowers.

So focused was The Smile on his impending maneuver that he was caught completely unawares by the car that came flying up from behind, pulled out, and flew passed, only to swerve and brake sharply in front of them, barely stopping as it shot through and took the exit into a retail park.

"Let it go." The calm voice of reason split the silence and almost deafened him.

"What?"

"Let it go. Remember where you are. This is small town Scotland, not The Village. We don't need the hassle nor the attention so just let the cocksucker go. Let's just turn in here and we can finally figure out this GPS." The passenger pointed towards the 24-hour superstore that was open on their left and watched as the offending Mini shot towards the cinema complex further into the park.

The Smile had been so preoccupied with his pursuit that he hadn't noticed he'd successfully navigated his first roundabout with ease; it brought a sudden, yet ridiculous pride. Reluctantly, he followed the instruction all the while wishing, and not for the first time, that they were back on familiar territory.

They found a far corner of the car park and, before he could bring the BMW to a halt, his ears were once again assaulted by the radio playing at full volume. Finding the mute button on the steering wheel, he silenced the car and saw that his passenger had successfully found the GPS. The menu allowed for both *postcode* or *street address* options.

They had neither.

Undeterred, his companion touched the street address and started to type, phonetically reciting the name of the estate as he did so.

"O-c-t-e-r-s-h-i-n-i-n." He pressed enter.

The car's response was immediate. *No results found. Please try again.*

The Smile realized they had made a huge mistake. They had never thought to have Melissa write down the address nor the postcode. It didn't help to know that she could have easily supplied both. *How could I have been so stupid?* He couldn't even send anyone else to extract this information from her, *NOBODY* else could be trusted. He didn't need to be told, that was completely understood between him and Tony: this was his only ticket to freedom.

To disappoint him was unthinkable.

"I'm going to use the restroom; you want anything?" To the passenger, all their options had been instantly exhausted and so best to leave The Smile to reach that conclusion on his own. He knew what temper lay bubbling just under the surface and it was always best to never be the object of that rage. He took the silence as a no and quickly scurried towards the bright lights of the store. In five short minutes, he returned and passed a flyer to his friend. On it was promotions for all types of booze and liquor.

"What the *fuck* is this? We have more important things to be concerned with than this shit. Have we not got enough booze back home for you?" The reaction was unsurprising.

It was the passenger's turn to smile. "Look there." He pointed to the bottom right hand corner of the glossy page.

"A fucking dollar off a bottle of scotch? So what?" He hadn't noticed that he used the wrong currency; his patience was all but done.

"Look at the name of it. *'Auchentoshan'*. Look how it's spelt. Maybe that is how you spell *'Auchtershinnan'?*" He didn't wait for a response, as he was already typing in his suggestion.

A-u-c-h-t-e-r-s-h... The GPS completed the spelling – *Auchtershinnan House*.

Before he could hit enter, The Smile grabbed his head and kissed him *"Genius!"* Two young lads were walking passed them, each with a slab of beer under an arm, and saw the exchange. *"Get a fucking room, will you? Nobody wants to be seeing that. Dirty bastards!"* They raced back to their car and swung it around to shine their lights into the BMW; all the while shouting abuse through their open windows. One drive by wasn't to be enough and the abuse continued as they drove around a second time. It was only as they started a third that The Smile was ready to snap. As he put his hand on the door handle, he froze.

The blue lights lit up the whole car park and drew in behind the young lads' car.

They watched as the two police officers exited their car and walked towards the open window on the driver's side. The driver stepped out with his head heavy on his shoulders, instantly contrite, and started pleading his case. An arm quickly appeared out from the passenger window and was pointing back towards the BMW. Ignoring it, the policewoman pulled out a black box and took the protective covering off a straw.

The Smile hit enter on the touchscreen and followed the instructions, slowly making their way out from the car park to slip back onto the roundabout. They drove in silence through the city – it was more like a town, and nothing like The Village – and crawled back out into the darkness. The eerie reflection of the full moon lay gently upon the long narrow strip of water that had appeared from nowhere, and disappeared far into the distance. The road hugged one of the steep hills that emerged from either side of its bleak depths.

The passenger was mesmerized, it was both captivating and beautiful.

"I wonder if there really is a monster?" The Smile posed the question while pointing to the side of the road. The passenger followed the finger to the signpost, *Loch Ness – Home of Nessie*. The very thought sent a shiver through him and suddenly he felt very cold, and his skin began to crawl. He quickly turned in his seat, placing his back to the water and facing the hillside, his eyes set firmly askew as he watched the road.

Then he saw it.

Although he had no idea what he was actually looking at; just a soft glow hidden behind the trees and bushes on the opposite side of the cove. There, basking in a soft light atop the craggy outcrop, were the hauntingly beautiful remains of Urquhart Castle. Once again he twisted in the seat, his fear defeated by curiosity, in a desperate attempt at a second look. It was hopeless. As quickly as it had appeared, it was gone, protected by the night and the bracken and the brush that conspired to make a natural fortification against all unwelcome attentions. The fleeting glimpse was all it had allowed him and was instantly framed in his mind; it would be one he would never forget.

The road dipped down and around to the right, dragging them away from the loch to head inland. It meandered for a while beside a river that became a stream until, like so many other things here, it was lost altogether in the night – it was quite enchanting. Suddenly their peace and solitude was shattered by the tinny female voice that startled them both and, once again, made them wish they were home.

"Your final destination is 300 yards on the right."

As instructed, the BMW pulled off the main road and came to a halt. They were parked on a wide expanse of gravel that quickly narrowed to form a single track road that stretched well beyond the aluminum gate. It was only as they went to open it did they notice that it was secured to a steel post by a thick chain and sturdy padlock. A wooden plaque was bound by old wire and the words reflected from the car's headlights.

Auchtershinnan Estate –
TRESPASSERS WILL BE PROSECUTED.

"She certainly doesn't want to be found, huh?" The question was aimed at The Smile, although it was exactly the same thought that was running through his head.

"Well she has been. Let's go." The Smile pulled their backpack from the car's rear seat and they both made their way to the gate. They quickly climbed over and headed off down the disused driveway, completely ignorant to the fact that the GPS settings had been for the *shortest* rather than the *fastest* route to the main house. As such, they had been directed to a side entrance of the estate that was barely, if ever, used. The main entrance, complete with the lodge house that was available to rent, lay a mere half mile further on.

It had no gate whatsoever.

As they walked among the overgrown weeds that had long since made this road home, they had no idea they were being watched.

Chapter 21

Auchtershinnan Estate, Invernesshire, Scotland

Saturday 16th January

Penny had used all her powers of negotiation and manipulation to convince my parents to stay for dinner. They had been fully intent on leaving in the afternoon – *"while we have the light, Son"* – as they have one of their very best friend's surprise birthday party tomorrow. It was more of a surprise to me that anyone should have a birthday party on a Sunday and I said as much. Apparently this only further authenticates the surprise as the actual birthday was today, and so it would be a day later that expected, and they wanted the person to believe that they had all forgotten.

It seemed more cruel than funny to me.

I had suggested that they stay the night

and use the light of tomorrow morning but, again, that suggestion was of no use. There is a local car boot sale that they like to attend every week where a lady baker sells the most amazing empire biscuits; Dad has none left so needs to restock. So, the compromise was that they would stay for dinner and then leave immediately thereafter.

To my surprise, this is exactly what they did.

These days, it is always sad for me to say goodbye to my parents. It never used to bother me before, but now that I am settled and in love with someone that they idolize and who, in turn, adores them, it only makes me appreciate them even more. Especially after my dad's little health scare. Seeing him as human instead of Superman gave me the frightening realization that he is as mortal and as fragile as the rest of us.

Akin to discovering that your parents actually had sex, it was knowledge I could have happily lived without.

As an orphan with no siblings, Penny quickly adopted my parents as her own and their relationship has only grown in our time together. It's testament to their wonderful parenting skills that they had managed to develop that relationship with her whilst always making me feel, as they always had, their very special little boy.

We said our goodbyes at the front door as we walked them to their car. Under normal circumstances, I'd have shown off a little – well, actually, I'd have shown off *a lot* but, you know, whatever – by switching on the outside lights. These show the house in its full glory and continue along the driveway to where it meets the main road. It was as a mark of respect to my parents that I decided to let them slip away without the fanfare. Well, that and the fact that Penny had taken my hand and entwined her fingers into it when I had reached for the switch.

So the mark of respect was actually my idea; she'd just thought of it first.

We watched their car's taillights disappear into the night before turning back inside and closing the door. It was not yet 8pm and my parents were under the strictest instructions to call Penny… *us*… to let her… *to let us, damn it, to let US know*… that they had arrived home safely. That would be at least 2 hours from now, so I went to head for the only room that houses a television.

Penny had a different idea.

"Where are you going?" She didn't wait for an answer as she once again found my hand and pulled me towards the stairs. "I thought we could pick up from where we left off this afternoon…" The lingering image of my parent's car leaving the estate was suddenly replaced by that of our frantic and passionate love making on the floor of the library. Seeing her naked in my mind's eye had me suddenly desperate to make it a reality and I quickly lifted her in my arms and raced up the stairs, two steps at a time.

Her laughter echoed throughout our house and I instantly knew that love was home.

The bedroom door was barely closed before I was inside her. Once again, writhing in lust and passion saw me spent almost immediately although it really didn't seem to bother her. It did, however, bother me. "I'm sorry. This never happens to me and now *twice* in one day?" I felt that my shame and embarrassment would enlighten the darkened room.

"It's okay my love, we have *all* night." Her soft features basked in the moonlight that shone through the window. Her eyes were staring deep into mine and a lover's smile played on her lips. One hand was gently stroking my cheek as the other played with a fresh bead of sweat in the small of my back. I could feel myself almost ready for a second, more prolonged session of lovemaking.

So lost were we both in the moment that we hadn't heard the approach. The first we knew of anyone being outside our bedroom door was when the rapid fist started banging heavily upon it. Penny instinctively pulled the covers over herself as I leapt from the bed and, completely naked, stormed towards the door. This was fight or flight and I would not be found wanting.

Not for my Penny.

Not for my girl.

Not for my love.

I had almost made it to the door when the voice stopped me in my tracks. *"Penny, Z, can I come in? Please? I need to talk to you both, NOW!"* The unmistakable tone belonged to Andy, but the panic and desperation were new. I grabbed my recently discarded jeans and quickly threw them on; they were still warm. As I turned to see Penny, she'd flicked on the bedside lamp and was now back on her side of the bed. The bed covers were tucked tightly around her and she nodded. Following her instruction, I opened the door.

"Andy, what the fuc…" I wasn't allowed to finish as he barged in, brushing passed me, and speaking directly to Penny.

"We have a problem. I think it's *THEM.*"

Penny's face visibly crumbled and she quickly buried it into the duvet. The sobs were immediate and hard, instantly causing her whole body to shake violently. I watched as her shoulders heaved and she screamed long and deep into her hands that held the quilt around her head. Through the eiderdown I could hear the single muffled word.

"NOOOOOOOOOOOOOOOOOOOOOOOOOOO!"

"What the actual *FUCK* is going on here?" It was my turn to take some control and try and find out what was going on. Not two minutes ago I was making love with the love of my life and the world was locked outside. Now, the world had, quite literally, barged through our bedroom door and completely destroyed my girl's happiness. Mine too as it happens, but that could wait, one thing at a time. "Who are *THEM*?"

Penny had removed her cumbersome veil and was staring through bleary eyes, still full of tears, directly at Andy. "How do YOU know who THEM are, Andy?" The cold steely grit and determination that I knew she had was back, and she wanted an answer.

"*Kristy*, now is not the time for this. We need to move, and move FAST." Andy gathered her so recently abandoned clothes from the floor and threw them beside her, onto my side of the bed. Her face betrayed her thoughts as, whatever he had meant by

'*Kristy*' had obviously had the desired effect, and she was dressing very quickly underneath the covers.

Andy had turned his back to her and so never saw that her eyes never left him.

"Z, *please*, I beg of you, get dressed and let's *move*. I can answer all your questions later." Although this was said to me, it was directed at Penny.

"What do we do?" She was out of bed now and obviously ready to follow his instructions.

"Leave that light on and come with me. It should be enough of a distraction. Close that door after you Z." I was pulling on a shirt as Andy took Penny's hand and pulled her towards the stairs. The light could still be seen around the edges of the door, although I gave it a gentle push back to make sure it was properly locked. It was obvious that Andy was in control and I didn't want to be found wanting with the one thing he ordered me to do. It obviously took me too long for they were now standing at the bottom of the stairs and both looking impatiently back up at me; it was quite disconcerting.

"What?" I had done as I was told. What more did they want from me?

As I raced down to meet them, Andy started to talk. "Now, please, no questions.

Okay? I will *happily* answer everything you need or want to know later. For now, we just need to get through this. Okay?" That was twice he had asked if everything was 'okay' when everything was far from fucking 'okay' and he *knew* that. So, two stupidly redundant questions and I was still none the wiser. Everything was happening so fast. My brain, along with my consciousness, was still upstairs trying to get myself ready for round two of the lovemaking.

What had happened with that?

This was the very question I was wrestling in my head as I watched Andy reach down behind the plant pot that resides at the bottom of the staircase. He seemed to press, or knock, or push, or pull something, but whatever he did, a panel on the wall swung inwards to reveal a small passageway. Now a completely new set of questions came flooding into my head and I was struggling to pick just one when Penny beat me to it.

"Andy...?"

"As I say, all questions will be answered later. For now, *PLEASE*, just hide in here until I come back and get you. You will be safe here, I promise." He held Penny lightly by the shoulders and looked straight into her eyes as he made his promise.

I believed him.

Penny nodded, turned, and stepped into the wall. Andy caught my eye and tilted his head sideways, gesturing that I should follow. "These are dangerous men Z, and I know you want to help but, believe me, you would be more of a hindrance to me. This is something I need to take care of on my own. Trust me *my friend*."

I hadn't given a single thought to helping him face these guys, whoever they were, so completely focused was I upon protecting Penny. However, no sooner than he had said it, I realized that he was allowing me to save face. Never have I been more grateful to him. I entered the wall and, turning to close the panel, I gave him a nod and my best smile of reassurance – it was a smile I never knew I had. "Be safe *my* friend."

"There is a bank of CCTV monitors at the end, you can watch what is going on. This room should be soundproof, but keep all noise to a minimum, now is not the time to test that particular theory. Now, close the door and I shall see you soon."

I didn't need telling twice.

Penny was already sat at the far end of the small corridor and was intently watching one of the nine screens. Following her gaze, I could see two men in the distance, skirting in the shadows along the side of Andy's workshop, and approaching the rear of the house. They were in the top-right screen, yet it was the center-left that drew my attention. There, racing along the tree line of the driveway and out towards the main entrance of the estate, was the unmistakable figure of Andy.

"They're inside." Penny had switched to the top-middle screen that showed both men silently entering the back entrance to the kitchen. Looking down to the center-middle screen, it showed both figures making their way along the hallway. They were, quite literally, a few feet from us. Seeing them on the screen, wandering around our home, among all our familiar things, was surreal. It felt like I was part of a game.

Then I saw it.

The unmistakable outline of a gun in the second man's hand. They were stopped at the bottom of the staircase, just through our newly discovered door; so close that I could hear their whispers.

"She isn't here?" The man with the gun seemed genuinely disappointed. I could only imagine why.

"Oh she's here, look." The man in front nodded in the direction of our bedroom. *"See the lights?"*

"Oh, yeah." The glee was evident in the

gunman's voice as he followed his companion deftly, if not silently, ascending the stairs. The squeaks and groans of the old staircase seemed deafening in the silence of the house, yet were somewhat contained under the ornate carpet that adorns it. Still, it was obvious, even to my untrained eye, that these men were no strangers to creeping around other people's homes uninvited. The gunman held the bannister in his left hand and hugged the wall, using only the front of his foot on each step to minimize the contact area. His partner in crime – quite literally in this case – was mirroring his actions on the right-hand side of the staircase. When they reached to top, they took their respective sides to our bedroom door and stopped to listen.

Silence.

The man on the right reached down and slowly turned the door knob as the other man raised his gun. In a second, the door flew open and the gunman rushed in first, aiming at the bed. Quickly realizing that it was empty, he scanned the room, searching for an occupant. Finding none, he lowered the weapon as his companion entered. He walked straight to the bed and placed his hand under the duvet on Penny's side.

I felt violated.

"It's warm, she's here. Somewhere."

We had watched the whole scene unfold in the center-middle screen. I had no idea that there were cameras in, evidently, every room in the house. Why would we need them and, worse, who has been watching us? It was obviously not Penny. Was Andy a secret pervert? Another question for him when that time comes.

If that time ever comes.

The gasp from Penny seemed to deafen me and certainly gave me a fright. The companion was looking directly at the camera. She stepped back as if he was going to walk straight through the screen and catch her. Instinctively, I stepped between them.

"She's watching us right now." He pointed right at us as the other man followed his finger and raised his gun. For the first time in my life, I looked directly down the barrel of a very real gun. I mistakenly assumed that this was a first for Penny too. I wasn't even close. As we courageously stared back at them, helpless and hiding, they were staring at us, calculating and conniving. The impasse was broken by the shrill tones of the telephone. As the answer machine took control, the pleasant tones of Penny filled the dead air and wafted past us and up the staircase.

Hi, I am very sorry, but I am

*unable to take your call at the
moment. Please leave a
message and a contact
number and I will be sure to
return your call. Thank you
so much and have a great
day!*

The beep was very quickly followed by
a voice that was all too familiar within the
house.

*"This is for the two men
currently searching the
house. Listen VERY carefully.
I have found your BMW and
your backpack. I have your
passports, gentlemen, so I
know that you are a Mr.
Marco Lombardi and a Mr.
Dominic Rossi..."*

The gunman shot a confused look at
The Smile and pointed the gun in the general
direction of the telephone, "That's fucking
great, he knows who we are. What do we do
now?" Thinking was not his forte.

"For now, we listen." The Smile was
still staring directly at us and, bizarrely, it
was me who was the first to break eye
contact.

"...I have also found the 2

kilos of heroin..."

"2 kilos of heroin? Seriously, what is going on?" Evidently, thinking isn't quite my forte either, although I did at least manage to contain my questions within a whisper. My head was spinning; this must be a bad dream.

"Shhhhhhhhhhh. Please." Penny knew most of the answers, but now was still not the time for any of my questions.

> *"So, you men have a choice. You can wait where you are until the police arrive, or you can make your way back to the airport and get on the plane that brought you here from New York, never to return. Either way makes no difference to me. I shall, of course, be handing over your passports, drugs, and backpack to the police when they get here.*
>
> *There is a car around the back of the house that you passed when you broke in. It has the keys in it, I suggest you use that and go.*
>
> *NOW."*

The line went dead.

In the fresh silence, my eyes were transfixed upon the two men on the screen but I saw three people in the frame. Even in the dim light, I could see the tears falling from Penny's cheeks and she was biting hard into her bottom lip, struggling to contain her emotions. Her hands came up to cradle her face as she turned to lean back against the wall; her gentle sobs were hidden behind a web of interlocking fingers. The usual confidence that held her head high had slipped from her shoulders and dragged her down with it. She seemed quite vulnerable and, for the very first time, I felt that she actually needed me.

It was such a wonderful feeling that made me instantly hate myself.

All of the questions that were racing through my mind evaporated as I turned to face her. My hands scraped against the exposed brickwork as they wormed behind her shoulders and tried to tenderly coax her into my arms. Her whole body went rigid to the touch. My lips grazed the side of her head as I spoke softly into her ear, *"It's okay my love, it's me, Z. I'm here now, everything will be okay, I promise."* It was a promise that I had no idea how to keep, but one that I fully intended to honor; for the moment at least. She buried her head, still hiding behind her hands, deep into my chest. I placed an arm both high and low on her back to pull her tight into me, I wanted her to feed from my strength.

She felt so frail.

"They found me… they found me… but how… how did they find me…?" The questions were barely audible through her web of fingers and was yet another for which I had no answer. They did, however, have the unhappy consequence of raising yet more questions for me. Questions to which I began to wonder if I actually wanted to know the answers. My head was swimming and I suddenly needed air.

This was all just too surreal.

Fortunately, my pointless and meandering thoughts – from which, I knew from experience, no good could ever come – were abruptly interrupted by the sound of two sets of feet racing down the staircase just beyond the wall panel that doubled as the portal providing us refuge.

Not that 'we' were of any consideration to them now.

Penny's head was now turned and resting on my chest as she watched them flit from one screen to another, then vanish completely. Her hand found the control panel underneath the bank of screens. It had a button marked with its corresponding camera, and she quickly pressed the one that read *Rear Entrance*. The two figures were already in the vehicle and the gravel scattered silently as they sped around the house. Another click and we saw our second set of taillights head over the crest of the driveway tonight. The final button was marked *Front Gate* and Penny was barely quick enough in pressing it as she saw them fly out into the main road and head towards Inverness. They initially took to the right side of the white lines as they accelerated away. Before they made the first bend, the brake lights flashed and the car visibly slowed as it switched back to the legally correct side of the road.

It seemed like forever that we stood there in silence, just staring at the last screen that they had so recently vacated. I had been so consumed by their escape that I hadn't noticed that Penny's arms had found their way around me and she was now holding me tighter than I had ever been held before. Her head still faced the bank of screens, but was buried deep into my chest. It seemed she was terrified to look at me.

Afraid to face me.

Afraid to let me go.

This was the exact moment that I knew how much she truly loved me.

Truly needed me.

"Are you okay?" The question was devoid of any confidence and was delivered by a genuinely scared little girl.

"No, I really am not." I couldn't lie.

"I understand Z. I should have told you everything, but there was never the right time. I just wanted to…."

I cut her off, now was not the time for this conversation. Now she needed me to be her man. "That's not what's bothering me."

"Really? What is it that is bothering you?" She released me from her embrace to step back and her eyes searched my face for answers that weren't there. Her hands held my arms at the elbows, fully prepared to both let go or re-engage, depending on what I said next.

"They took MY fucking car!"

Never have I been so happy to hear her laugh.

Chapter 22

Harrison, Westchester County, New York

Saturday 16th January

The light tap at the door did little to rouse Melissa. The second tap, slightly louder, had a similar result. Michael's patience was reflected in his third attempt, this time demanding her attention.

"Yes?" Her slumber was not yet ready to let her go and she had no idea who she was actually answering.

"Good afternoon, Melissa." He had been up for a few hours, but thought it best to let her rest as sober Michael had taken a little longer than expected to appear. He'd taken a cold shower to clear his head of any lingering effects from the alcohol and years of practice had helped perfect this particular technique. Fresh and almost alert, he had taken his time to thoroughly rifle through her handbag, purse, and all the pockets of her coat. He still had no clue that it was a jacket, nor would he ever care. He had resisted the temptation of searching the rental car, but only because her room faced out onto the street and he could have been too easily caught.

That would have blown all his goodwill, credibility, and trust-building efforts.

In any case, he already had all the information that he needed on her. He now knew her name, age, and address; that was more than enough to ensure her compliance.

"Melissa? I have made some fresh coffee. It's almost 5pm, I can only feel flattered that you have managed to sleep so long in my home." It felt good to be able to exercise his charms once again upon yet another stupid woman within the confines of his own house. He allowed himself to close his eyes and for a second to enjoy the moment.

It was in being told the time that brought her crashing back to reality. Never in her life had she slept all day, even when she was sick. The easiest option, and the one that provided the most solace, was to blame the jet lag. She knew that, in reality, her body clock was 5 hours ahead and so only making things worse, it being almost 10pm in Scotland. She chose to ignore this particular fact as it did nothing to appease her conscience.

"Coffee sounds great, can I meet you downstairs? I need to…" She needed to use the bathroom and also rid her mouth of the ghastly taste and odor that comes from eating practically nothing and living on liquids for the last few days. However, she couldn't exactly tell him that. That would be uncouth and unladylike. Whatever was happening here, and whatever she had embroiled herself into, she had standards that she would never compromise. Well, not at least whilst she had an option. "…freshen up." She let out a sigh of relief at finding the right words.

"Okay, great. The bathroom is just across the hall. I shall wait for you downstairs."

She heard him make his way slowly from the door as she pulled back the curtain that was next to her bed. Her rental car was covered in a fresh blanket of snow and the whole street appeared tranquil and serene. Completely unspoilt, it was like a scene from a postcard. It was easy for her to see why Michael and Penny – *or Kristy as he knew her* – would want to settle and raise a family here.

Anyone would.

From his seat in the kitchen, Michael

traced her every step from the bedroom to the bathroom and then down the stairs until she appeared before him. "Help yourself to the coffee. I like mine strong, like tar." He let go a little chuckle at his own weak joke while searching her face for a reaction. She obliged by forcing an equally weak smile. *Bitch. Can't she see I'm being charming?* He acknowledged and congratulated himself on his self-control. *If she was mine, I'd teach her manners and respect, that's exactly what she needs. What they ALL need.* "If it's too strong for you, only fill half the cup and we can top it off with hot water. What do you take in it? Milk? Cream? Sugar?" He stood and made his way to the empty fridge that only had milk and cream.

And ice. Lots and lots of ice.

"Black is fine, honestly." Under normal circumstances, she didn't touch coffee, tea was her drink of choice. As these were anything but normal circumstances, she forced herself to take a sip of the bitter liquid and swallowed quickly. *How can anyone drink this? It tastes like liquefied cigarettes!*

He watched her closely as she drank and saw her obvious discomfort. It was pleasing. "Let's take a comfy chair, shall we? After you." He gestured towards the living room. Leaving the cup of coffee on the counter, she walked past him and out of the kitchen. From her reconnaissance in the early hours of that very same morning, she already knew which chair he favored and so she chose a seat furthest away from it. He never seemed to notice as he sat in his throne.

Ready to be regaled.

"So Melissa, as you know, I am Michael Bradley. I think I should properly introduce myself, now that you have slept in my bed." Another joke that was as crude as it was unfunny. His polished smile was back and it made her skin crawl. He stood and walked towards her with his hand extended, looking for hers. She more leaned forward in her seat than stood as she shook his hand. As she expected, he almost crushed her hand and she got the message.

This was his house. His home. His rules.

As he sat back in his seat, his mood instantly switched and became more somber and serious. "So, is it true that you have proof that my darling Kristy is alive? Please tell me you have? You can have no idea the torture I have endured, constantly wondering if I'll ever see her again. As you can imagine, I miss her terribly. As you can see, our home is so empty without her." He reinforced his points with one hand waving aimlessly around the house, while the other quickly gave his head a place to rest and covered his mouth as he finished. He thought his performance was exemplary.

Every instinct in Melissa's body was screaming at her to get out and run.

She should have gone with the cop. She knew that now, but that was yet another lost opportunity. There was no other option now but to tell him the little she knew and then, hopefully, he would simply let her go. In less than five minutes, Michael knew all that she did. He was now Penny's problem and no longer hers.

"How absolutely intriguing. So she now owns an estate in Scotland and is running around calling herself 'Lady Penelope'? This would be hilarious if it weren't so tragic." He was too shocked to be angry. The words were tumbling out, but only because he couldn't allow himself to believe the story until he told it to himself. Melissa was a mere woman and, as such, could never be trusted.

She could, however, be believed.

"Actually, she just goes by 'Penny' but, yes, she holds the title. Or, at least, she certainly uses the title." Melissa's correction fell on deaf ears.

The plan was already formulating in his head. "So she transfers money to your bank in Scotland from a mysterious account in the Caymans? Do you know the details of this account?"

"Details? What do you mean 'details'? The money is simply transferred to my bank from one in the Caymans. What else is there to know? I have no idea from whom, how, or why this happens. Indeed, all I know is the account number that it comes from. That's it." Melissa omitted to say that she also engaged in trivial email chats with her contact there; Robert. No-one at her bank knew and certainly Michael had no need to know as it was personal, nothing to do with anything; an inconsequential detail. Otherwise, she was certain that her lack of knowledge would end this charade and she could leave. She was wrong.

"Only the account number? Can you tell me what that is *please*?" For his new plan to work, this was all the information that he needed.

"Why?" Melissa had no idea why he would want to know. What difference could it possibly make to him? No matter, if telling him was enough to end this, then fine.

"Well it could greatly help the police with the investigation. You see, it is still ongoing, even although they already have a man in prison. Obviously, if what you say is correct, then he was wrongly convicted. So any information you can provide to exonerate him can only be useful. It should also help in bringing my darling Kristy home." A new face, one rarely seen, was facing Melissa. It held all the warmth, care, and compassion that Michael could muster. It was almost convincing.

"Can I have a pen and paper please?" Melissa knew the account details by heart. She wrote them down and passed them to him.

"Thank you so much, Melissa, you have been a great help. I shall contact the police with this information on Monday morning. Now, can I get you anything to eat or drink?" There was a sincerity behind his smile.

"A glass of water please." She was parched and desperately needed to hydrate. She watched and offered another weak smile as he passed her and headed for the kitchen.

"There you go." She gratefully accepted the glass from Michael and drained it of the clear liquid. Within seconds she overwhelmed by a desperate need to use the bathroom. Excusing herself, she casually walked towards the staircase, but the sense of urgency was just too strong. She broke into a run and barely managed to lock the door before wrestling with her jeans and underwear and successfully landing on the toilet.

Her relief was as real as her embarrassment.

It was only as she was washing and drying her hands did Melissa wonder if the sound of her digestive distress had been confined within the four walls that surrounded her. She certainly hoped so. It was only this hope that she held onto as she collapsed onto the bathroom floor.

Michael waited patiently for the crash and sat back in his chair with a fresh scotch poured from the neighboring bottle to the one he had consumed the night before. Melissa could wait. The Rohypnol had been redundant since the bitch left, now it had a new purpose.

He raised the crystal glass, with its heavy base and four cubes of ice, to toast himself on his ingenuity. Not one to be rude, he finished the contents in a single gulp and reached for the telephone to make the first outward bound call in months. *"Directory enquires, which name please?"* Michael knew exactly who to ask for and gladly accepted the operator's kind invitation to connect him. As expected, he heard it ring twice before being forwarded to a cell phone. It was answered on the second ring and Michael interrupted the usual pleasantries. The call was completed in under two minutes. The private plane would be ready for take off at 4pm sharp the following day.

There were two passengers listed on the manifest.

Chapter 23

Auchtershinnan Estate, Invernesshire, Scotland

Sunday 17th January

It was just after midnight when we saw the police car slip through the main gates and creep down the driveway to the house. The fresh promise that comes with each new day was to be sullied by the continuing nightmare that was yesterday. Although we had watched the two men escape there was still the very real risk that they may have thought better of the idea and came back. In that event, and with still no sign of Andy, I'd have been left to deal with them on my own. In a fist fight, I fancied my chances. Not so much with a gunfight; especially when I didn't have a gun.

Better a live coward than a dead hero.

It was only at the very welcome sight of

the two men exiting the car did Penny speak. "Can you deal with them please? I really have had enough for one day and there are more than enough questions of our own without answering theirs. I shall remain here and you can tell them I have gone away for a few days or something. They are another problem for another time." She looked exhausted. The events of the last few hours had taken a visible toll and I could see she was beat.

For tonight at least.

"Sure, I get that. I'll try and get rid of them as quickly as possible. You can watch from in here." It was an offhand remark meant to provide her with comfort through control; it had the exact opposite effect for me. I left the relative safety of the newly discovered panic room and made my way through what had previously been my home. At least, it was when I last entered. Now, it felt like a house full of secrets.

There was a surprise for both of us when I opened the door to greet our latest guests. "I thought there were two of you?" The one in the uniform was missing. I found myself trying to recall when was the last time we ever had just a single visitor to the house. In answering my question, the officer interrupted my unresolved thought.

"Good evening, Sir, so sorry to bother

you. Yes, you are quite correct, there are two of us, but how did you know that? The whole house is in darkness and it looks like we woke you and I haven't yet alerted you to our presence."

I had to admit that this did look suspicious. A report of heroin – *a lot of heroin at that* – on the grounds of the estate and me looking like I was waiting in the dark. Yes, that is definitely suspicious. I berated myself for not waiting until he had knocked the door or rang the bell. "Between you and me officer, this is something we don't advertise so I would appreciate your discretion, but we have a silent intruder alarm at the main gate. It's built into the cattle grid and so goes off whenever a car crosses over it. It works in concert with the main burglar alarm within the house and so I knew you were coming. At least, I knew *someone* was coming and so I waited and watched to see who. We get more than our share of pranksters down here, kids mostly seeking a chase, as I'm sure you can imagine."

His pensive nodding indicated that he understood.

"You should report such activity, Sir. We would be delighted to take care of that for you. It is, after all, what we are here for." He seemed genuinely concerned.

"You do enough sterling work, Officer and our problems are nothing in the grand scheme of things. They usually get fed up quickly enough, once they see that there is someone here. So, anyway, what can I do for you? Oh, and where did you say your colleague had gone?" I stepped beyond him to look around the grounds. There was no sign of his companion.

"He has just gone to check and secure the perimeter of the house Sir, for your own safety, of course. Can I come in please? It would be better that we spoke inside."

I stood to the side and pointed him straight ahead towards the kitchen. It was further away from Penny and I knew she could watch the developments. "Certainly, it's actually nice to have some company. This old house can be quite creepy when you are here alone." I said this more to the stranger that was my home than to the one who had newly crossed the door. "You'll take a cup of tea?"

"I think you might need something stronger than tea, Sir, but tea certainly works for me. Milk and two sugar please." I was delighted that he took a seat without waiting to be offered as I filled the kettle.

"So, what brings you to our little slice of paradise?" I already knew, but had to maintain the pretense.

"Sorry, Sir, I should have said this earlier. It's actually the owner of the house we need to speak with." He had taken his notebook out and flicked through a few pages. "Yes, here we are. A Ms. Penelope Munro; could I speak with her please?"

"I'm sorry, I'm afraid that isn't possible. You see, she has gone away for a few days. Is there anything I can help you with? I'm her fiancé, Zacchaeus McLeod, but my friends and family call me 'Z'. So you can call me Mr. McLeod..." His face betrayed the shock and hurt reaction I was looking for. "Only joking! Please, call me Z." His serious features relaxed as he smiled for the first time. "Forgive me, but I never caught your name, Officer?" I quickly thrust my hand into his, taking him off guard.

"Yes, of course, sorry Sir...I mean, Z. I am Detective Inspector Marple and, yes, I'm perfectly serious. I have had to suffer this moniker my entire life and you could say that the police force was a natural fit for me. Anyway, please call me John."

It was my turn to smile, but not at his name. I was still wondering why I had introduced myself as Penny's fiancé? Whatever the reason, it was a thought that I took a selfish second to fully enjoy as I turned to fix his tea. The knock at the back door brought me crashing back to reality and startled us both, it was far more violent than required for its desired effect.

"Oh for goodness sake, Wilson!" John said exactly what I was thinking, only he more barked it as the fresh tea began seeping into his shirt and suit. I pointed to the kitchen roll as I made my way to unlock the door and let him in.

"Good evening, come in. Constable Wilson, is it?" I was actually beginning to enjoy this charade.

"Yes, Sir. Thank you, Sir." As he entered, he spoke directly to his tea stained colleague. "Perimeter is clear, Sir. They must have abandoned the vehicle."

"Very well. Go wait in the car, Wilson. I shall be out in a minute." There was no doubt who was in charge. Oddly, he chose to leave by the very door from which he entered. As I returned from relocking it, my face obviously held the question. "Don't ask. We both know it would have been far easier to simply walk out the front door. Maybe the night air will clear away the cobwebs in his head, but I very much doubt it." He sounded exasperated. "Anyway, the reason why we are here is…"

As he relayed the story that I already knew, the biggest surprise was that my shock and horror were actually genuine. Until that point, I had all but convinced myself that this was some sort of nasty dream that we would all laugh about in the morning.

Only now it was morning and no-one was laughing.

As he was nearing the end – *when will this ever end?* – he reached into his pocket and pulled out his phone. He was still talking, although no longer fully focused, as he drew his finger across the screen. "I'm sorry, there seems to have been further developments. A private jet left Inverness Airport within the last hour and the flight plan has its destination listed as New York City with two male passengers on board." He continued reading, completely oblivious to my sense of relief and desperate need for a seat; I was certain I was going to faint. "We have reason to believe these were the men who parked the stolen car on your estate."

It was Penny's estate, but I was in no condition to correct his error.

"Oh, this is interesting. They have found a car registered to you at the private hangar in the airport."

"Bastards…" I could barely muster the disgust and contempt his revelation demanded, I was exhausted.

"Obviously they had some issue with the first car – I see here that it's registered to the airport manager – and so they abandoned it and stole yours to hightail it out of here. I guess they forgot all about their backpack. Well, I shall bid you goodnight Z and sorry for being the bearer of such unfortunate news." *Unfortunate? Now there's an understatement.* "We shall, of course, keep you appraised of all developments from our enquires. If you have any questions, please just call." He placed his card beside the remnants of the tea. I thought better of highlighting that he was wearing more than he drank, although it would be something I would always remember.

Especially whenever I heard or saw the name 'Marple'.

"Goodnight, Sir." It seems that we are, once again, back to being formal and professional. If this was meant to throw me off, it wasn't working. I was far too tired to care.

"Goodnight, John." I watched my defiant response follow him down the hall and out the door. It would appear that all unwelcome visitors simply let themselves out now. It's not a practice that I care for and it certainly never happened back in the good old days when this house was my home. I slipped back into the kitchen and quickly unlocked the back door. A few steps outside had me safely hidden under the blanket of darkness and gave me a clear view of the driveway. I watched in relief as they headed back from where they came.

It was my turn to do the same.

With both front and back doors locked and bolted, I returned to the foot of the stairs and knocked on the wooden panel, *"Penny?"*, I had no idea why I whispered her name, there were only us two now in the house.

Nothing.

No response, no noise, no indication at all that she was there. I knocked again, harder this time, *"Penny?"* My voice was more authoritative this time.

Still nothing.

Panic began to settle in my mind and a multitude of scenarios ran through my head, each worse than the last. *Was she okay? Had she collapsed? What if she was unconscious? Was this a dream? Is there really a panic room?* Scrambling to push the plant pot out of the way in a frantic search of Andy's secret switch, lever, whatever it was that granted the magical access, I nearly died from fright upon hearing my name coming from behind me.

"Z, it's okay, I'm here."

"Where are you?" I recognized her voice, but there being a distinct lack of her physical presence only made this house that little bit more creepy. After tonight's events, it certainly didn't need the help.

"Drawing room."

Strangely, I caught myself returning the plant pot to its original position without discovering how the panel opened; yet another secret that the house would keep.

For now, at least.

She had already begun to talk as I opened the door and entered the room. "I couldn't stay in there any longer, it was claustrophobic and suffocating; I now understand why it's called a 'panic room'. It didn't help to be watching you protecting me whilst being unable to protect myself. Thank you. I shall, of course, thank Andy when I see him. The police didn't suspect that we had any involvement with the events of this evening?"

The fire was beginning to catch in the hearth, but its light was yet to find its way around the rest of the room. The flickering of the flames cast a gentle but weak glow that found her curled up in a ball on the rug. It was oddly romantic yet suitably dramatic. Once again, I fell under the gaze of her ancestors who were hanging on the wall and it only served to remind me that I have never felt comfortable in this room. There had been one occasion where Penny had wanted to make love in here, but I had been rather reluctant, almost to the point of refusal. *Almost*. She thought it funny when I explained that I felt it was something more akin to a sick voyeuristic orgy with all her family in attendance and that we were being watched.

Now I knew it was true and that we were being watched.

In every room.

"Everything's fine." Everything was far from fine, but neither of us wanted the conversation. Not now. Ignoring her family, I slid in behind her and felt her melt into my arms. She let her head rest on my bicep and I placed a soft kiss on her neck. The fire hissed and crackled, but it was in my heart that the sparks were flying. She drew a heavy breath and, as she exhaled, I felt her body relax. I went to kiss her neck again when she spoke, there was no mistaking the sense of mischief in her voice.

"So, I'm your fiancé huh…?"

It was a moment that was as inappropriate as it was welcome.

Chapter 24

Auchtershinnan Estate, Invernesshire, Scotland

Sunday 17th January

"Are you awake?" Penny whispered the question at the smoldering embers of a once proud fire; I was left to presume that it was meant for me. She hadn't moved all night and, consequently, neither had I. Her head was still resting on my bicep with my other arm draped around her waist. Only her shallow breathing gave any indication of life; it held such a comforting rhythm that it almost lured me into believing that she had managed to rest.

Almost.

"Yes." I lied. Dawn had finally broken on a day that had already proven itself too long. It chased the darkness out from every corner and yet failed to shed any light upon the fresh problems that had deprived me of sleep. At least, I thought I hadn't slept until she asked me.

So much for my heroic vigilance.

"I know you have questions and you will think you have a right to answers. The truth is, you really do not." The voice came from Penny, but wasn't one that I recognized. This one was cold and calculating, one that was devoid of emotion and full of fight. It was one I instantly feared and admired in equal measure. "The men who came here last night were from my past; a past that I thought I'd managed to escape but evidently, that is not the case. A past that you were no part of and that I cannot allow to take you. It has me and, God willing, only me. They know nothing of you and I must ensure that it remains this way."

I couldn't believe what she was saying. "Penny, what are you talking about? I *am* part of this, whether you like it or not. I told you *on this very spot* only a matter of days ago, how *I love you*. I don't love you when everything is going well, I don't love you when it's convenient, I love you because I simply love yo…"

She cut me off.

"Don't be so naïve. This isn't about *LOVE*. This is about *LIFE*. Something, if you will forgive me, I know a lot more about than you. You love *me*? You don't even know *me*. You know the caricature that I created when I bought this place. You *love* the Lady of the Manor. The Lady of THIS Manor. Not *ME*."

Who was this horrible person in my arms? Never in my life had I been so hurt, and all by mere words. Never could I have imagined that she – *my Penny* – could have been so capable of causing me so much pain.

"Please, leave now. I can have your things sent to your parents. Just go. Forget all about me. Forget you ever met me. Forget all about this place. Go, and start over with someone who can give you what you want, what you need. It will be better for us both if you did so." She threw my hand from her waist and freed my bicep as she shuffled forward to remove all physical contact, resting her head on her own arm.

I was frozen in shock, my mind racing with a new set of problems. Worse still, she had rendered me mute. No words would come. Nothing. We had both wrestled with the issue of the intruders, only she had the advantage of knowing who they were and their true purpose for being here. Yet in every single scenario that I had imagined, never once had I considered her facing these alone.

Without me.

"Please, just go." The words echoed around the vacuous room and suddenly I felt very lonely. Not knowing what else to say – *words still eluded me* – and not having any idea of what I could do to change her mind, I quickly gathered what was left of my dignity and pride and stood to leave.

Only then did I hear it, the all too familiar crunching of tires fighting with gravel on the driveway. I looked down and saw that Penny heard it too. Still with her head on her left bicep, her right pulled her legs up into the fetal position and she held herself tight. It was impossible to believe that the cold, heartless voice that had just broken my heart and ordered me out of her life belonged to this helpless soul in such desperate need of protection.

The car had pulled up at the front of the house; that was never a good sign. We both knew that only guests – *those that were expected and otherwise* – drove up to the front door. Everyone else parks at the rear. This was either the police or new 'friends' who were here to finish what the others had started – not that I would ever actually know what that was. Not now. Penny didn't move. She just stared at the now blazing fire; a scared and defeated little girl resigned to her fate.

Never have I been so angry.

"Well Penny, this may be what you want, but there is no *fucking* way that I will simply stand back and watch you like this. Let's just see who we have here and, whatever happens, they will have to go through *fucking* me to get to you."

Foolishly, I didn't even check the window to see who was waiting for me. Leaving her alone, I stormed out the room and slammed its door behind me. I secretly hoped to have dislodged at least a few of her patronizing ancestors from their lofty perches and had them crashing to the floor. The silence told me I was out of luck. Before I reached the front door, the doorbell rang. That only served to infuriate me further.

"I'm fucking coming!"

"Z? What are you swearing for? It's me. Open the door will you?"

A wave of relief flooded over me. Although fighting with far too many locks and bolts took more time than expected as I couldn't wait to see the familiar and friendly face beyond.

Andy.

"You have *no idea* how good it is to see you!" I genuinely meant it.

"Don't be soft, what's wrong with you?" His smile betrayed his sense of relief although he could never actually say that.

This was a time when we were expected to be men – *real men* – those men that are emotionless and feel no pain. I've never been much of a real man. However, I knew Andy to be and so there was no way I could lose face in this particular moment. I'd already lost enough for one day.

"I wasn't talking to you; I was talking to my car!"

"Oh that. Yeah, the police told me I could take it. They have enough evidence with the passports and all the other stuff that they didn't need the car. I also told them you would whine like a girl if I couldn't give it back to you." He smiled at his manly jibe. He was only half joking and he was only half right. "Talking of girls, where's ours?"

"Not *ours* anymore I'm afraid. She's all yours now and she's in the drawing room. Are the keys in it?" I nodded towards the car, I couldn't face him for fear of losing whatever shred of dignity and pride I had left.

"Ah, I wondered if this would happen. Do me a favor, come with me for a second." Andy asked as if I had an option, but his grabbing and locking me by the elbow proved otherwise. We entered the drawing room to find Penny where I'd left her.

"*Penny...? Penny...? Get UP!* We have no time for this nonsense. We need to act and act *NOW!*" Childishly, I was delighted to see that there was no reverence or respect from Andy for any of the faces in the still intact gallery.

She never moved.

Andy dropped my arm and made his way towards her; I took it as my cue to stay exactly where he left me. He bent down and whispered into her ear. Try as I might, I could not make out what he was saying. In a matter of minutes that seemed like an eternity, he gently helped her to her feet. Holding her around the shoulders, it could have been either as support or reassurance, possibly both, he continued talking with her and I continued to be ignorant of the conversation.

"Z, go and get packed." Andy's attentions had returned to me although his hands remained on her. A pang of jealousy knotted deep in the pit of my stomach. I really hated having no control, especially in this bloody room.

"Look, I'll just go and Penny can send my stuff on. That's what she wan…"

"Z, *listen to me*. Go and get packed. We are ALL leaving in a thirty minutes."

"We are? Where are we going?" I had no clue what was happening, but if this was to include me with Penny, it really didn't matter.

"They have found us. They know where we are and they will not make the same mistakes again. However, they WILL come back. I have a plan, but it needs all of us to work together. So, go and pack some things. Enough for a few days, but make sure you pack light. This is not a vacation."

I didn't need telling twice and raced for the bedroom.

Andy watched me leave. As the door closed, he looked back at Penny. He saw her tear-stained face that reflected her broken heart. *"I love him Andy. I'm only trying to protect him."* She collapsed into his arms and he held her.

"There now, shhhhhh. It's okay. It's all going to be okay. Trust me, I have a plan and it's a plan that includes Z. Penny, he is stronger than you think, believe me on that, and he wants to help. You are trying to protect him and I get that, honestly, I do, but sending him away isn't the answer. Please, for now, just trust me." Andy broke their embrace and clasped her shoulders once again. He looked straight into her eyes before speaking again.

"And trust him."

Chapter 25

Harrison, Westchester County, New York

Sunday 17th January

Melissa opened her eyes, but had to check again to ensure she was awake as the room was in absolute darkness. Her head was throbbing and fit to burst and it was only as she went to massage her temples did she realize that she was shackled, with handcuffs on each wrist. Suddenly afraid and alert, she felt along the chain and found that it fed through a large metal ring that was set into the wall. She grabbed the chain at either side of the ring and pulled.

Nothing.

She gave herself a little slack from the chain and, anchoring her feet on either side and using every last ounce of strength she had, pulled again. The effort caused her to involuntarily cry out loudly into the void,

"Aaaaaaaarrrgggggghhhhhhhhhhh!!!"

Still nothing.

Sitting back on the cold floor, she was taking a second to recover and think on what to do next when a light came on and almost blinded her.

"Ah, I thought I heard you. Did you sleep well?" Michael stood at the doorway with a tray that had a sandwich on a plate and a glass of milk. "I figured you'd need some sustenance before our trip. Do you like what I've done with the place? Shame I haven't been able to use it for a while but, thanks to you, that will change soon." He looked around with a genuine pride and, as her eyes adjusted and everything came into focus. Her body froze in shock. He recognized her instant look of horror and the terror that immediately followed. "Don't worry, this is not for your enjoyment. It was the only place I could keep you safe and secure. Oh, and quiet of course."

His words took a moment to penetrate. When they did, she instantly felt guilty for the relief that they provided, for she recognized that this was his basement – although one unlike any room she had ever seen before. There was blood spattered on every surface, blood that she could only imagine once belonged to Penny. Various contraptions seemed to be randomly placed all over, but then she saw that they were firmly anchored to the floor. Every one of them had shackles to hold a recipient securely in place and all of them were of a sexual nature. Trying desperately to make sense of this place, there was only one logical conclusion forthcoming.

This is a torture chamber.

"As you will appreciate, it is fully soundproofed. So, scream away if you like. Alas, it would only be for my benefit – and enjoyment." It was as if he could read her mind, for Melissa desperately wanted to scream. Scream loud and scream long. Until someone, somewhere, heard her.

He placed the tray on a line painted in a semi-circle around her on the floor. "Kristy used to scream. She also used to fight. Oh, how I miss her…" Bizarrely, his sentiment seemed genuine and Melissa believed him. Although he continued talking, it was no longer to her, but himself.

And the chamber.

"It won't be long before she is back, old friend. We can deal with her then. She will atone for the misery she has caused us. She will have ample time in here to contemplate the sins that she has conferred upon her husband. I can only hope that, with my help, God can forgive her."

Melissa sat still and quiet, afraid to

bring any attention back upon herself. Obviously he still had a use for her or else why would she be here? *'A trip', he said?* Penny is coming back here? She immediately recognized that her best chance of walking away unscathed was back in Scotland, on her home turf. In New York, she knew that she was liable to numerous charges given that she knew Kristy to be alive and living under an assumed identity, and that an innocent man was languishing in prison.

In all likelihood, for the rest of his life.

In Scotland, New York had no jurisdiction over her and so there she would be safe. Safe and sound. And home. Similarly, she would have no jurisdiction over him. She could simply walk away, but what could she say to the police? *He kidnapped me and brought me home.* What kind of a kidnapper does that? He could simply deny it and it would be her word against his. Anyway, he was after Penny. That much was obvious, and that wasn't her problem. Although she knew that this assertion was simply untrue and she was lying to herself, but that was a problem that could wait.

She had more pressing concerns.

As Michael turned to leave the room, Melissa spoke for the first time. Her tone was calm and measured, she wanted to keep on his good side – *does he have a good side?* – she quickly dismissed the thought. "Michael, can you please leave the light on? I promise, I won't be any trouble. Please?"

He gave her a sinister smile that had so long been absent from this particular room. Oh you poor bewildered soul. *You still believe that you ever could be trouble for me?* He turned and took his thoughts with him as he left the room in the trust of a complete stranger.

To her relief, the light remained on.

Chapter 26

Pelham, Westchester County, New York

Sunday 17th January

Joshua McCall had the auspicious distinction of being the youngest judge ever appointed in the state of New York. Everyone knew that his appointment was due solely to his highly successful prosecution of Anthony Di Silva. After that, the offers had came flooding in; all partnerships at top law firms with large offices and bigger salaries.

He had delighted in refusing them all.

His was an altogether nobler cause, a deep-rooted belief in the principals of justice and service. To the whole legal community, he had it all. A brilliant mind and a career that was only heading in one direction. To add further misery to his esteemed peers, colleagues, and professional acquaintances, he had also been in the enviable and somewhat unusual position of being a bachelor.

Until he met Christine Smyth.

She was the most beautiful woman he'd ever seen, who also happened to be highly intelligent with ambitions of her own. He had pursued her relentlessly and unashamedly until she had, at long last, finally agreed to a date. He hadn't known at the time that she only agreed in order to prove to him that his assertions of their suitability were completely wrong; not that he would have cared. However, and she still hated to admit it, he had been perfectly correct. Within two quick years, and in front of their delighted family and friends, they were married in what was widely described in the city tabloids as the *'Wedding of the Year'*.

In the seven months since, they had spent almost every Sunday enjoying lunch at the Carnegie Golf and Country Club. Well, more endured than enjoyed. Pretentious in the extreme, it was the accepted meeting place for the great and the good, full of self-important people further indulging their self-inflated egos. Where talk of making money was seen as repugnant yet the talk of how it was spent was expected.

The car park was testament enough to

that, where an outdated model was enough to clearly indicate that the owner was suffering from financial woes.

In reality, for Josh, it was a burdensome chore that had to be tolerated to ensure continued career progression. For Christine, it was a means of justifying the $25,000 membership fee that they paid each year. Ever prudent and incredibly shrewd, she wanted at least some return for that level of investment. Although she understood the social demand for them being members it did not, in itself, mean that she agreed with it.

A point that she took every opportunity to remind her husband.

Their weekly misery was almost over when they were approached as they stood to leave. "Ah, Josh, there you are, I was hoping to run into you." They knew the friendly voice belonged to Robert Webster, one of the most ruthless operators to frequent the club. Universally disliked, but powerful enough to demand toleration, his presence was a fitting end to an unpleasant lunch.

He also knew that the McCall's had a standing 12.30pm reservation, so they all knew this was no coincidence.

"Bob, good to see you." The lie came as easy as the handshake to Josh. "What can I do for you?"

"Well, as you know, there is an election coming up in November and we are looking at suitable candidates to put forward for consideration. I hope you don't mind, but in our discussions, your name came up. Presumptuous as it may be, it was actually my suggestion so I'd better check and make certain it was something that you may be interested in before we went any further with it?" Among the few titles that Robert Webster has – some not as pleasant as others – is that of the chairman of the local Democratic Party. He also knew that Josh McCall was a party member who had discreetly expressed political aspirations.

"Why sure Bob, I'd be interested. As my record shows, I'm a committed public servant, only interested in serving the people." It was an open secret that Josh coveted the nomination.

"Great, leave it with me. Lovely to see you again, Christine. Although, for the life of me, I have no idea how Josh here managed to convince you to marry him. That one's a thinker!" He laughed too long and too hard at his own joke, undressing her with his eyes.

"Yeah, I often ask myself that very question, Bob." She dutifully laughed along as she slipped behind her husband, her arm wrapping firmly around his waist. To her,

Bob Webster was a loathsome and vile individual who had used his power to bully and badger people to his will, and Josh would be expected to show loyalty and a return for his act of kindness and generosity. It was an arrangement that already made her feel deeply uncomfortable, and the conversation wasn't yet over.

However, she also knew that Josh was fully aware of the expectations and he was an expert at playing the game.

"We'll be in touch, Josh. Always a pleasure, Christine." Bob made to lean in for a kiss, but Josh grabbed his hand once again and shook it.

"Excellent, looking forward to it. Really appreciate your time, thanks again, Bob." Josh felt his wife's grip on his waist tighten as Bob returned the handshake. This time, he squeezed a little harder. Josh returned in kind.

The drive home was short without being very sweet. Christine eloquently expressed her unease in having to deal with the likes of Bob Webster and his ilk in order for Josh to achieve his political ambitions. In return, Josh all but managed to convince her that Bob would be the least of their concerns and, indeed, dealing with him would actually be 'good practice' for the big leagues.

As they pulled into their driveway, they managed to at least agree that this was much too good an opportunity to resist – and one simply too good to ignore.

Chapter 27

Pelham, Westchester County, New York

Sunday 17th January

It was my first time on a private jet and the flight was as luxurious as it was awkward. A single air stewardess was on hand to tend to our every whim and, much to her annoyance, boredom seemed to be the only passenger that she needed to care for. For the most part, Andy sat at the very rear of the cabin, rarely looking up from his laptop. Occasionally, he would use a headset and cover the mouthpiece as he spoke on what I presumed to be Skype. Penny sat at a window seat in the middle that faced backwards towards Andy. Every once in a while he would call her over and they would chat quietly, hands would cover their mouths for maximum privacy, with the occasional finger being pointed at the laptop screen and this always seemed to generate further discussion. All the while I sat with my back to the cockpit, merely watching it all, and wondering what the hell I was doing there.

Sometimes I caught myself wondering if I was there at all.

"...where the local time is 11:56am. Thank you so much for..." The pilot was all but finished with his announcement before I realized that he had actually started. It was the time that caught my attention. It was only as I began adjusting my watch that I noticed that we had landed a mere forty minutes after we had taken off; we had been in the air for almost six hours. I would never have thought it possible, but the longest day of my life just got a whole lot longer. *Will this day ever end?* It was a question I had no time to contemplate for, as we stepped off the plane, there was a car waiting for us.

"Mr. Jamieson?" The man who was stood by the open driver's door stepped forward at the nod from Andy and handed him the keys. Nothing more was said as he turned and walked towards the looming hangar that was behind the car and facing us.

"Z, are you coming?" Andy's impatience with me was heavy in his tone, as both he and Penny were already in the car and ready to go. I hadn't noticed. The idea of landing and taxiing directly to a private hangar and then stepping into a waiting car was something I had only ever seen in the movies. It was always a dream of mine to travel like this, but not under these circumstances. Try as I might to enjoy it, I couldn't help but wish that we had arrived by more modest and conventional means. Without Andy. Just Penny. Both of us exploring this magical city as mere tourists. Normal, everyday tourists.

She still hadn't spoken to me since we had left the estate and did all she could to avoid even looking at me.

"Z, get in!"

I took my seat in the back, behind Penny in the passenger seat, and convinced myself it was because it had the most legroom. In truth, it was to save her any discomfort when she talked to Andy, as I'd have fallen into her peripheral vision if I'd sat behind him. I still had no idea why I was here, but knew that I didn't want to be anywhere else. She was in danger, that much was obvious, and Andy seemed to think I could be of use. I was in no position to question his judgment; he had more than proven himself worthy of my trust with his recent heroics.

It was the first time I'd ever actually

seen the familiar skyline that captivated me as we drove through the city. Looking around, each window in the car seemed to frame an instantly recognizable landmark. Andy and Penny once again started talking in hushed tones and I was successful in ignoring their conversation. Instead, I kept myself occupied by searching the faces in the other cars, hoping to spot someone famous. It soon became apparent that, in the city that never sleeps, the stars stay at home.

At least they do on drab and grey Sunday afternoons in January.

It was just over an hour after landing that we pulled into a deserted street. The road and sidewalks were clear, as were most of the driveways, but everything else was hidden under a blanket of clean snow. Penny held Andy's laptop on her knees and the full screen was a Google Street View of exactly where we were, only this was taken in the summer. All the flowers were in bloom, the lawns manicured to perfection, and the trees and hedges trimmed to perfection in various shades of green. It was almost impossible to imagine that this was the same place.

"It's definitely that one." Penny was pointing to a house that, to my untrained eye, looked much the same as every other.

"Yeah, I think so. Let's see if anyone's home." Andy reached into his pocket and pulled out his phone. He must have pre-programmed the number on the plane as he pressed one button and held it to his ear. In the silence of the car, I could hear the ringing. As it clicked to the answer machine, he hung up. As he did so, he looked at Penny. It was a look that needed no explanation.

"So, we wait." She settled down into her seat. Andy did the same. It was obvious that this was not for comfort, but to make themselves look small. I followed their lead and did the same.

We didn't have to wait long.

It was almost 2pm when the car drew into the driveway. No sooner had it crossed the sidewalk but the garage door was opening. In seconds, the car had vanished and the street was exactly as it had been before. The same, but different.

"Showtime." Andy turned in his seat so he could easily see us both. "Z, you're with me. Penny, you stay here. Right here. Okay? Now, do *not* do anything rash. If you have any problems, blast the horn and we'll be out here in seconds."

She nodded, but said nothing.

"Right Z, listen to me. I need you to be cool, calm, and collected. Act just like we belong here and are popping in to see a friend, okay?" His instructions were clear and simple enough yet the adrenaline that was pumping through my veins was now throbbing in my ears. I had to suppress the bizarre image of mutant butterflies that seemed to be tying huge knots in my stomach, along with the overwhelming urge to use the bathroom. I had no idea what was happening and not really sure I wanted to know, but it was clear that this wasn't a visit to an old friend.

That could never be a good sign.

The sharp winter air attacked me as soon I stepped from the car. As I closed the door and stepped forward, I caught Penny watching me.

My wink found a smile.

It was only as we made our way up the driveway that Andy spoke. "Stop looking around, pretend like we belong. Focus on the door, only the door. We need to be invisible and so do nothing that draws attention. Now, when we get there, let me do the talking."

I had no intention of doing anything to the contrary.

The American national anthem wafted through the house immediately upon Andy's pressing the doorbell. Muted voices could be heard from within. *"I have no idea, but at least if I answer it, I can let you know."* The male voice sent the joke into their home in search of his wife as he opened the door. "Yes, how can I help you?" It was an altogether less friendly tone that he used to greet us.

"Judge Joshua McCall?" I followed Andy's instructions and said nothing although my mind was racing. *A judge? Why are we at the home of a judge?*

"Yes?" This was a judge who obviously wasn't happy with a house call.

"Your Honor, we need to talk. It's about Anthony Di Silva and the kidnapping of Kristy Bradley. Trust me when I tell you that it is in all of our interests that we have this conversation. May we come inside? I believe the fact that we are troubling you at home and on a Sunday reflects the seriousness and importance of the situation. Please, all I ask it that you just hear us out then we will go, if that's what you want." The judge never said another word, but Andy had obviously said enough to pique his curiosity as he stood back and pointed straight through to the sunroom at the rear of the house.

Kristy Bradley? 'Kristy' is what Andy had called Penny when he came into our bedroom only last night. 'Kidnapping'? Snippets of answers that only gave rise to yet more questions.

As I followed Andy, I realized that I

was entering the home of a man I never knew, with a man I hardly knew, for the love of a woman that I thought I knew.

Chapter 28

Pelham, Westchester County, New York

Sunday 17th January

"Well, gentlemen, although I am most reluctant to admit it, you do have me intrigued. However, this is an old case and, more importantly, *a closed case*. So let's make this quick. You have five minutes; I suggest you use them wisely." It was clear we were not welcome and that we shouldn't take a seat. The judge spoke while ushering Andy through his house.

I was expected to follow, but couldn't.

The house's humble façade gave no indication of its truly palatial interior and only now could I see that it was almost as deep as it was wide. It was quite magnificent and completely captivating. At least, it was to me. Intimidating and yet strangely homely, it exuded wealth and power; exactly what one would expect from such a prestigious and established person. The small coatroom entered onto a marble floor where a beautiful fountain took pride of place in its center. Basking in the natural light that was streaming in from the glass ceiling directly above, it held fish that were lazily swimming around with an attitude befitting their sumptuous surroundings. As the marble met the walls on either side, it rose to form two separate and wonderfully ornate staircases that led to an open balcony on the upper level, from which I only half-expected two opera stars to appear. I caught myself scanning the full balcony a second time, just to be sure, and was actually disappointed when they didn't. Yet, for some reason, the *Floral Duet* started playing softly in my head.

"When did they start…?" The question was gone before I could catch it. I'd closed my eyes for the briefest of seconds to enjoy the music, only to find the judge's words lurking in my head; so lost in the moment that I'd forgotten myself.

I'd also forgotten Andy's explicit instruction of silence.

"I beg your pardon?" I knew it was the judge who was asking the question, even though he was obscured by one of his own cherubs that was randomly perched around the top of the water feature. Thankfully, the water that was cascading from its coronet successfully blurred Andy's face although could not prevent the penetration of his burning glare.

"Well, you said we have five minutes and I was just wondering when they started? Was it when you answered the door, or when we came in, or is it from just now, when you said it?" Originally, it was an impulsive, if rather insolent question, but now I genuinely wanted to know. At the very least, by asking the question, I hoped I could maximize the full five minutes for our own benefit.

The judge's reaction was better than I could ever have expected. His laughter echoed around the house and it returned with a lady's voice, "What's so funny?"

"Nothing, darling. I'll tell you later." The judge stepped around the fountain and held a curious look as he eyed me up and down. It was truly unnerving and I instantly knew that his was not a court I'd like to be standing in. "Now, if I'm not mistaken, that is a Scottish accent?"

"Guilty." I immediately regretted my response, but it was the only one that seemed appropriate. I shuffled a few feet around the fountain, more to hide from Andy, and saw that the judge was smiling.

"My grandfather was born there. I've been over a few times but, sadly, not as much as I'd like. Well, now things just got a little more interesting. Why on earth would a Scotsman be interested in the kidnapping of Kristy Bradley?"

"It's a question I've asked myself more than once, Your Honor." It was the absolute truth although his laughter suggested that he thought I was joking.

"Okay, well let's go through and hear why you gentlemen are here." He turned and made his way through the house. Following at the back, I entered the sunroom to find the judge had already taken his seat. It was strategically placed to enjoy the splendid view down the sprawling gardens that backed onto a distant ravine. The trees lined the border of the property. All covered in snow, they provided a natural barrier from prying eyes and so ensured total privacy; it gave one the instant feeling of being both safe and secure. Andy had walked directly to the sliding doors and seemed to be fumbling with something under his jacket.

"Your Honor, there is something I need you to see before we talk."

What do you have in there Andy? Surely not a gun? I still had little to no idea why we were here but, in light of recent events, mine was a completely logical assumption.

Without thinking, I took a single step and placed myself between the two men. Andy turned and our eyes locked. He saw how I'd positioned myself and raised a disapproving eyebrow; it was only by seeing what he held did I understand.

There, in his hand, was the brightly lit screen of an iPad.

"Trust me, you do not want nor need to see this." He spoke directly to me and I knew this wasn't the time to argue, so I took a seat on the couch that faced the judge's chair. It felt like I was the only member of what should be a three-person jury. "Your Honor, what I am about to show you is the inside of the Bradley residence."

"And why do I need to see the inside of the Bradley residence?" The judge asked my question.

"This should give you a very different understanding of Kristy Bradley's situation. It isn't as black and white as was portrayed by you in the courtroom. I'd hoped never to have to show anyone this, but there have been developments that now demand that you see it." Andy crouched by the chair and placed the tablet in his hands. "For the sake of my friend here…" Andy gestured towards me. It was not lost on me that never once had he mentioned my name. I returned in kind. "…and for your own benefit, I shall let it play on mute. If you insist, I can provide headphones."

"That won't be necessary." As he spoke, the judge was looking directly at me; a friend helping a friend.

Andy pressed play and walked back to the screen doors, casting his gaze far into the distance in the hope of finding a happy thought. His was a forlorn hope. Watching him, it was easy to tell that he was replaying in his head exactly what the judge was now watching. The tears welling in the corners of his eyes betrayed him and set my mind racing.

What is on that screen?

I looked back to the judge. He was mesmerized. Watching intently, his eyes seemed to grow bigger with each passing second as he absorbed and processed every last detail. Holding the tablet in his right hand as his left quickly found and covered his now gaping mouth.

"Oh my God, what are you watching?!" The female voice was one that I now recognized and it belonged to the beautiful woman who emerged from the corridor on my right. I presumed it was his wife although there were no such doubts about her disgust – that was absolute. To his credit, he immediately hid the screen by setting it down against his chest. "Josh, what

was that? Tell me that wasn't real?"

"Sadly, I cannot." His tone was sad and weary. One hand was spread over the tablet, as if hiding it from her would somehow ensure she instantly forgot what they had just seen. Sadly, without success. The other hand raised to pinch and roll the skin on the bridge of his nose. As his index finger and thumb spread out to rub his eyes, it seemed to me that he was also trying to erase his own freshest memory.

"Who was that? And why are you watching it?" Ignoring Andy and myself, she walked straight to the center of the room and looked directly at him; she was determined to have the answers. Beautiful and feisty, I immediately liked her.

"Those are among the very questions that I have for these gentlemen. Although I can only imagine that the answers they have are not the ones that we wish to hear. I, for one, dearly wish that I had never seen what we both just watched. So, if this is any indication…" He tapped a finger on the iPad. "…I would strongly recommend that you not stay for this particular discussion and I can give you the abridged version later?"

"Indeed you will not. I want to know exactly what is going on." There was nothing more to be said as she sat down on the other end of my couch – second member of the jury. The judge was already settled in his seat. Our trial was about to begin and all eyes fell onto Andy. He was still to be found standing by the sliding doors, staring off into the distance. As he started to speak, each carefully chosen word was delivered slowly and deliberately. His voice constantly struggled to contain the cracks of emotion; this was a battle he was losing.

"I haven't seen it. I know about it…" He paused and took a deep breath. His own admission obviously caused him pain. "…but I haven't seen it. Nor do I ever want to." He turned and looked firstly at the judge, and then to his wife. I could see that they both understood, but said nothing. Andy ignored me and turned back to look out the window. In that moment, I understood.

He was looking for something unspoilt. Something pure.

"The scenes were a collection of snippets from different pieces of individual tapes that were filmed by Michael Bradley. The lady that is the object of his depravity was his wife, Kristy. She took these tapes before she disappeared and kept them in a secure location. They were only to be used in an emergency, and only for her own protection. Believe me, he has so many more that I very much doubt he knows that these are gone. However, before I continue, there is something you should know. Something that only I know. Something that I hope clarifies why we are here, looking for your help." Andy closed his eyes and I could see the tear glisten and fall down the side of his cheek. He valiantly tried to compose himself, but without much success. Drawing another deep breath, he raised his head proudly and straightened his back. His words came as a whisper and were deafening.

"Kristy Bradley is my daughter…"

Chapter 29

Pelham, Westchester County, New York

Sunday 17th January

Wait…what did he just say? If Andy is Kristy's father, does that mean…? Mine was a train of thought that was immediately derailed by the judge. As the words hung heavy in the air, Josh McCall picked himself out from his chair and sidled himself directly in front of Andy, acutely aware that he was trespassing upon the man's desperate attempt to find a happy thought. Gently placing both his hands on Andy's shoulders, I was all but certain he was about to hug him. Instead, he looked him right in the eye and spoke with a compassion that I could never have imagined, far less expect.

"I am…" Josh quickly glanced back at his wife before looking straight back to Andy. "I mean; we are so sorry for what your daughter went through. What we saw was undeniably gruesome and horrific.

Truly.

However, and please forgive my bluntness on such a close and personal subject, but I am somewhat confused. As I am sure you will appreciate, what we saw was obviously before Mrs. Bradley's kidnapping and there was never any complaint filed for that. Even so, there is still nothing that can be done as she is still missing and, without her, Mr. Bradley need only say that what we saw was consensual and the case ends before it begins.

You must surely know that?

Again, please forgive my bluntness, but I can only deal with matters as they present themselves. As such, this case is closed. I know, for I am the man who closed it.

But then, you already know that.

As Mrs. Bradley…" His head fell slightly as he peered from under his eyebrows in what we all could see was a sympathetic act of acknowledgment, "…*your daughter*, is still missing. Given the nature of the man convicted of her kidnap and disappearance – and considering the length of time she has been gone – it is only natural that we presume the worst. For that, Anthony Di Silva shall spend the rest of his life in prison. If that is why you are here, for that assurance, then *trust me*, you have it.

Otherwise, I really have no idea why you are here, nor what you think I can do for you?" The judge once again left Andy to his thoughts and found a seat on the couch, slipping a protective arm around his wife. Our jury panel was now complete with Andy as the new adjudicator – all eyes were upon him.

Suddenly the wailing of a telephone rudely broke the silence.

"Let the machine get it." Our jury forewoman's order was redundant, for her husband hadn't moved. His actions speaking louder than her words. After the second ring, she sat in silence as her voice from a happier time filled their home; the instructions she gave were as precise as they are universal.

> *"Hi Josh, it's Bob Webster. So sorry to bother you at home, but just wanted to follow up on our earlier conversation. I have spoken with a few other people regarding your standing as our nominee and it's looking good. I mean, really good. Are you free on Tuesday evening to meet and discuss further? Say 8pm at the club?*

*Great, see you then. Have a
great day! Oh, and say hi to
that lovely wife of yours!"*

"What a fucking sleaze." It was
becoming a pressing source of concern to
me that I now seemed to impulsively talk
without neither thought nor consideration. I
also noticed that I was scratching my arms
this time as I did so. This guy had literally
made my skin crawl.

"Absolutely! And in *every* sense of the
word." Mrs. McCall turned to me and was
nodding. The contempt she held on her face
was not meant for me.

Andy ignored us both and had turned
his head in the general direction of the
telephone, as if trying to better hear the
message. It could have been considered rude
had his eyes not been scanning the floor, as
if searching for something. After a long
minute, he seemed to have found it. "Your
Honor, would I be right in saying that the Di
Silva case made your career?"

It was a question to which he already
knew the answer.

"Well, yes. I suppose that's fair to say."

"And, well, there is no delicate way to
put this other that to say I'm sorry, but there
is no denying that we all just heard the
telephone message." His hand gestured in

the direction of the phone, but his eyes found me. Suddenly I felt quite claustrophobic; I pulled the collar away from my neck and quickly found something that was nothing to look at in the garden. There, the snow was gently falling and it felt like we were locked in a snow globe. I left myself outside as Andy continued. "So, should the Di Silva conviction be overturned, would it also be fair to say that this could cause you considerable embarrassment and, potentially, destroy your career?" He slowly and deliberately emphasized the word '*destroy*' whilst repeating his hand gesture towards the telephone.

The question took Josh McCall completely unaware.

"Well…. yes, I suppose. However…" As he scrambled for both composure and words, I let my head wander around his garden. It was there that I came to the lazy realization that the word '*however*' is just a snobbier way of saying '*but*'. It was an odd time to have such an epiphany, however, it eased the tension in my head and the seriousness that surrounded me.

It also brought me a fleeting smile.

"…it was all circumstan…" The judge tried to continue, but came to an abrupt halt when he saw that Andy wasn't paying any attention. Instead, he had pulled out his cell phone and, after a few taps on the screen, held it to his ear. He only said one word.

"Okay?"

He immediately returned the phone to his pocket. "Mrs. McCall, we have another guest joining us. Would you be so kind to answer the front door please? For my own peace of mind, and for safety's sake, I really think the judge should be seated when they arrive." He had barely finished speaking when we all heard the soft knocking from beyond the fountain.

"Okay?" Mrs. McCall left us with the question as she made her way to the door.

Once she had left the room, Andy spoke directly to her husband. Not Josh McCall the judge, but Josh McCall the ex-District Attorney. "I must ask you to trust me one more time. It really is for the best that you are seated for this. As I said to you at the door, now we *ALL* have a problem."

Chapter 30

Harrison, Westchester County, New York

Sunday 17th January

In the end, the decision was a relatively easy one for Melissa. She had no clue how long she had actually wrestled with it, but it felt like days. In reality, it was under an hour. She knew it was either the sandwich or the glass of milk that contained the fresh dose of Michael's drug of choice.

Probably both.

It had presented her with a problem that, when considered its logical conclusion, amounted to no real problem at all. Given that he had already drugged her, and that she was now held in restraints in a chamber that no amount of therapy would ever erase from her memory, then one way or another, he was going to have to incapacitate her again.

She reasoned it was better on her own

terms.

There had been the fleeting thought that the dose might be lethal, although it was a notion she quickly dismissed. Even the most casual glance around his chamber would determine that he was a sick individual who was undoubtedly sadistic, but that is a long way short from a killer. Anyway, this might very well be Penny's idea of a sexy and fun time too; Melissa had no way of knowing. One way or the other, and she was beyond the point of caring. She quickly devoured his offerings then sat back and waited for the darkness to take her.

A few minutes later, Michael heard the familiar sound of glass smashing from his favorite room.

He checked his watch. There was still ample time before their flight; she could wait. Turning his attention back to her small suitcase that he had brought into the house from her car, he sifted through her belongings and was surprised to find nothing of interest. *Was she really so noble? Her quest was purely one in the pursuit of love, all to play her part in the real life fairy tale? Oh, how deliciously naïve!* He enjoyed the thought and allowed it to take his imagination to that wonderful place where he was, once again, reconciled with Kristy. It had the happy coincidence of ensuring that this interfering bitch Melissa would get her wish too.

It would just be perfect.

Only, this time, things would be different. The long days and short nights had afforded Michael the opportunity to think and reflect. And pray. There was only one obvious conclusion; he had been far too lenient with his wife. He now realized that this would have to change, for her own sake and safety. How could she be trusted on her own, by herself? He knew she could not. The Holy Bible – *God's own word* – told him so. That wisest of tenets is to be found in Ephesians 5:22 and one, to his eternal shame, he had failed to adequately convey to his own wife. He hung his head in shame and embarrassment as the passage, once more, rang through his head.

> *Wives, submit to your own husbands, as to the Lord. For the husband is the head of the wife even as Christ is the head of the church, his body, and is himself its Savior. Now as the church submits to Christ, so also wives should submit in everything to their husbands.*

He conveniently ignored the rest of the

passage.

God's will be done.

The plan had come quick and easy, as he knew it would. Of course, it was something in which Kristy could never have dreamed. *Stupid bitch.* That would have to change and he knew exactly what to do. The 'conditioning room' needed to be extended to incorporate the basement toilet. That only required the removal of some drywall – no great feat.

It was the mirrors that would be the greatest challenge.

He would order from two separate sources on the pretense he was fitting out a gym room. Only his gym would have a fully mirrored ceiling for a totally different workout – a spiritual workout. All his previous efforts had obviously been in vain, and this was a mistake he would learn from. In time, his wife would thank him for another opportunity to cleanse her soul. Not that he was one to judge. No, that was between her and the Almighty. His onerous responsibility, and his alone, was to ensure that she fulfilled her sacred duties as a wife.

It was a responsibility that he had, and continued to take, very seriously.

Kristy would need to regain and earn his trust and respect. She already had his love. *Unconditionally.* Truly for better or worse, for richer or poorer, in sickness and in health. Until death. She would remain in the room until she proved herself as a worthy wife. The mirrors would allow her to see herself, whenever and wherever she looked. She would see the reflection of evil manifest in her own likeness. The evil that had caused him such pain.

Such sorrow.

Such heartache.

The only escape from seeing that evil in her own image would be to look down. Down into hell. The very word he intended to paint clearly on the floor, to run along each wall, so she could not escape it. She would see it reflected everywhere. In the center of the room, there would be a single flame burning. It would be too weak to provide any warmth, but strong enough to create the illusion, and so let her see what awaits those who turn and ignore the will of God.

Unfortunately, there were just a few loose ends to tie up first.

34 million and one of them to be exact…

Chapter 31

Pelham, Westchester County, New York

Sunday 17th January

    "You...? But... But... It can't be... You...?" All color drained from Josh's face and he looked like he'd seen a ghost. Slowly and unsteadily rising from his seat, he left his jaw firmly on the floor and dragged his heavy feet and an uncomprehending mind in the direction of his wife.

    His eyes never left their latest guest.

    "Kris...? Surely not...? It can't be, can it...? Krist.... Kristy Bradley? But you... you? You are... You're well..., well, you're dead!" The judge still could not grasp what was happening.

    Neither could I.

    "Kristy Bradley *IS* dead, Your Honor." Andy stated this as a fact that left no room for any doubt.

"That's preposterous! How can you say that when she is standing here – *right here* – in my home? *This* is Kristy Bradley. *Right here.* There is absolutely no question in my mind that this is Kristy Bradley. None whatsoever. Who else could this possibly be and why else would you all be here?" Josh had almost regained his composure and was desperately trying to retake control of the situation. He shook his head in a valiant effort to clear his thoughts, and used his right hand to rub his eyes as he continued. "Do you have any idea what this means?"

The last question was more for himself than us. Obviously, he did. His new career would be over before it began. His old career wouldn't fare much better.

"Your Honor, may I introduce Miss Penelope Munro. Who, I must admit, bears a striking resemblance to the missing Kristy Bradley. However, it is that very resemblance that has brought us to your home today and presents us all with a very real, and very serious, problem." As he spoke, he had walked over and stood beside Penny.

A father beside his daughter. *How was it possible that I hadn't seen it before?*

Her big eyes hid under a heavy frown and the weight of the world seemed to hang from her shoulders. Never would I have thought she could look so vulnerable. So frail. So small. Seeing her like that made me feel so helpless; it was an all too familiar feeling to me now. Andy recognized what I could see and placed a protective arm around her, squeezing her tightly into him. A reassuring hug from a loving father. The loving father she had never known.

Yet my shame and envy came all too easily with the immediate wish that his arm was mine.

"You cannot be serious; a blind man could see that this is Kristy Brad..." Yet again, he wasn't to be allowed to finish.

"Josh, my darling, can I talk to you for a second?" A very composed Mrs. McCall stepped daintily around both Penny and Andy and walked to the sliding doors. En route, she caught her husband by the elbow and, in one fluid movement, turned and guided him with her. She ignored the annoyance and frustration on his face and only spoke once they were stood at the closed gateway to their garden. Obviously uncomfortable in the warmth of their own home, their soft voices directly contrasted with the expressive gestures – more from the judge than his wife – with his hands often flying in the direction of Penny and Andy. Although I couldn't hear the whole conversation, I was able to discern a few choice phrases that set my mind racing.

The judge was all business.

"...call the police...duty bound...legally obligated...ruin my reputation...laughing stock..."

Mrs. McCall's comments were altogether more reasoned and temperate.

"...calm down...hear what they have to say...it might not be that bad...she may not be...even if it is, you saw it too, she deserves to be heard..."

They were still in deep discussion as I looked over to Andy and Penny. He now had his back to the room and was talking into her ear. She was still looking straight at the floor and saying nothing by way of response. Then suddenly, another voice filled the room and drew everyone's attention and surprised us all.

Mine.

"Your Honor, I understand your misgivings and the very serious predicament that we have placed you in *but*..." I almost said *'however'* and was actually quite pleased with myself that I hadn't. Yet another example of the stupidest things that go through my mind at the most serious of moments – something for me to berate myself about later no doubt. "...as my colleague here said, this is *not* Kristy Bradley. If we were to admit that it was, then I completely appreciate and understand the legal obligations and consequences that you would be exposed to. I should stress that, although unable to practice, I do hold a couple of law degrees and so know that there is a huge difference between the letter and the spirit of the law."

It could only be hoped that *'a couple'* sounded more impressive, although not exactly confidence inspiring, to a man of the bench. After all, I was hardly his peer. I paused long enough to quickly glance at everyone individually in the hope that I had their attention, if not quite their respect. The implication of what I'd said seemed to somewhat appease the judge, and so too, his wife. Penny's eyes were already waiting to meet mine. I recognized the pride and gratitude and my heart sang. *God, I love you.* I sent the thought in return, in the hope she could read my mind. Was it just my imagination or was there the faintest glimmer of a sad smile hiding in the corner of her mouth? Could she actually be proud of me?

I chose to believe she was.

In fear that I was wrong, I immediately switched my attention to Andy. The weak smile on his face was very real. So was the single nod of approval. My heart sang for a second time, but for a very different reason.

He slowly threw his eyes back in the direction of the McCall's and I understood exactly what he wanted me to do – *keep going.* Now I also knew exactly why he had brought me here.

For this.

"Can everyone please just sit down and we can discuss this rationally? As my friend has repeatedly stated, this situation raises serious issues for all of us, but I think there are possible resolutions that would be satisfactory for everyone." To my complete surprise, everyone found a seat.

I remained standing to directly address both Mr. and Mrs. McCall.

"Okay. Firstly, I am really sorry that we are here, but please understand, we certainly wouldn't be if we had any other options. Obviously, we don't. Please believe me on that. *However,* let me first establish a fact that is irrefutable." It was time to play a hunch and take a calculated risk.

Please God, let this work.

"To the world, Kristy Bradley is dead. That includes the law. This woman that you see here may look like Kristy Bradley and, indeed, actually may – *just may* – have been Kristy Bradley, but that would've been once upon a time. Now, she is Miss Penelope Munro and she has all the legal documentation to verify this fact."

"That all sounds rather fanciful and, indeed, plausible. However, the fact remains, that Kristy Bradley is still missing and I'd bet dollars to donuts that this young lady's DNA is a match. So, no matter how you present this, the facts are the fac…"

Once again, the judge's wife interrupted him.

"Josh, please let him finish. From what we both saw…" The realization of what she was saying became instantly apparent to her as she spoke, and the words trailed off. Christine McCall left her husband's side and moved directly towards Penny. Crouching down in front of her, she clasped both of her hands into her own. Their eyes locked and they had a silent moment. One of those moments that only applies to women, where they can have a complete conversation without anything being spoken. That moment of sisterhood. That moment where they forge an eternal understanding.

A sincerity.

A truth.

That moment that men can witnesss, but could never emulate, and will never understand.

"I am truly sorry for what we saw and for what you went through. It was absolutely horrific. Something I can never too soon forget and yet can only wish that it had never happened to you." I believed every single word. The two women exchanged a nod and a weak smile of recognition and understanding. Tears of sorrow, relief, pain, heartache, suffering, blended as one and slowly trickled down Penny's cheeks. The very same tears were also to be found on those cheeks belonging to Christine McCall. "What I can promise you is that whatever we can do to help avoid this ever happening to you again, we will."

Once again, I believed every single one of her words.

So too, did Mr. McCall. He was biting his bottom lip and fighting his own emotions as he watched his wife embrace the stranger in their home. All the while, he was slowly nodding in agreement with the promise that his wife had given on their behalf. He cleared his throat and mustered up the confidence and composure that was so desperately needed, to say the words that we so desperately hoped for.

"So, Kristy Bradley is dead. What is it that we can do for you?"

The pride shone through his wife's tears as he said 'we'.

From somewhere deep inside the cavernous house, a bell tolled. Three long chimes, each seemingly louder than the last, signaling that our long five minutes were up.

Yet nobody moved. Nothing was said. All eyes were waiting.

And all our thoughts were with Penny.

Chapter 32

Pelham, Westchester County, New York

Sunday 17th January

"I knew Kristy Bradley."

We could all see that it was Penny speaking, but there was no doubt it was Kristy Bradley talking. The soft voice, barely audible, belonged to a very frightened woman; one devoid of confidence or self-worth. Yet still, it held something. Something I recognized. That grit, that resolve, I knew it and could see it there within her, only now it too had a name.

Penny.

"She was loving, warm, and kind. A really nice person. Full of fun and full of life. At least, she was until she married Michael Bradley." She said his name without any malice or spite, but rather as if recalling a dim and distant memory of an old acquaintance; someone she once knew. "The man she dated was not the man she married. Michael Bradley – the husband – was, and is, a bad man. A wicked man. An evil man. There was no doubt in my mind, he would eventually kill m…"

She suddenly stopped.

She had almost been quick enough to catch herself. *Almost.* Genuine fear spread over her face and we could all see her body tense. Her hands, knotted together, were clasped so tightly they were white. She looked desperately at everyone in the room, to see if we had realized. If anybody did, nobody gave any such indication. There was only love and kindness in this place. Her relief was palpable as her eyes fell back to the floor. That was where her shame was to be found. She took a deep breath and held it for a second, as if trying to contain the thought, but then bravely let the words drift out as she exhaled.

"…that he would eventually kill her." She tried to take another deep breath, but it caught in her throat. The silent sobs overwhelmed her as she desperately tried to compose herself, without success. She closed her eyes and hid her head in shame. In seeing his wife's attempts to calm Penny down, Josh McCall disappeared into the house and returned with a glass of water.

"Here, drink this. It's okay, just take your time."

It struck me as oddly ironic that the glass was only half full. I could only imagine that Penny saw it the same way, but it was easy to see, and completely understand, that it would always be half empty to Kristy Bradley. Although, as Penny accepted the glass and tried to take a sip, it was immediately apparent why it wasn't filled any further. Her hands were shaking so violently that she was in danger of spilling out what little she had.

A thoughtful and wise gesture on the part of the judge, who respectfully sat back down and patiently waited for Penny to continue.

"In the end, Kristy really had no choice. Whilst he had been caught up in his case against Anthony Di Silva, a case that had consumed him, the beatin…" The word got stuck in her mouth and she took a second to muster all her powers of concentration and determination in an effort to force it out. As she did so, her eyes darted to every corner of the floor. I followed her gaze, trying to aid in the search for what she was looking for. It took me a second to understand. It wasn't anything that she was looking for, but rather running from; trying to escape the memories that the bastard had left her with.

"The beatings…" The word was said with purpose and defiance. *That's my girl.* "…were less frequent then. Once the trial was over, she knew that they would start again. There was no doubt about that. Kristy saw the receipts for his new equipment. Equipment that was to replace some that I believe you have already seen…" She took a second to find the right word.

"…utilized?"

Josh and his wife both looked away in sorrow and shame. The sorrow was understandable, but the shame did not belong to them.

"So, Kristy was persuaded that she had an opportunity. She could get out, once and for all. She could also ensure that another bad man, another evil man, would be punished. It would also mean she could start afresh, start anew, far away from there. Far away from here. The money would help as it would be one less thing to worry about. There had been enough worry. Worry if she would survive another week, another day, another hour. Nobody – *nobody* – will, or could, ever understand what life was like for her.

The waiting was the worst.

Waiting at home, although it was hardly that. A home is a place of refuge. A place where you are safe. A place where people in love reside. For Kristy, her waiting was done in a *house*. Waiting for a man who had promised to love her forever. Waiting to see what man returned. Waiting to see what mood he brought with him. Waiting in fear. Waiting for him to decide what would happen that night. Rape? Torture? Sodomy? Bondage? All of it? None of it? Going to bed, wondering if this would be yet another night that she would wake briefly to find the rag loaded with Rohypnol held over her face. Most often, hoping so, for it took both consciousness and memory. No recollection was far more desirable than…"

She could take no more. She slipped from the chair onto the floor as her face fell into her knees and she wrapped her hands tightly around herself. The heaving sobs were long and torturous for us all. Her new sister placed both her arms around Penny and gave her a light kiss on the side of the head. Words of comfort were whispered into the ear just below where the kiss was left. None of us, certainly not me, could hear what was said. Thankfully. We were already too close to the pain. Andy moved and took a place beside Josh.

The look that they exchanged spoke volumes.

We all knew that Penny had not yet said what the judge could do for her, how he could help. Yet we were all completely engrossed in her story. Unbelievably, I found myself wanting to know more.

I wanted to know everything.

What kind of man did that make me? Was I as bad, as nasty, as evil, as this man Michael Bradley? Curiosity was, for the most part, a natural and positive trait, yet now, right at this moment, I knew how negative and ugly it could actually be. Was it at all possible that I was actually feeling the guilt that belonged to another man? I chose not to believe so, for I had only ever loved her. I felt guilty because I couldn't protect her. Not then, but I could now. Knowing what she had gone through might, just might, help me understand her better. That could only help us.

If 'us' would ever again be what she wanted.

"I'm sorry that you need to know. But it's only in knowing will you understand, and it is only once you understand that I can ask for your help."

As Penny continued to talk about Kristy in the third person, it was apparent that there was no real need as the judge had long since waived all of his legal concerns and accepted that the dead Kristy Bradley was sitting here in front of him. Yet, when I realized why she had chosen to do so, a new bout of shame and no small amount of stupidity came over me – it was simply easier this way. Easier to separate the past, who she *was*, with the present, who she now *is*.

The loving, tender, caring, vibrant, funny, happy, strong, focused, and independent woman that I loved.

"One time, she was… well, *'restrained'* is perhaps the best word for it. He brought in a laptop and, placing it just out of her reach, pressed play. On it were images of herself, naked and unconscious. There was blood. Lots of blood. He started to laugh when he saw her reaction, rewinding and tormenting, reveling in her agony." Her voice was as calm and clinical as her story was chilling. Her eyes had found mine although I could barely see her through my tears. I dared not wipe them for fear of breaking the contact. I couldn't let her see me be weak. Not now, when she needed me to be strong. She needed to know that I was here for her. *Always.* "He told her that he had hundreds of hours of such tapes. They were all of just her. He didn't appear in any of them and, from what she saw, there was no reason to doubt that he spoke the truth. If she left, he promised to release them onto the internet. Her career, her life, would be over. Kristy believed him."

We all did.

"As the protracted negotiations with Di Silva were drawing to a close, he kept dreaming of his new life. Whatever the amount would be, it guaranteed him financial security. He would be able to afford to retire and it was something he discussed, mainly with himself, openly and often. He also threatened to enforce retirement upon Kristy. Then life would fall back to 'normal'; only the sanctuary of work would no longer be available to her. She dreaded, but almost accepted it.

Then her mom died.

It was four days before the end of the settlement negotiations and Kristy didn't even know she was sick. He always hated her having any contact with any of her family or old friends, anyone at all who could influence her. There were constant and meticulous checks of the phone records, emails, text messages, anything that could be used for communication. He even demanded access to her work emails. Numbers or email addresses that weren't recognized, he would always follow-up on. It was easier for her to just agree than to take the punishments for perceived disobedience, real or otherwise. As such, she had no idea that her mother was terminally and, worse, that she had died alone.

Sadly, the daughter's guilt did not die with Kristy.

The case was used as an excuse but, in truth, she knew he was relieved not to have any part in dealing with the arrangements and the estate. Naturally, Kristy immediately left for Virginia Beach and took care of it all by herself. There, her mom's lawyer handed her an envelope and told her that he was under the strictest of instructions that it was for her eyes only." Penny wiped the fresh tears of mourning that she now shed for the woman who gave birth to Kristy.

Two very different daughters sharing a single grief.

"The letter contained a suggestion. A suggestion that became a plan. A plan that became an escape. She was a woman who gave birth once, but provided new life twice – a mother right to the end.

The only family both Kristy and I have ever known."

All eyes but Penny's fell to her father. Here was a man hiding in plain sight, who obviously had his reasons for doing so. How I desperately wished I knew what they were, but these were simply yet more questions that would have to wait. Although it did prove something; curiosity will undoubtedly be the death of me. Whatever his reasons, yesterday's handyman was today's handy dad, and for that I was eternally grateful. It bore no thinking about what might have become of Penny and myself had he not intervened with our sinister visitors to the estate.

Try as he might to fight it, Andy's face betrayed the raw torment and pain that Penny's words of ignorance so easily inflicted. He turned his back on her to hide the struggle that he was having with his own emotions. Cruelly, I couldn't help but wonder if this was just the second time that he had turned his back on his daughter? Indeed, how many times had he done so with her mum? Yet I knew nothing of the circumstances nor reasoning that led us all to this juncture.

How easy it is to judge.

"However, I have been far luckier. I now know the real meaning of true love and the love of a family." Both Andy and I turned as one to see Penny looking straight at me.

Chapter 33

Harrison, Westchester County, New York

Sunday 17th January

Michael checked his watch. He knew it was less than five minutes since he had last looked, but he didn't care; time had never been his greatest ally. Indeed, it had been a constant companion throughout the longest and loneliest years of his life and had proven itself extremely loyal, if not always welcome. All it brought was misery and contemplation; opportunities to think and reflect. He had been moderately successful in his attempts at silencing it – *killing it* – with alcohol. Now, it was taunting and teasing him once again, obviously conspiring with Melissa against him.

Foolishly, he hadn't anticipated that she would finish his entire snack.

The Rohypnol had been in both the

sandwich and the milk. He reckoned that a desperate thirst might have forced her to drink some of the milk, but probably not all. The sandwich had been the back up. Finding both glass and plate empty, with her unconscious and unresponsive body slumped out on the floor, had been a surprise. An unwanted surprise that brought with it a troubling dilemma. He could not administer the fresh dose needed for the full duration of the flight. To do so, would be to kill her.

I'm no killer. The very thought filled him with disgust.

He looked back at his watch. Another two minutes had passed. He watched the second hand creep up and over the twelve. Three minutes. He knew that she would need another four hours before it was safe to give her more, but their flight left in just over an hour. To give her it on the plane was risky, yet there was no other choice. It was a realization that tormented him. He hated risk. Always had.

To risk is to relinquish control.

He had already pulled her car rental into his empty drive. The Porsche was going to be his first purchase with his new wealth, but that dream had vanished faster than his wife. She obviously hadn't realized that he would have allowed her in the passenger seat when she was needed; functions, dinners, charity events. Those occasions where his genius was to be celebrated and he was to be courted by the local elite. *The completely selfish and utter bitch.* He would have it yet, the Porsche and the status.

It was only a flight away.

Melissa had been a dead weight and completely unresponsive when he set her into the back seat and pulled the seat belt around her. Now was not the time to be drawing unnecessary and unwanted attention from the police; now was not the time for such stupidity. How he loved Rohypnol, one of life's constants, one of the only things that could be relied upon to constantly and consistently deliver. Like himself, it was completely dependable. He felt the small bottles in his pocket, safely wrapped in the cloth that would be used on Melissa later, and only to be used when there were no prying eyes in the cabin. Ever vigilant, he'd packed an extra bottle, just in case. He took pride in his forethought. There were any number of eventualities that could scupper his plan, not least of which was turbulence.

The timing would be essential.

It was a short journey to the airport and Michael took his time, almost enjoying the Sunday drive. It had been a while since he had cause to drive and so knew that he was a little rusty. It was yet another of his qualities, the ability to recognize his own failings and adapt accordingly. He pulled up to the private entrance as helpfully provided by the confirmation email. Second to their home, this was the most expensive purchase he had ever made; as is always the case, the short notice ensured it was also far more expensive than it would normally have been.

The destination didn't help.

The deposit had been paid when he'd initially called to book the flight and it instantly wiped out his meager savings. That left him less than 24 hours to find the balance, a hefty $28,000, and it stretched his two credit cards to the limit. Actually, it would have taken his American Express card over its limit, but a precautionary telephone call to the company had been met with an obliging supervisor. *"Please, it's literally a matter of life and death. It's my wife, you do know the situation with my wife?"* He knew they did, and the female supervisor felt his pain.

> *"I know that it's an unusual request but, please understand, I wouldn't ask if there was any other option. I have a lead, but it's time sensitive. I need to get there –*

314

*to get to her – now. Right
now. Please!"*

The limit was immediately raised, with
an extra $5,000 to cover 'unforeseen
expenditures'. He'd made the payment in
full over the internet as the supervisor
remained on the line, to make sure there
were no issues. Thankfully, it had cleared
immediately.

"Good luck, Mr. Bradley, I hope it all
works ou…" He had hung up before she had
finished talking. Just another stupid bitch
whose very existence was trying his patience
– why God? Why me? – and she had, after
all, served her purpose.

He drew into a free spot and strode
confidently into the office at the hangar.
There, behind the counter, was another
woman who was already annoying him; all
hair and teeth, with a cheery tone that was as
fake as almost every other part of her.
Certainly the breasts, that were straining
against a white blouse that was obviously
intended to snare an unsuspecting, but rich,
fool. "Hello there, Mr. Bradley is it?" They
both knew who he was, just another part of
the charade. His experience dictated that it
was always smoother and easier to play
along.

"Hi. Yes, I'm Mr. Bradley. Please, call

me Michael." The charm offensive cranked up to 'full'. He returned her fake smile as he handed over both their passports. "My travelling companion is in the car. I'm sorry, but she absolutely hates to fly and so has taken a little something to ease her nerves. Unfortunately, it has taken effect rather quicker than expected. I hope that won't be a problem?"

"That's fine. It happens all the time… *Michael.*" She flashed a new wall of teeth. "Do you need a wheelchair or can you manage alone?"

"I should be fine. She, like your lovely self, is a slender slip of a girl." The compliment found wanton eyes and an elaborate laugh, as he expected it would. The passports were returned with her left hand with the vacant ring finger elevated ever so slightly.

"Ah now Michael, what a wonderful thing to say. Two compliments in one, too. Not one two, but one too. Oh, I'm sure you know what I meant." She saw that Michael had understood and threw yet another smile at him, this one containing nothing but her embarrassment. "Well, you have a safe and pleasant flight and, if there is anything else we can do. Indeed, anything else *I* can do for you. Anything at all, just give me a call." She took a business card from her purse and handed it to him. "My cell number is on the back. I can be reached anytime, day... *and night.*" He turned over the card and saw the number already handwritten in blue ink. There on the counter, in a clear plastic holder, was a stack of the exact same business card.

Michael wondered how many she had in her purse, already prewritten with her personal number.

"Thank you..." He looked at her card. "*...Allegra.* What a fittingly beautiful name for such a lovely girl like yourself." He never counted lies like these as sins as they did no harm, only good.

"I'm not always lovely..." Her tongue shamelessly traced its way around her top row of teeth.

"Oh, really? Well, in that case, I shall be certain to keep this *very* safe and be sure to give you a call upon my return." He placed her business card into his wallet, to be discarded at the earliest possible opportunity.

The boarding was completed without any further delays and the plane took off on time. He settled back into the sumptuous cream leather chair that he'd deliberately chosen as it faced the cockpit. Melissa, still asleep, was in the opposite seat facing him. He reckoned there were still a few hours or so before she roused. He kicked back the recliner and allowed his eyes to close.

"Sir…? Mr. Bradley…?" Michael awoke to the soft nudge of their private stewardess. "So sorry to bother you, Sir, but the pilot thought you should know that, due to some adverse weather, he has had to alter the speed and route slightly. This will only add another 20 minutes or so onto our flight time. Of course, this will be of no extra cost to yourself."

I should fucking hope not. He knew better than to verbalize the thought. He quickly checked his watch to see that he had been asleep for almost three hours. Panic instantly gripped him as he shot a look at Melissa. It was a relief to see she was still sleeping, but he knew she wouldn't be for much longer. Now he had to get rid of this annoyance in the uniform so that he could deliver the fresh dose. "Thank you, yes, that will be fine."

Like there was any other choice?

"Thank you Sir, I shall let the captain know. We appreciate your patience and understanding. Is there anything I can get for you?"

"No, thank you. We would like to try and get some more sleep. So, if you don't mind, can you leave us please?" He was already feeling in his pocket for the cloth and one of the vials.

"Certainly, Sir. Thank you again, and please just let me know if you change your mind." She was delighted to be so readily dismissed. This was one of the easier flights, these two weren't demanding at all. Yet he gave her the creeps. There was just something about him, he was just too...too.... *smarmy.* The cockpit provided the welcome refuge that she craved; this flight couldn't be over soon enough.

Michael waited for a few minutes more after the curtain closed to ensure they had total privacy. Still, he knew better than to be too blasé, and so slipped out the cloth and vial from his left pocket and took it into his right hand. He unscrewed the vial inside the cloth and, turning it in his hand, emptied the full contents into the rag. He always loved this part. A final glance around the cabin confirmed they were alone. His free hand unbuckled his seatbelt and, in one fluid movement, he stepped forward and knelt in front of the unconscious Melissa. He could see there was no need to restrain her head, so he simply covered her nose and mouth with the cloth. The vibrations of the plane made it impossible to count how many breaths she had taken – usually four was his magic number. In the interests of safety, he chose to simply count to ten. Satisfied, he stepped back into his seat where, at long last, he could relax again. Once more he kicked the recliner back and closed his eyes in a new search for sleep. For a second, he caught himself being envious of how easily it had come to Melissa.

If he only knew...

In reality, Melissa had actually roused a few minutes before the stewardess had appeared and heard every word of their conversation. She thought better than to alert Michael of the fact, instead preferring to assess her situation whilst pretending to still be asleep. A situation that involved his attempt at drugging her for a third time. An unsuccessful attempt as it turned out, for she had managed to hold her breath for the full duration of his endeavors. She would maintain the pretense until after they had landed in Scotland. Only there, at home, would she feel truly safe and finally be able to actually help Penny. Although that required a new plan and, hopefully, the rest of the flight would give her just enough time to figure one out.

"Excuse me, sir?" The stewardess once again found cause to disturb Michael. It had been almost two hours since she had last troubled him and, this time, it took him a little longer to rouse. She'd never know that it was because he'd, at last, been able to relax, secure in the knowledge that Melissa was contained.

"Yes?" He tried to clear his head through rubbing his eyes.

"We are on our final approach to George Town. Could you please prepare yourselves for landing? Thank you." She didn't wait for an answer.

George Town? Surely she meant, 'Fort George'? Melissa had heard the instructions, but quickly concluded that the stewardess had made a simple mistake. An easy mistake at that, for Fort George is the old fortress that sits less than five miles from Inverness Airport. She felt the plane touch down onto the runway and taxi to a halt.

Home at last. In a matter of minutes, this nightmare will all be over.

She heard the door being opened and felt the heat rush into the cabin. The now familiar voice of the flight attendant used only five words to destroy her new plan.

"Welcome to the Cayman Islands."

Chapter 34

Pelham, Westchester County, New York

Sunday 17th January

"Well I guess that brings us neatly back to the reason why we are here."

Neatly? Hardly. The silence in the room had drifted from respectful through awkward to completely uncomfortable. Andy was the one hurting the most – everyone but Penny knew that – and so it just seemed appropriate to wait for him to take the conversation forward. He was, after all, the reason why we were here.

Thankfully, he used his professional pride to mask his personal pain.

"Your Honor, do the names Marco Lombardi and Dominic Rossi mean anything to you?" He knew perfectly well that the ex-District Attorney knew exactly who these men were. Thanks to Josh, everyone in the New York legal system knew who they were.

"Yes, I know them. Why do you ask?" It was Josh's turn to revert back from the personal to professional.

"Would I be correct in my assertion that these men are associates of Anthony Di Silva?" Andy was pursuing his own agenda and so ignored the question.

"Your assertion would be correct, but I'm afraid that they are a little more than mere associates. Well, that is certainly the case with Marco Lombardi. He is Di Silva's nephew and the man that, if the rumors are to be believed, controls the money and looks after Anthony's interests on the outside. Again, why do you ask?" The tone left no doubt that this was a question that demanded an answer.

"These very men were in Scotland last night, paying Penny here a very unwelcome visit." Andy paused long enough for this information to fully register with Josh. His surprise was expected. "We managed to intercept and chase them off, but I believe they will be back. Well, what I should say, is other associates of theirs will be back. They are of the mistaken belief that Penny here is Kristy Bradley. As we have all seen, she most definitely is not that person, but there is still the possibility that a DNA test would provide enough evidence to convince a judge…" He paused to look directly at Josh, using his raised left eyebrow to fully convey his fears. "…that Kristy Bradley is alive and well. As such, that judge would have no option but to release the man falsely imprisoned for her kidnapping.

We all know what that would mean for your career, Your Honor."

Andy walked to the window and waited for the full implications of what he was saying to hit Josh. He had played his best hand and hoped that it was enough. Yet it wasn't his own career that concerned the judge.

"Oh my God, it'd be a bloodbath…" His eyes were wide and fixed firmly upon his wife.

"Josh? What do you mean? What do you mean, *'a bloodbath'*?" Christine McCall was suddenly afraid. Very afraid. She had never seen her husband like this.

"Anthony Di Silva was the Boss of Bosses, but *nobody* knew, only him. At the trial, I was able to show who and what he was and so he became a target. *Damn it!* In all honesty, I never thought he would've survived this long in jail. There are contracts on his head – *big contracts.* He should be dead already. Him free? It really doesn't bear thinking about. The repercussions…"

His eyes shot to the heavens. "If he was ever freed, and for as long as he is alive, nobody and nowhere in this city would be safe.

Shit.

Shit, shit, shit, shit, SHIT!"

Christine had never really heard Josh curse before; it only served to heighten her fear and alarm.

"So it would be in all our interests to ensure that Anthony Di Silva remains where he is. Yet, it's a fairly reasonable assumption that he now knows about Penny here." Andy was more thinking out loud than engaging in the conversation.

"I think that it's more of a certainty than a 'reasonable assumption'. Lombardi and Rossi would never have got on a plane without his say so. In fact, he'd have paid for the jet." Josh was beginning to see the whole picture. His mind was racing, desperately searching for an acceptable solution.

"You know they won't stop, don't you?" The question was said to the room, but it was meant for Penny. "One way or another, you are the golden ticket for Di Silva's release. If they can prove that Kristy Bradley exists, in whatever guise and whatever persona, then he walks."

"Are there any other options?" Christine McCall draped a protective arm around

Penny and pulled her close.

"Other than ensuring that they never find Penny? None that I can see. Are you prepared to run for the rest of your life? Not that it would matter. Ironically, they would be able to utilize the law for their own benefit. They need only relay their suspicions to the police and they would be duty bound to follow up. Their counterparts in Scotland would oblige their request to investigate and, as part of that investigation, they would ask for a DNA sample. It's standard procedure." The defeat wore heavy on Josh.

"Your Honor?" A thought had struck me but I'd, once again, been unable to contain and process it in my head before blurting it out. It really was becoming a serious concern.

"Yes?" He sounded like one of my exasperated old professors, tolerating yet another one of my stupid and mundane questions.

"We all know that there is a huge difference between what you know and what you can prove. So, is there anything that you know that could help us? Anything we could use that would ensure this guy stays off the streets?" A shot in the dark and something that I wasn't entirely sure of what I meant, but worth asking anyway.

"Hmmmmm, now that is an interesting thought." The judge's hand found his chin. A few moments passed when a strange look fell upon him. His eyes narrowed and it seemed that he was contemplating the full implications of what he knew before telling us; something I myself should learn. It was certainly a most curious look. A final nod of his head indicated that he had reached a consensus with himself. "Di Silva is Lombardi's uncle through marriage. His wife and Lombardi's mother are sisters. There have long been spurious rumors that Di Silva is actually his father, but we ran a DNA comparison and so know for a fact that he isn't."

Whilst this was interesting, it was hardly the kind of information that could help us; it seemed that the judge had drawn the same conclusion.

"However, what we also know for certain, but never had quite enough evidence to prove, is that Di Silva had Lombardi's father killed. His father was undoubtedly a clever man, but not an evil man. All his actions were considered and measured, a Capo who was actually rumored to be the 'Boss of Bosses'. Yet, as we now know, that was Di Silva himself. This information only came to light after the trial. With Di Silva gone, the whole Mafia organization fell into disarray. Everyone started scrambling for a bigger piece of the action, and the pushing and jostling of every family head to fill the top spot. In that struggle, we were inundated with information – solid, actionable information – that helped us put a lot of others away. However, the information regarding the murder Lombardi's father was from a witness whose credibility would have been destroyed under cross examination, so I decided against pursuing it. The risk wasn't worth it to me, but this information may be useful to you?"

The look shared between the judge and Andy told us all that it was, although I had no idea why.

"Could I talk with you…" Andy started to ask the question before realizing that he was talking out loud. He quickly scanned each face in the room and, when his eyes fell upon Penny, he swiftly turned back to the judge. "…in private?"

"Sure, come this way." He rose and disappeared down the same corridor that his wife had emerged from earlier. I caught myself thinking that it was more than five minutes ago. As Andy followed, he casually picked up the iPad that held the full horrors that the McCall's had so recently and reluctantly witnessed. It had been placed, face down, on the side table beside the judge's seat. It was an obvious attempt to minimize the risk of himself, or anyone else, seeing more.

A thoughtful and selfless act, especially now that Penny was here in the room.

Just as I was considering how to fill the void with small talk – *the silence was killing me* – a familiar noise came drifting in, one known the world over, and one that left the three of us looking at each other in puzzlement. The ascending tone of the Skype application being opened. We could hear each keystroke as the number was entered and, once complete, it started ringing almost immediately.

"Hello?" The voice filled the house, and while I knew that he was saying 'hello', the thick New York accent made it sound more like 'yellow'. Ordinarily, this would have been funny to me but, right now, humor was in short supply and would have been completely unappreciated. *"Hello? Who da fuck is dis? Fuckin' answer me you cocksuc…"* Thankfully, yet another familiar sound cut the voice off mid-sentence. The frustrating Skype 'woop woop' tone that, in my experience, normally indicates that your call has been dropped.

We really do need better coverage on the estate.

Andy and the judge's voices could be

heard, faintly at first, and then louder until they both appeared from the same corridor down which they had so recently disappeared. Under the iPad was a thick wad of papers contained within a brown folder, although they were both focused on the screen.

"It's not too far from here. Ten, maybe fifteen minutes. Too close for comfort, that's for sure. Anyway, as I say, he is recently married. That should help. Good luck and, please, let me know how it shakes out." Josh turned to Penny. "Good luck to you too. I am truly sorry for what happened to Kristy but, hopefully, you can go back to living your life. You have two men here that truly care for you. That is a great start. Take care."

His wife gave Penny the hug that the judge deserved.

"It's only in times of adversity does one find who they can really trust, and I know you to be correct. I am so thankful to both of them, and also to the both of you. Thank you." Whilst her sincerity was absolute, this was the first time I had ever seen Penny humble. It was cute and endearing, certainly, but it was also unbelievably sexy. Even in these most ridiculous and perilous circumstances, perhaps because of them, whatever the reason, I really just wanted to rip her clothes off and take her. Right there, in their fountain.

"Z? Z? Are you coming?" It was Penny talking, and it was the right question, but the wrong situation. Reluctantly, I walked passed the smirking cherubs and headed for the door.

Smug bastards.

Chapter 35

George Town, Cayman Islands

Sunday 17th January

"With our compliments, Sir." The stewardess opened the door that doubled as steps and indicated towards the stretch limousine that had pulled up alongside the plane. *I should think so too, I've more than paid for it.* Gratitude was a redundant quality as far as Michael Bradley was concerned. As it says in the Bible, "a hard day's work deserves a fair day's pay". That was, after all, the reason why he became a lawyer. He had never worked harder than the day he earned his $34 million, only to have it all stolen from him.

That was the day he lost the love of his life and, coincidentally, his wife.

Vanity prevented him from recognizing that his share was actually 30% as, to do so, would merely dilute his sense of triumph and his overwhelming sense of loss. It would also dilute the well-deserved respect that he demanded and enjoyed from his peers and from those people in the community. Arrogance blinded him from recognizing that they pitied rather than respected him, as he had been left with nothing and no-one.

Well, now he'd arrived in paradise – and in befitting style – to reclaim it all.

With interest.

"Thank you." His fake smile was returned in kind. She already knew that Michael was thinking ahead and had retained their services for a late morning flight back off the island and destined for Scotland. It wasn't a flight she was looking forward to. His confirmation email had come through mid-flight and, not for the first time, she'd cursed the inbuilt Wi-Fi. The balance was due before he boarded; otherwise, they wouldn't be going anywhere. The deposit had been paid from the last of Michael's available funds, although it was of no real concern to him. Tomorrow, *oh the glorious day that is tomorrow*, he would have enough cash to buy the plane, far less hire it; then a delightful flight to Scotland where he would dispose of Melissa and reclaim Kristy. He took a second to enjoy the thought of taking her home to where he could begin to make her pay.

Oh and how she would pay.

The chauffeur – 'Henry' was the name embroidered onto his short-sleeved shirt – was already standing to attention and holding open the back door of the limousine, when the stewardess subtly indicated that his help was required with one of the passengers. It was not unexpected. Indeed, it was an almost daily occurrence and an implied part of the service. In his experience, such passengers were passed out from being either drunk or high. Usually both. Providing such assistance, along with absolute discretion, was often generously reflected in his tip.

Today would be one of the few exceptions.

The plane's small door was only wide enough for one person and so Michael positioned himself behind Melissa, holding her under the arms and trying to walk her out. Henry stepped forward and clumsily took her feet. Between them, they managed to manhandle her into the back seat of the waiting car.

Although, to Henry, it was more than just a car. It was a status and a livelihood. It had been bought new a mere eight years ago and, since then, if it wasn't being driven, it was being polished. It had been a huge investment but one that had paid off, and handsomely so. One of only seven on the small island, it had yet to have its third major service and it had never exceeded 60kph. There had never been any need as when he breached the city limits, it was generally to tour the island. On those occasions, his clients had wanted to enjoy the experience; less speed with even less haste.

As they say on the island, '*when they made time, they made plenty of it.*'

Henry could already tell that it would be a fruitless exercise to suggest such a tour to Michael. His one question was to ask the name of their hotel and, in less than ten minutes, he safely drew into the main entrance. *Another satisfied customer.* Sarcasm was a prerequisite among his profession. On his way to open the back door, Henry discreetly tilted his thumb into his mouth to indicate drinking, gesturing to the concierge that he had yet another intoxicated and incapacitated passenger.

The concierge gave a simple nod of understanding.

Michael begrudgingly helped to push Melissa's shoulders around so that she was facing Henry, who leaned into the car and pulled her out. In one swift movement, perfected from far too much practice, he turned to the bellboy whom he knew was waiting in place with the required wheelchair. However, Henry underestimated the drop and Melissa inelegantly flopped straight into the ready seat. Michael couldn't have cared less as he exited the car through the same door and quickly grabbed both their small cases. Striding towards the hotel, he left the bellboy in no doubt that he was to push Melissa. As he passed Henry, he said an insincere "thank you" and extended his hand and slipped him a folded bill. Etiquette dictated that Henry wait until he was alone before he checked what princely sum with which he had been blessed. He watched as Michael walked and Melissa rolled into the foyer before returning to the driver's seat and opening his hand. Either his eyes were deceiving him or else he must have inadvertently dropped the rest. Graciously, he gave Michael the benefit of the doubt and quickly jumped out of the car and ran around to check, searching the ground as he did so. Nothing. He looked back into his hand and wondered what he would do with the five dollars.

It was the most consideration he had ever given any tip.

Chapter 36

George Town, Cayman Islands

Sunday 17th January

It was the first time in her life that Melissa had ever stolen anything. Well, other than all of Penny's personal details and banking information. Still, breaching that confidentiality – *twice* – had been, quite literally, done as a matter of life or death.

Her own.

She promptly ignored the fact that she had flown across the Atlantic to place herself in such perilous situations; now was not a time for such contemplation. Now was a time to act in an effort to clean up the mess that she had created. It was in the course of this very action that resulted in the first physical theft of her life – to Melissa, it was an important distinction – and, secretly, she was actually quite pleased that she'd managed to do so without being caught. As she was being wheeled into yet another new room, this one infinitely more agreeable than her last, she surreptitiously slipped the spoils inside her pocket.

There, she gently caressed the unmistakable form of Henry's cell phone.

"Where would you like your wife, Mr. Bradley?" Michael successfully fought the urge to tell the bellboy – the name on his badge said 'Isaac', but nobody ever noticed far less cared – in no uncertain terms that this was most definitely not his wife. Instead, he quickly checked through the sumptuous rooms and, once again, cursed their greed and his own bad luck. Predictably, the honeymoon suite was all they had at such short notice and he knew better than to challenge it. To do so would only have driven up the price and his attitude could very well have driven down the availability. As a man of the world, although one who rarely ventured out of New York State, he knew how the game was played. Now that he was here, he could see that it was everything he could have expected, although no less than he deserved.

Ah yes, this is the life that I was destined for.

"Just there will be fine." He threw his hand in the general direction of the two luxurious sofas facing each other over a fittingly ostentatious table that was set in front of a fireplace that had never been used. In its hearth, in a vase that was as vulgar as it was ugly, there was an extravagant bouquet of fresh flowers with an overpowering perfume. Isaac wheeled Melissa towards the sofa closest to him. As he did so, he realized that this faced the balcony doors and so she would wake to a perfectly framed view of paradise.

It was a happy coincidence for which he gave himself full credit.

He took a moment to discreetly observe Michael making his way through a set of double doors and disappear into the bedroom. It was an obvious, if somewhat thoughtless, gesture that indicated there would be no help forthcoming. Not yet sixteen, although his birthday wasn't far away, he was small for his age and all he'd desperately wanted for Christmas was a growth spurt.

Santa hadn't obliged.

As tough it was to accept, and as much as he hated to admit it, he simply lacked the physical strength to lift the dead weight of Melissa. He also knew that to ask for help would result in him being fired for incompetence. Isaac had been lucky to get this job and there were plenty of replacements to be had; other, stronger, boys that were ready, willing and...*able.*

That left only one option.

As he drew the wheelchair back a few feet, he reasoned that the plush carpet would muffle the noise from the tires and so ensure maximum discretion. A final look towards the bedroom confirmed he was still alone. He turned and ran as hard and as fast as he could towards the sofa, taking it on the angle, and stopped just short whilst lifting the handles. Melissa stifled a scream as she was shot forward and landed face first among the plump cushions down at the opposite end of the sofa; barely managing to keep herself from rolling onto the floor. Isaac immediately abandoned the wheelchair to race around the back of the sofa and, reaching over, he roughly grabbed Melissa by the shoulders to set her upright in the middle seat. Snaking his hands under her arms and locking them behind her neck, he took a deep breath and held it as he summoned all his strength and concentration to drag her one seat over and back to his end of the sofa. As he lifted, Melissa surreptitiously pushed. Between them, they managed to settle her into the corner, and he wedged her into place using one of the cushions. Satisfied that she was comfortable, Isaac swiftly removed himself and the incriminating wheelchair back to the main door of the suite. He took a second to wipe the sweat from his brow before standing attentively and calling back through to the bedroom. "Is there anything else I can do for you, Mr. Bradley?"

"No, that will be all, thank you." Michael's voice called out from the bedroom. He checked his watch and let Isaac wait an awkward twenty seconds before emerging with a malevolent smirk, one that had been redundant for far too long. *Oh how I've missed this.* He stood in the bedroom doorway and never paid the slightest attention to Melissa. Instead, he casually held out his hand, palm down. They both knew it was his tip but, if Isaac wanted it, he would have to come to Michael to claim it. Yet, to not do so, could be reported as a slight by the guest. Another sackable offence. Isaac walked lamely forward and left his pride in the wheelchair, not once did his eyes leave the floor. As he slipped his hand up to accept the folded note, Michael seized upon it. Holding it tightly for a long few seconds, Michael stripped away the final vestiges of Isaac's dignity.

All for five dollars.

He watched with a conceited satisfaction as Isaac returned to reclaim the wheelchair, but not his pride, and hastily exited the room. As the door closed, he checked to see that Melissa hadn't moved. He would never know how sickened she was by what she had just witnessed. Not that he would ever have cared. Instead, he walked over and stepped out onto the balcony. The sun was setting on the horizon and he could taste the salt in the balmy sea air. Suddenly, he yearned for a drink – a good, long drink. He hadn't had one for a whole day now and that was the longest he had gone since he had lost all the cash.

And Kristy.

Sadly, the alcohol would have to wait. Tomorrow was going to be such a wonderful day, one where his dreams would be realized in paradise, and then to Scotland. Scotland? Of all the places she could have gone, why had she gone there? That promised to be another long ass flight there, and then yet another back home; home to the house that had missed his wife as much as he had. It desperately needed a woman's touch. His woman's touch. It would have that, and more.

Yes, tomorrow would be the best day of his life.

First, he needed to be sober to take care of business, then the money would be all his. He would hide it away so nobody would be any the wiser. All of it. Every last, single penny. Without the money, Kristy would have no choice but to come home with him. What other option did she have? None that he could see. In any case, if she dared refuse to come home, he would simply let her know that he would pay a visit upstate to see Anthony Di Silva and let him know where she was. That was, after all, his civic duty. How could he possibly be expected to sleep at night with the knowledge that an innocent man is incarcerated? His conscience would never allow it. Of course, he'd overlook this knowledge to ensure her safety. For his wife's safety. That would show her how much he loved her and would also be enough encouragement to get her home. It was only once she was home could begin the process of exonerating her sins.

He was, after all – *as God himself decreed* – a gracious and forgiving husband.

Michael let the delicious thought settle in his head as he closed the balcony doors; for now, tomorrow could wait. It would not only be a great day, but also a long one. He needed to be alert and ready, fully prepared to enjoy every last second of it all. It was time to freshen up and have an early night. He tossed his coat onto the arm of the sofa facing Melissa and set off for the bathroom. She listened intently as the toilet was flushed and, a few seconds later, she heard

Michael step into the shower.

This was her chance.

Melissa knew there was only one logical reason why they were in the Caymans. Penny received transfers from here and so this must be where the ransom was deposited. Michael obviously had a plan to access it and she needed to know what it was so that she could warn Penny.

Before it was too late.

She slowly opened her eyes and sat completely still, drinking in the room, and taking a second to memorize how she was seated and the position of his coat. Satisfied she could replicate the scene, she reached over and checked his front left-hand pocket and found both vials of Rohypnol, one was heavier than the other. The thought of replacing it with the water from the vase flashed through her mind, but the risk of being caught was too great. She checked the front right-hand pocket and felt the rag that he had used on the plane; she fought every one of her instincts to take it.

To retake the control that it stole from her.

That he stole from her.

Illogically, she caught herself wondering if this was a rag that had been used on Penny. Why else would he have Rohypnol, if not to use it on her? She chased the question from her mind, as now was not the time to dwell on it. Even under normal circumstances, it didn't bear thinking about, and these circumstances were anything but normal. Now was a time to help, both herself and Penny. She took a second to listen for the shower.

It was still running.

Melissa slipped back the coat's lapel to reveal his inside pocket. There, peeking just over the lip, she could see the familiar burgundy cover of her own passport. Behind it, there was a white envelope. She carefully extracted it from the pocket and lifted the unsealed flap. As she looked inside she only read two words. Two words, but they were enough. Her jaw dropped as she gasped for air, all caution was abandoned for the very real need to simply breathe.

The silence instantly deafened her as the shower was turned off.

Melissa fought to compose herself as she raced to replace the envelope and hastily threw the lapel back into its original position. She settled herself as best she could back into her seat, struggling to hear as over the sound of her own heartbeat as it coursed loudly through her ears. *Was that exactly how his coat was placed…? Was this my exact position…? Where was the wedged cushion…? Think, damn it, just THINK?*

Never had she been more thankful than to hear the sound of a hairdryer. She quickly drew a breath in a useless attempt to calm herself before feeling inside her pocket to pull out Henry's cell phone.

Please don't be locked...

It wasn't.

Please have internet connection...

It did.

Melissa's fearful eyes darted between the bathroom door and the cell phone. *Come on...come on....!* There wasn't much love in this honeymoon suite. It took three attempts before she managed to enter her own email address and password correctly. She hit the compose button and typed in the recipient's email address from memory. The message was taking longer than expected and she listened intently to the bathroom whilst her right thumb danced over the phone's keyboard.

Suddenly, silence.

The hairdryer had been switched off, only to be replaced by Michael's soft but irregular humming. It was apparent that he was now having a much needed shave. She recognized the distinctive sound of a razor being tapped against the side of the sink. *Perfect. All I need is a few more minutes....* As she turned her attention back to the email, the hauntingly melodic tune drifted into her head. Melissa recognized it, but from where? It took a few seconds before she realized it was the same one that was playing in the hotel foyer when they were checking in. As the irony sank in, so did her panic and she completely lost her concentration. It was *Vide Cor Meum*, the theme tune to the movie *Hannibal*.

For her, not so much a *Silence of the Lambs*, but rather a lamb to the slaughter.

The door opened abruptly and Michael stepped out, fully wrapped in one of the hotel bathrobes. *When had he stopped humming?* He was rubbing aftershave balm over his face. Still set rigidly in place, Melissa instantly closed her eyes and froze, hiding the phone in her right hand beside her leg; his blind side. Her breathing was labored and, as she tried to consciously regulate it, she was overcome with the irrational fear that he would hear her heart beating.

Shit!

It immediately became the least of her concerns as she realized that the screen was facing upwards in her hand. *What if he sees the bright light of the screen? I've not yet finished the message. Oh God, please, if ever I needed your help!* She knew she had no option. As slowly as she dared, Melissa turned the cell phone in towards her body, and held it tightly against her leg. It was over in a matter of seconds but it felt like it had taken forever. Just as she was congratulating herself on having successfully completed the herculean task, it happened.

The cushion that Isaac had used to wedge her in fell lazily off the sofa.

Fuck! Panic gripped every fiber of her being. She stopped breathing. A single bead of sweat escaped from her brow and came to rest at the end of her right eyebrow. She never noticed. The blood threatened to burst through her ears. She ignored it. All her senses were completely focused on Michael. He had looked over as the cushion settled upon the carpet. He watched Melissa for another few seconds and, seeing no indication of her rousing, turned and disappeared into the bedroom. She heard him switch on the television and gave him a few seconds before she dared to gently draw the phone back out. Opening only her right eye as slightly as she dared, she used just her thumb to tap the individual keys and complete the message.

She hit the send button.

Melissa watched as the tiny envelope whisked off the small screen, followed by the very welcome words: *Your message has been sent. View message.* Her relief was momentary as she realized that Michael could still discover the cell phone. She quickly turned it off and swapped it into her left hand, then stuffed it as far down the side of the sofa as she could. Satisfied that that she had done all she could, a fresh sense of relief overwhelmed her and she suddenly felt exhausted. As she settled back into her seat, Michael once again emerged from the bedroom and walked directly towards her. She allowed her eyes to open just wide enough to watch him.

It was a decision she immediately regretted.

He lifted his coat and rifled through both front pockets. Opening the fresh bottle of Rohypnol, he emptied its contents into the rag. Stepping forward, he bent down beside her and held the back of her head as he pushed the cloth into her face. She held her breath for as long as she could, but she knew it was pointless. As she exhaled, Melissa opened her eyes wide and bit into the rag with all her might.

She felt his hand in her teeth.

Michael reeled in shock. *What the…?* Instinctively, he tried to pull his hand away from her, but she held it firm. In just a few seconds, it was over. As she inhaled, the drug immediately started to take effect, forcing her whole body to relax. He, however, couldn't wait and repeatedly pushed and pulled his hand in her mouth until it was finally free. The cloth fell as he adjusted himself to complete the task with his other hand.

As she slipped into unconsciousness, the last thing that Melissa saw was Michael's blood on the falling rag.

Chapter 37

Scarsdale, Westchester County, New York

Sunday 17th January

The sprawling house nestled comfortably on an expansive lot in the corner of an exclusive cul-de-sac. There were only three other homes on the street and each sat in quadrants around a large oak tree that served as both a center piece and turning circle for friends and family alike.

Strangers were not welcome here.

The doorbell was one more commonly found adorning those grand old European homes from a bygone era. Its large ornate knob protruded from deep within a circular recess and was one to be pulled rather than pushed. It was installed more from a sense of folly than function. The obvious intent was to radiate a unique style and elegance that perfectly complimented the newly constructed house. Instead and, ironically much like the house, it was both tacky and ridiculous.

Not wishing to have to ring it twice, the visitor yanked it with an excessive force that proved altogether unnecessary.

As the bell rattled violently throughout the house, he stepped back to wait under a garish portico that had been clamped onto the front of the building, and one that served absolutely no practical use whatsoever. The snow was falling lightly once more, lazily drifting in and around him, but he took no notice. Although his head faced forward, his eyes were alert, sweeping and scanning every window for signs of life. He already knew of the two discreet security cameras that were focused upon him, but they were of no concern as they couldn't cause him any physical harm. From inside he could hear a man's voice heading in his direction. The man opened the front door and took a step outside, his arms hanging loosely by his sides and chest puffed out. He used his chin to lift an arrogant sneer in the direction of his own suspicious eyes. His was not a friendly demeanor. It was obvious that this was a man unused to having fresh faces knocking on his door and it seemed that this was a practice he seemed keen to discourage – especially on a Sunday evening.

"Who the fuck are you?"

"Auchtershinnan."

Andy waited for a second to enjoy the look of recognition then realization settle upon Marco Lombardi's face. His sneer immediately fell and disappeared off his chin. His eyes widened as his mouth dropped. As his head struggled to process and understand exactly what was happening, the questions instantly flashed upon his face and were an easy read.

Auchtershinnan...? Scotland...? Here...?

Andy decided that the moment was over as he drove the palm of his hand straight into the center of Lombardi's chest. It was both hard and fast and instantly incapacitating – just as he knew it would be. The force drove Marco staggering back into his own home and left him fighting to breathe. His body was doubled over in pain but his eyes, instantly filled with a very real fear that he had never before experienced, were fully focused upon Andy. The arrogance had vanished, replaced with a feeling of helplessness and the instant realization that he was alone. Alone and vulnerable. Now at the mercy of this stranger who had invaded his home.

The irony was not lost on him.

In one fluid motion, Andy bent down to

his right and grabbed Marco by the throat, driving him up and back as he stepped inside the house, forcing him to stand up straight. The vice like grip was hardly needed, but it was used to convey more than mere strength; this was a demonstration of power. And control. At that very moment, Marco Lombardi was in absolutely no doubt that his life was in this stranger's hands. As a man who dealt in fear, he knew that the mere threat was often greater than the action. Whilst his very reputation was most often enough to ensure compliance to his will, this stranger's actions now spoke to him far louder than his single word. Still struggling to breathe, he realized that this was the man who had not only chased him from Scotland but had, quite literally, followed him into his own home. He had known scary men, tough men, crazy men, but this man was something different altogether. This man was calm, calculated, controlled. In his entire life, he had never been afraid. Even now, he wasn't afraid.

He was absolutely terrified.

Andy almost pulled his ear off as he drew it to his mouth. He whispered each word slowly and deliberately, he was not a man in a hurry, and they both knew his control was now absolute. *"You do not speak. I ask the questions and you blink*

*once for 'yes' and twice for 'no'.
Understood?"* Andy let go of the ear to face
him. He knew that, even if he wanted to,
Marco couldn't speak whilst he had his
throat. Looking for the response, he saw the
tears welling in his eyes.

One blink. A single tear escaped from
his left eye.

"Good. Are you alone?"

A double blink. A second tear escaped.
This time from his right eye.

"Any of your men?"

Two blinks.

"Your wife?"

A second single blink.

For the first time, Marco broke eye
contact. Andy watched as a tear fell from
each eye, and he knew why. The man was
ashamed. Ashamed that he had brought this
danger to his wife's door. Ashamed that he
couldn't protect her. That shame was exactly
what Andy expected.

"Just her?"

Another slow, single blink. He raised
his eyelids to convey the answer but left his
defeated gaze on the floor.

Andy could see through an open door
into a study that was on their left. Gently
closing the front door with his free hand, he
walked Marco backwards into the vacant
room. He flicked on the light switch before

once again closing the door. Every wall was covered in books, from Shakespeare to Tolstoy, yet none had ever been opened.

"Okay, I'm going to release my hand from your throat. Do anything stupid and I will end you. Understood?"

Another long blink.

As Andy opened his hand, fully prepared to react if needed, Marco stood silent and still. Andy walked around the large mahogany desk and opened all the drawers. As expected, he found two loaded guns. He checked that the safeties were on and stuck them in his pockets. Pulling out the seat, he ordered Marco to sit down and quickly made his way to the side of the window and closed the drapes. Satisfied they had total privacy, Andy reached around his back and pulled a folder from inside his waistband and placed it on the desk. He tapped his finger on the pile of papers.

"Read."

"What is it?" To Marco, it really didn't matter. He knew instantly what it was – it was a lifeline. If he was being asked to read this, then this stranger needed something from him. Something other than him to be dead.

"Among other things, it's the police report into your father's death. I thought you might want to know that he wasn't the man you think, or have been told he was. Your father was an intelligent man, shrewd, honorable, and decent. A man of wisdom. That made him dangerous. A man who commanded so much respect that he was ordered to take the position of Caporegime, or 'Capo' as you know it." The judge had come through with all the information and, until that point, Andy had no idea who or what a 'Capo' actually was. He did now. *"A high ranking 'Made Man' who heads his own crew"*, was how Josh had described it. "The 'Capo' position was one he didn't want from a life that he didn't want. And he certainly didn't want it for you. Your father was a man who got caught up in a situation that cost him his life."

Before Andy had finished talking, Marco Lombardi had opened the file and had started to read all about his dad.

"Holy shit, my father called a meeting of 'The Commission'?" His was a voice of confusion, shock, and awe as he looked up and sought confirmation from Andy.

"Yes."

"But why? That hasn't happened since '85. Why would he do something so foolish?" They both knew the importance and implications of calling such a meeting. 'The Commission' had been formed in 1931 by Lucky Luciano and established a board of directors to replace the singular entity that had been the 'Boss of Bosses'.

As such, it was the governing body of the Mafia.

"It was the very same reason why he was killed. Contrary to what you were told, your father was murdered because of what he knew. He was the first man to realize that 'The Commission' had actually been duped. So duped, in fact, that it had been replaced. Only they didn't know it. They had been replaced by a new 'Boss of Bosses'. The very same 'Boss of Bosses' was the man who had your father killed. His own brother-in-law, and the man you know as an uncle, a man who took you under his wing after he ordered the hit. The same man who today, as I understand it, treats you as a son.

And the very man who sent you after _MY_ daughter: Anthony Di Silva."

Marco sat in silence, elbows on the desk with his head in his hands, looking down on the papers. Andy gave him a minute to process the information before he continued. His voice, once again, full of menace and malevolence.

"So now, Mr. Lombardi, we have reached an impasse. You came to my daughter's home to do her harm, on the orders of a man who, in all likelihood, will never again be free. Unless, of course, he can prove that my daughter is Kristy Bradley. Once he does that, he can prove she is alive and, then, he can prove that he had no part in her disappearance.

As I am sure you now understand, I cannot allow that.

You were unsuccessful in your endeavor. I, on the other hand, am standing here in your home. You have no idea who I am, but you now have a slight inclination of what I am capable of. My being here should show you that I have no fear of you, or your friends. My friends and I have dealt with men far more dangerous than you in Bosnia, Afghanistan, Iraq, and a great many other hell holes around the world.

You have this city – if even that.

My understanding is that you are not a stupid man and so you will no doubt recognize my predicament. As you will appreciate, I will stop at nothing to ensure the safety of my daughter. *Absolutely nothing.* I'm assured that you are the only lifeline to Di Silva. You control his money. Money is the power in your business. At the moment, given his current situation, it would take time for me to get to him. Again, as I understand it, there are many men just as keen to do him harm and that tells me that he enjoys some protection where he is. To me, that would suggest that he has somehow managed to secure a cozy life in solitary confinement. So, as I am sure you have already determined, that leaves me with only one option.

As I cannot cut off the head of the snake, I take out the closest part."

As he finished, Andy could hear soft footsteps shuffling along the hall. The door opened slowly and a heavily pregnant Sophia Lombardi labored into the room and struggled into a seat on the opposite side of the desk, never once taking her eyes off her husband. The tears were flowing freely as her hands protectively held their unborn child. Marco, his hands tightly wound into his thick black hair, was too ashamed to face her. She totally ignored Andy and simply pointed to the telephone on the table.

"I heard everything."

The thick Italian accent was instantly recognizable, although the young lady's voice belonged to someone older and wiser. It was not a voice full of the impending excitement of parenthood. It was tired and weary, resigned to its fate of raising a child alone. Another woman without a husband. Another child without a father.

Another widow of the Mob.

In that moment, Andy saw them through different eyes – through a father's eyes. He no longer saw them as a threat, but as a family. A family seeking an escape, seeking asylum, seeking safety.

The Lombardi's were refugees of the Cosa Nostra.

Chapter 38

Scarsdale, Westchester County, New York

Sunday 17th January

"Okay, there may be another option." The plan came quickly to Andy and it was far more preferable to the alternative. He hadn't wanted to kill Marco Lombardi – he had long thought those days gone – but he would, if it was needed. He would take a life for Penny to have a life. After all she had been through, it was the least he could.

A father's duty.

"There are no other options. We both know how this plays out. You and I, this is what we are, what we do. We reap what we sow and, at some point, the reaper comes calling. For me, it's tonight. All I ask is that you spare my wife, and our child. Please." Marco Lombardi was a man resigned to his fate.

"Hear him out, Marco. What do we have to lose? *Please*, continue." Sophia's eyes never left her husband as she spoke to the stranger. A stranger that had brought fear and death, but now offered hope and life. His plan, *any plan*, was worth considering as the alternative was unthinkable. Certainly to her. Deep inside her, their child kicked.

Already it had its father's spirit and its mother's fight.

"You won't like what I am about to suggest, but please hear me out before making any rash decisions." Andy outlined the sketchy details of his idea. After he finished, a few moments of silence passed as they each thought through the proposal.

"It's perfect. Marco?" Sophia had never before interfered with her husband's business affairs and, to her mind, she still hadn't done so. This was about their life as a family, and on that subject, she would never be silent. Her husband raised his head to meet her eyes. Andy recognized the look of love.

He also recognized the look of agreement.

"What do we do now?" Sophia allowed her husband to ask the question on their family's behalf.

"Now, I need to make two calls and you..." Andy pointed to Marco, "...you need to make one. Mrs. Lombardi, take only your jewelry, those items that have sentimental value. Everything else can stay, that will buy us some time. Mr. Lombardi – *Marco* – I'd suggest that, in the meantime, you transfer every single cent of Di Silva's fortune into a secure offshore account of your own. Oh, and how much cash is in the house?"

Andy's calm tone demanded respect and left no-one in any doubt about who was in control; it brought a strange comfort to both Marco and Sophia. To them, there had never been any doubt about trusting Andy; even when that meant trusting that he would end Marco's life. Marco trusted that he would do it. Completely. As such, they both knew that now was a time for compliance and honesty. Their lives depended upon it, as any mistakes would have deadly repercussions. For *every* Lombardi. That fact was not lost on any of them, even the little one had stopped kicking and was now peaceful and ready.

It seemed that all three Lombardi's were happy to conform with Andy's plan.

"Just over $2 million. Why?" Old habits die hard.

"Bring it with you. You're going to need it." Andy said no more as he reached for the phone. Marco was already working on his laptop and Sophia could see that the numerous tabs all had names of different banks. In just under an hour, Marco sat back to look at the screen and see the new balance in their joint account in Switzerland.

It was just over $893 million.

It may have been the fact that he had just stolen it from Tony that reminded him of Kristy. It may have been the fact that it was her father that was helping his family. It may have been a number of other reasons that he would never care to consider, far less understand. Whatever it was, it didn't really matter. He just thought it best to let Andy know. "Oh, I don't know if this is of any interest to you, but you may like to know that Tony ordered us to have Michael Bradley's place bugged, just in case Kristy ever got in touch."

"Yeah, that makes sense. Why are you telling me this?" Andy's question betrayed a little too much concern.

Marco was still looking at the long line of magic numbers in the current balance section of their bank account as he spoke. "Well I thought you might like to know that, yesterday, he hired a private plane for himself and a passenger to take him out of the country. This afternoon they flew out to the Cayman Islands."

"We have to move, NOW!"

Chapter 39

Scarsdale, Westchester County, New York

Sunday 17th January

"Z, budge over would you please? These two are coming with us." Andy was a welcome sight. The silence in the car had been unbearable, but I didn't want to risk upsetting Penny any further although I desperately wanted to know that we were okay.

That we were still a couple.

That she still loved me.

I knew this wasn't the time to have such a conversation, but that only prolonged the agony and exacerbated the problem, especially when we had the privacy for the discussion. Although, with Andy, we never knew for how long. He had simply told us to wait in the car and, as usual, had vanished to God alone knew where and only God knew for how long.

It was one of his less endearing qualities.

As requested, I had folded myself in a corner of the back seat. I wasn't built for back seats and never understood the whole obsession with them. For me, fooling around there was always a fool's errand and anything but romantic. I guess it was a job for 'smaller' guys. My own joke made me smile until I saw the first face getting in beside me.

"Wait a fucking minute, you're the prick that was in our house! What the fuck is going on here?"

"Z, now just calm down. Everything will be explained in good time. Unfortunately, time is in short supply at the moment so, please, let's just get moving." There was obviously no discussion to be had and to push the subject would have been stupid. Churlishly, I turned my back as best I could and looked out the window. Not another word was spoken, and I had no idea how long we were driving, until we pulled back into the same airport that we had landed at earlier in the day.

Is it still the same day?

We drove back to the hangar and, as we drew up to our readied plane, I went to get out before the car came to a halt. Whatever

Andy's reasons for having this asshole in the car, they were certainly not mine, and I didn't want to waste another second beside this guy. This was the point when I discovered that Andy had engaged the child locks. Given my feelings and predicament, I begrudgingly recognized that his was a rather shrewd and altogether apt measure. "Wait here." He turned and said this directly to me as he stole my dramatic exit.

The bastard.

Andy disappeared up the small steps and, unusually, I used the plane windows to look inside rather than out to see him talking with our pilot and stewardess. Whatever was said, the conversation was over in a few minutes as he shook both their hands and came hurrying back to the car, coming directly to the back door and opening it.

Only not on my side.

"Okay, they are ready for you. Everything has been organized and you should be safe enough. The plane is registered in the UK and has three on the manifest. They have agreed to sign for three on the return flight to Scotland, where it will touch down and refuel. There they will report that all three passengers disembarked and, an hour later, they will take off with you hidden on board. All going well, you will be having lunch with your family in

Sicily tomorrow evening.

Please leave the bag in the truck and I can use that for our own flight. You three please stay safe. This is the best I can do just now but, should you need me, you know how to find me." Andy stood aside and held out his hand to help the woman out.

Only now did I see she was pregnant.

"God bless you." The woman kissed Andy on both cheeks, the tears falling freely as she held him in a tight embrace. The asshole shuffled along the seat, but didn't step out. Instead, he turned and tapped Penny on the shoulder. She looked at him with a defiance that I expected. This was the man that had come after her and she refused to be afraid. He spoke directly to her with an unmistakable sincerity.

"You are incredibly lucky. Your father is a remarkable man and, believe me, I am sorry that we invaded your home, but I cannot regret it. Not now. Your father is giving us, like you, a second chance at life and at a family. We won't ruin it. I hope and pray that you do the same. God bless you." The man paused for a second, then turned to me.

"I understand why you hate me. Trust me, scaring a woman is not something I am proud of. However, please believe me when I say, I had no choice. Now, I do. Thanks to her father. All I can say to you is I am sorry for the pain and hurt I have caused you. I will take that regret with me to my grave."

I believed him.

Once again, the words tumbled from my mouth without any forethought or consideration. "Thank you. Take care and good luck with the little one."

I meant it.

As they made their way onto our plane, Andy jumped into the driver's seat and took us to another hangar in the airport. There sat an even bigger private jet than the one we had just left. "Okay, let's go." Andy popped the trunk and went to the back of the car as Penny made her way towards the waiting pilot.

The waiting female pilot.

My own surprise at her gender instantly annoyed me. She warmly welcomed us on board and then stepped out to meet Andy. The conversation was brief and she accepted the new bag that he brought from the car. We all settled into seats that made the other planes seem positively spartan in comparison and I was determined to enjoy this flight home. In a matter of minutes, we were climbing through the latest flurry of snow and into the skies. Just as we broke through the clouds, the beautiful night sky stretched out like a celestial carpet towards the heavens. The soothing tones of the captain's voice came through all of the many speakers.

"Welcome on board, Lady and Gentlemen. It truly is my pleasure to be flying you tonight and please just kick back and relax. In a few short hours the harsh winter weather of New York City will be an unpleasant memory as you all enjoy the friendlier climate of the Cayman Islands."

The fucking what…?

Chapter 40

Somewhere over the Atlantic Ocean

Monday 18th January

> *'Anthony Di Silva is dead!'*

The shock mixed with an obvious relief as Penny's eyes scanned the screen of the iPad, desperately searching for more information. I'd been delighted that she had taken a seat opposite me and it'd been far too long since I'd seen anything other than the side or back of her head. Andy was also facing me, but on the other side of the aisle. I still couldn't understand why they would face a different direction from the way we were flying. My only conclusion was that some people are just odd.

"Early and, as yet, unconfirmed reports are claiming he committed suicide with an overdose."

For some reason I sensed that Andy had

something to do with this development. It was just too coincidental. I turned to look at him, to see his response, to gauge his reaction. Nothing. He was looking out the window and, quite literally, lost in space.

Or so I thought.

My eyes drifted to his portal in search of his thoughts when I suddenly realized that he was using the reflection to stare directly back at me. Mine was an immediate embarrassment that caused my face to flush instantly, it felt like it was on fire. Still he held my gaze and I was powerless to break the contact. It was then that it struck me – he was entirely responsible for Di Silva's death.

He seemed to read my mind.

For just a second, a small knowing smile found the corner of his lip until his single nod chased it away. I was dismissed and he was, once again, to be left with his thoughts.

Thoughts that replayed the events in the Lombardi home.

Thoughts that recalled his telephone conversations with the judge and Anthony Di Silva.

Josh McCall was only too happy to oblige Andy's request for witness protection for Marco Lombardi and his wife in exchange for credible information that he knew would end the careers of most of New York's major players in organized crime. The only condition had been that the Lombardi's be released into Andy's care to be made available to Josh – *and only Josh* – at any time he saw fit.

The judge had readily agreed.

The call to Anthony Di Silva would forever remain one of Andy's favorite conversations. *"Check your bank balances."* Di Silva did as he was told, without uttering a single word.

"I'm talking with a dead man." Di Silva's weak reply was missing all his usual gusto.

> *"Funny, I was thinking the exact same thing. Unlike you, I believe that every man has the right to know why he died. For you, it was for coming after something that belongs to me. For that, you die. I'd prefer tonight, at your own hand. However, I can wait until tomorrow, when you are replaced back into the general population. You should know that I have placed an extra $5 million on your head. Oh, and here's*

*something that only a man
like you can appreciate.*

*I am using YOUR own money
for the bounty.*"

Andy wasn't to be allowed to fully
savor the moment.

"Is it true?" Penny had put down the
tablet and was looking out of her own
window. There was no way to know who
she was talking to, so Andy and I both
remained silent. Her tone was not friendly,
and whilst I was delighted that yesterday
was over, it somehow didn't yet feel like it.
Engaging in this conversation would only
confirm that.

"Is it true that you are my father?"
Penny's question visibly shocked Andy and,
for once, he seemed to be somewhat
flustered. I watched as he rubbed the bridge
of his nose with his thumb and finger, trying
to manipulate an appropriate response.

"Who told you that?" His eyes had
settled back upon me. It was an
uncomfortable feeling, and one I wanted rid
of instantly.

"It wasn't me." My heroic reply that
somehow made me feel like I'd just saved
myself.

"It was the man in the car, if you must
know. The same man who broke into my

home. Does it really matter? It still doesn't answer my question." Penny was determined to have the conversation whilst I just wanted to be anywhere else but here.

Andy quietly rose from his seat and stepped towards her as she raised her head to look him straight in the eye. He reached into the inside of his jacket and removed a letter. As he handed it to her, and before releasing his grip, he said softly, "You weren't the only one that your mum wrote to." Penny looked at the battered and bruised envelope and instantly recognized her mother's handwriting. Andy left her to read as he returned to his seat and stared deep into the abyss.

I sensed that this wasn't his first visit.

"So, you are *my* father." She had finished reading and held the letter in her hand, but she couldn't look at him. Instead, she too stared out into the night's sky.

"Yes, I am." He spoke with a pride that was resolute and absolute. "If I had only known earlier, I would have happily, *proudly*, been a part of your life. As you just read, your mum had her reasons. Reasons I understand. However, that doesn't mean to say I agree with them, nor her decision. When I did find out, as you can see from the date on the letter, it was shortly before she..."

He couldn't bring himself to say the word 'died'.

His attention returned to the void, searching through the pane in an effort to ease his pain. "You should know that, although brief, your mother was the only woman I ever loved and I can see so much of her in you. Fate was unkind to us, but yet I always loved her. I still do. That letter has brought me incredible joy, in finding out and getting to know you. It also brought me terrible pain, for just seeing her handwriting stirred up feelings I'd thought long since gone. I used to call the hospital daily for updates. All too soon thereafter, I was calling the hospice, always pretending to be her brother. Until, one day, she was gone."

His voice was fighting his emotions and the tears came easily. His was a profound and palpable sense of loss. A loss of the woman he loved, the mother of his child, the wife he never knew. He cast his eyes out among the stars, solemnly searching every corner of the vast emptiness, looking for the face that was now forever a memory. He continued to talk, but with a different tone. Softer, tender, caring. One filled with love. He was speaking to us, but talking with her.

To paraphrase Shakespeare:
"When she shall die,
Take her and cut her out in little stars,

And she will make the face of heaven so fine,

That all the world will be in love with night,

And pay no worship to the garish sun."

He paused for the briefest moment; a moment to share with her.

"It was only right that I respected her wishes, as she knew I would, to wait until after she passed to contact you. Then, you disappeared. Naturally, I read the newspapers, but something didn't sit right with me, so I broke into your home and found..."

We all knew that he meant the tapes. Andy had lied to the judge about seeing them, although I couldn't help but wonder if he was more lying to himself, hoping he would forget what he had seen.

"I wanted to kill him. Desperately so. Yet, as I observed him in those days and weeks after, I saw that what you had done hurt him far more than I ever could. It was more satisfying to just let him live with the torment of not knowing what happened. The torment of having had so much money in his account yet having to send it all back to you, thinking he was paying Di Silva's ransom, and all in complete ignorance. It was quite brilliant."

His admiration shone through brighter

than any star in the night sky.

"Then I found you. It wasn't easy and I called in more than a few favors, but still, I found you. My intention was always to come clean, to tell you I'm your dad, but it just never seemed to be the right time and I was just happy to be close, to watch you grow and find yourself as a person on your own. To protect you. That's why I told you I was the estate's caretaker who had merely been on holiday for a few weeks. If you questioned it, then I would have had to concoct another equally plausible plan.

Thankfully, it didn't come to that and I have loved every minute since.

Then, Z here came onto the scene and you changed. Oh, and how you changed! You were suddenly happy, excited, full of spirit. That same spirit I recognized and had known in your mum. It was so wonderful to see. I desperately wanted you two to get together as I could see – *a blind man could see* – that you two are right for each other. Over time, I, like you, met his parents and, together, these have been the happiest days of my life. Telling you could have ruined that and I couldn't risk it.

Not then. Not now. Not *ever…*"

The last words drifted in a whisper as Andy desperately tried to regain his composure. Penny was fighting a similar battle, and losing.

I was a blubbering wreck and no use to anyone.

"So what would you like to happen now?" It was me speaking, again. Whatever happens from here on out, when we get home, I really need to get to the doctor. There must be some sort of medical cure for these sudden, and seemingly uncontrollable, outbursts.

"Good question." Penny seemed relieved that I had filled the silence with a pertinent question. "Andy?"

"Actually – if you don't mind Andy – Penny, the question was for you. I have no idea, once again, what we are heading into down here, but I am guessing it's something to do with money. However, that doesn't matter to me. It has never mattered to me. I just love you. Simple. I want to be with you and I want us to be a family. If that means living in a tent in a field, then as long as it's you and me, then I'm just fine with that. Of course, we'll need Andy to take care of the tent.

The rest will take care of itself."

My eyes never left Penny's as I spoke and I saw our love there. My own mother's voice came ringing in my head, *the eyes never lie.* As she softly nodded in agreement, she gave me the same quick wink that her father had done earlier. Through her teary smile, she mouthed the words *"I love you"*.

All was right in my universe again.

I turned to see Andy watching us from the corner of his eye. He saw me and nodded, a single approving movement of his head, and he too mouthed a message.

Thank you.

Chapter 41

George Town, Cayman Islands

Monday 18th January

"Hello sleepy head, time to wake up."
Michael gave a couple of light slaps around
both of Melissa cheeks. "I ordered room
service as I know you haven't eaten for a
while and I figured you must be hungry.
You need to shower and freshen up before it
gets here. We have a big day ahead."

"Where am I?" Melissa genuinely
didn't know. Memory loss was one of the
drug's many side effects. Not generally a
positive one for Michael as it meant that
Kristy didn't always know that she had been
punished and, worse, why. It was yet
another trial that he had endured over the
years in his pursuit of her spiritual
purification. His martyrdom was a constant
curse and one for which he would reap his

just rewards on that glorious day in the true paradise.

With his grateful wife justly by his side.

"You are in the Cayman Islands."

"What…? *The Cayman Islands…?* No, that can't be…, but I was in New York… How…, how did I get *here?*" Melissa genuinely didn't know. She looked beyond Michael, who was sat on the coffee table in front of her, and saw the beautiful blue ocean trail off into the distance to meet the cloudless sky. The air conditioning was working overtime to keep the room cool, but it couldn't beat the humidity. She could already feel her blouse sticking to her.

"The details are of no importance. I just need you to get ready and then we can go. Room service will be…" The knock at the door interrupted him. "Ah, perfect, that will be them now. So, let's eat, shower, change, and move. As I say, it's a big day ahead. For both of us."

Melissa's head was pounding, whilst also struggling to process what she had just been told, the last remnants of the drugs were refusing to leave her system without a fight. As the server entered the room, the aroma of the breakfast overpowered her senses and she recognized that she was ravenously hungry. She was also in desperate need of the bathroom. Yet her instincts told her to eat now, and not to leave this man alone with her food.

"I didn't know what you might want, so I ordered a cooked breakfast and the fruit platter. Please, bon appetit…" He waved his hand invitingly over the trolley as the disappointed server disappeared out the room with another five measly dollars.

Melissa wasted no time in devouring the entire offering. Thereafter, she quickly showered and dressed, returning to the main room to find Michael standing on the balcony and enjoying the view. He came in as soon as he saw her, nodding in approval.

"Ah, you look positively resplendent." It wasn't the word she would have used to describe herself. Certainly not for wearing black pants and a cream blouse. "Shall we?"

"Shall we what?" Melissa wasn't sure she wanted to know the answer.

"Well, leave of course. The bank opens in a few minutes and I want to be there when it does."

Ah, of course! The bank!

"Why do you need me there?" She certainly wanted to know *this* answer.

"Well, I need to confirm that the bank account details you gave me are correct. From that, I can access all of her account records and see the total income and expenditure. Hopefully, she hasn't spent too much of my money.

I also thought that you would want to be there to enjoy the moment. I could always leave you here, if you like? I should tell you though, that once my business is concluded at the bank, I am flying directly to Scotland to... Now, how would you say it? Yes, that's it, to *rekindle the romance* with my wife. So, if you want a nice free flight home, I suggest you come with me. Either way, it's your choice."

Melissa grabbed her purse and overnight bag and followed him out the door.

Chapter 42

George Town, Cayman Islands

Monday 18th January

"Who is it I ask for in here?" Michael only realized as they were rapidly approaching the front door of the bank that he hadn't determined who he needed to be dealing with. It was a simple oversight and one that he instantly berated himself for.

Thankfully, it was an easy fix.

"What?" Melissa stopped and tried to stall for time, but he wasn't buying it.

"You heard me." The earlier charm was gone, replaced by his usual self. He slipped his hand under her elbow and squeezed. Hard. "Don't start playing games, now is *not* the time. Who is Kristy's point of contact? *Who do I ask for?*"

Melissa refrained from pointing out that he was essentially asking the same question twice, and took satisfaction in answering him once. "Robert Bowden."

"Thank you." Michael seemed genuinely relieved.

The International Bank of the Cayman Islands, or IBCI as it's known, is not like most banks. There are no tellers, but rather a single receptionist who sits behind a large and imposing desk, just waiting to deal with the immediate needs of every client that enters the building. Yet even the most mundane task of opening an account here requires an appointment along with the hope that your request is met favorably. To make the appointment list – which never has any openings for at least four months in advance – the proposed client must show immediately available funds of $25 million, along with a commitment that these will be retained as a guaranteed minimum in the account at all times.

There are severe financial penalties for those accounts that dip below this sum.

"Good morning, may I help you?" The question was absent of all sincerity and there was no accompanying smile, and it came from a beautiful young lady with an ugly demeanor who obviously had no intention of helping anyone. This was a place of serious business and so the tone was respectfully somber and professional. Her attitude, however, was one that was encouraged by her superiors to reflect the bank's exclusive status and prestige.

"Yes, please, I would like to speak with Mr. Robert Bowden."

"Do you have an appointment?" Her hands remained interlocked and placed firmly on the desk. The attitude was already beginning to irritate Michael.

"Not exactly. However, I was hoping that he was available to see me. My wife – Kristy Bradley, I'm Michael Bradley – has an account here and we have some urgent business that needs attending to. Can you please see if he can spare a few minutes? It really shouldn't take too long at all."

She lifted the receiver and tapped three numbers into the phone. "Good morning, Robert." The tone was light and airy, this time accompanied by a genuine smile. *She really is a beautiful woman when she tries.* Michael instantly sent up a private prayer for his instant sin of lust. "I have a Mr. Bradley *without an appointment*, but he was hoping you could spare a few moments to discuss his wife's account. He did say please." Her sneer was aimed directly at Michael and it instantly killed his attraction.

Thank you Lord.

"Perfect, thank you Robert." She hung up and pressed a button under the desk. The door immediately behind her buzzed open; only then could they see that it was at least six inches thick with five steel rods, each about two inches in diameter, that held it securely in place. "*Please* just go through, he is waiting for you."

"Thank you." Michael didn't wait for Melissa as he took off for the door. He could not wait to transfer his money out of this bank.

"Mr. Bradley?" As promised, Robert Bowden was waiting for them both and held out a hand that Michael shook in his usual manner, hard and tight. It was meant to convey strength, power, and control.

Robert Bowden had seen, and felt it, all before.

"…and you are?" He extended his hand to Melissa.

"Unimportant." Michael replied for her. Robert was already shaking her hand and she whispered her name. He returned a smile, and then her hand. "As I explained to the young lady at the reception, this shall only take a few moments of your time, then you can get on with the rest of your day."

"Certainly, come this way." Robert invited them through another door, thicker and more secure than the first, and into an open plan office. They passed by thirteen occupied desks before Robert slipped in behind the one that was empty, complete with his name plaque, and offered them both seats opposite him. "So, tell me Mr. Bradley, how can I help you today?"

"Well, *Robert*, mine is a rather sensitive although absolutely tragic situation. To save me any further upset, I think it may be best if you read this for yourself, then you will understand." Michael slipped his hand into the inside of his coat pocket and withdrew the envelope. He removed the single piece of paper and unfolded it, placing it onto the desk in front of Robert, and slid the document forward with just the index finger of his right hand.

Melissa looked away in disgust, as much with herself for playing a part in this charade, as with Michael.

Michael could not hide his grin of satisfaction.

"A death certificate? If I am reading this correctly, this is for your wife, Mrs. Kristy Bradley?" Robert was reading the document as he spoke.

"Tragically, yes. As you can see from the date, she died last week. We have had her funeral, a solemn affair, but she got the send off she deserved. As you can imagine, this is a very difficult time for me and so I am now here to tie up all her affairs as efficiently and expediently as possible.

Sadly, that includes closing her account here and, as her sole beneficiary, I would like to transfer the funds into my own account. As I said, it shouldn't take too much of your time." Michael sat back in his chair, satisfied with his day's work.

He could taste the money.

"I am so very sorry for your loss." As a mark of respect, Robert blessed himself and allowed for a moment of silent prayer before continuing. "Of course, I shall try and deal with this as quickly as possible for you. Do you have the account number please?"

Michael turned to Melissa. With the utmost reluctance, she recited the account number as slowly as possible. Robert entered each number and letter into the computer as it was recited.

To Michael, it was an eternity.

"Thank you. Ah, yes, here we are. I have your wife's account details here, but I'm very sorry to tell you, and this is rather embarrassing I'm afraid, but it looks like we have a problem Mr. Bradley."

"What do you mean, *'we have a problem'*?" Michael sat bolt upright in his chair, anger immediately mixing with adrenaline.

"Well, I'm afraid your wife's account is overdrawn in the amount of US $6.2 million. As you have stated that you are the sole beneficiary, in accordance with the law of the Cayman Islands, I'm afraid that this debt now falls to you.

So, how would you like to pay this today?"

Melissa's mouth dropped in shock behind her hand that had quickly rose to cover it.

"No..., wait..., actually, no.... She's not dead. She's alive. Here, let's just forget the whole thing. It's a mistake!" Michael reached over to grab the death certificate, but Robert saw what he was trying to do and pulled it away. He slowly folded it and placed it into his drawer.

"I'm sorry, a 'mistake'? You are now saying that Mrs. Bradley is alive? How can that be when you have a death certificate? Unless, of course, this death certificate is not authentic. Mr. Bradley, are you telling me this death certificate is a forgery?" Robert sought clarification.

"Well... no, but, well, yes... You see... she is alive, but she stole my money, so now I'm stealing it back. Don't you see...? It's *MY FUCKING MONEY!"*

"Well then Mr. Bradley, I'm afraid that you leave me no option but to detain you whilst we wait for the police. Bank fraud is a very serious crime here in the Cayman Islands. From what I can determine, either your wife is dead and, if so, you owe this bank US $6.2 million dollars; or she is alive, and you thought that there was money in her account and you were intent on defrauding this bank.

Either way, this is now a police matter."

Suddenly claustrophobic, Michael began gasping for air. He felt trapped; he needed water, he needed space. He stood to run but found that he was flanked by two armed guards who were, quite possibly, the largest men he had ever seen. They had no need to draw their weapons. Instead, one laid a gentle hand on his shoulder and guided him towards another door. "Can you step this way please, Sir?"

Everyone knew that it wasn't a request.

As Michael was being escorted away, Robert turned to Melissa. "Thank you Miss Chisholm. If there is nothing more that I can help you with, you are free to leave."

"Wait, how do you know her name? Robert...*ROBE...?*" The door closed on Michael's questions.

Chapter 43

George Town, Cayman Islands

Monday 18th January

> *"We're too late!"*

Penny's whisper managed to contain and stifle her desperate scream as she pointed towards the bank where we had spent the last few hours waiting for it to open.

"There's... *Michael.*"

She defiantly spat out the name. There was no hiding the disgust that the very word was offensive in her mouth, on her tongue, on her lips – she didn't even try.

"Yes, but who does he have with him?" Andy had now also caught sight of the man I had never seen, not even in a photograph.

"Wait, *where...?*" I was completely isolated from their conversation and it left me feeling both impotent and foolish. *Damn it, I want to help!* It was absurd that I was here and yet had no clue who I was looking for, although it certainly didn't stop me trying. Even now, when they had managed to identify the man, all I could see was a fresh raft of happy tourists who had so recently disembarked from one of the many monstrous leviathans masquerading as boats that were anchored in the bay. The same happy tourists that now swarmed around the city center square and had inadvertently provided the perfect shield that allowed Michael to slip into the bank before we could stop him.

Or, more accurately, before Andy could stop him.

"It doesn't matter now Z, they've both gone inside. As Penny said, we are too late. All we can do now is wait." Andy caught the barista's attention and ordered fresh refills. We had been passing the time at a table outside a friendly coffee shop that conveniently hugged the opposite corner from the bank and provided a clear view of its front door.

At least it had until the arrival of the countless and faceless tourists.

"So, let me get this right. We just sit here, all civil and nonchalant, while he wanders in there and stages, quite literally, a heist of your fortune? That's it? That's the plan? There's nothing else that we can do?" They heard my questions, but had no answers. Taking her hand, I managed to grab her attention, but I knew she would only allow me a moment. It was all I would need. "Well Penny, I want you to know, none of this…" I pointed directly to the bank. "…*NONE* of it means anything to me. I was born with nothing and I have most of it left." My weak joke found a weaker smile. "Anyway, I just want you to know as it's looking increasingly likely that we will have to live in a tent in the wilderness, that I was serious on the plane. I'd still be as happy as I could ever imagine, or expect to be, as long as I have you. The rest of it – the money, the house, all of it – really means nothing to me.

Without you."

As I finished, there was a familiar 'ping' of an email alert from Penny's purse. Whilst her eyes remained fixed on mine, she slipped her hand into her bag and pulled out the iPad. In order to give her privacy, I turned away to scan back through the crowd towards the bank. I saw her face in the corner of my eye as it instantly changed; confusion and elation seemed to blend as one.

"Wha… How…? How…? This can't be…?" Penny burst into tears as she thrust

the tablet into Andy's hand and vaulted from her seat into my lap. She kept saying, over and over, *"I love you! I love you! I love you!"* in between kissing all over my face and hugging me tightly. Once again, I was completely oblivious to this latest turn of events, but simply delighted to have my happy girl back.

"What's happening?" I'd done it again, blurting out a question without thinking. At least this time I knew that it was my own curiosity that was the cause. A medical breakthrough perhaps?

Penny spun on my knee to face Andy. "Show him. And…" She stopped abruptly. Her head dropped on an angle, as if no longer looking, but seeing him for the first time. It certainly gave her pause for thought, and then her face lit up as she gave him a smile that was full of genuine love and affection. With a slight nod of approval, she finished her sentence.

"…Dad."

The single word overwhelmed Andy. He held the tablet in my general direction and left me to take it, as he bit his lip and cast his head in the direction of the tourists, hoping to blend in as one of the faceless legions. A hand covered his mouth, but quickly spread over his face in an effort to hide the tears. It was an obvious effort to compose himself and it was the first time I'd ever seen Andy fail at anything. Not that I wanted him to succeed, for it was easy to recognize a father's emotions of love and pride.

It was a beautiful sight.

Penny tapped the screen that held the mysterious email and I recognized her subtle hint. Yet I had to read the email three times before it made any sense.

Dear Miss Munro,

Please be advised that this email is confirmation of the successful transfer of funds as outlined below. These funds are now cleared in your account and fully available.

Many thanks,

Geoffrey Brown
Inverness Branch Manager

Monday 18th January:

From:

Robert Bowden
International Bank of the Cayman Islands

To:

FAO Ms. Melissa Chisholm
Inverness Branch
Caledonian Bank

Dear Sir or Madam,

As per our existing arrangement regarding the account of Miss Penelope Munro.

Please credit to the account of Miss Penelope Munro, the amount of $68,200,000 (Sixty-Eight Million, Two Hundred Thousand US Dollars) only.

These funds are to be made available immediately.

Many thanks,

Robert Bowden.

"I think Andy and I need a raise." I was only half-joking. "You have $68 million dollars? That's an insane amount of money."

"That's just the thing, I don't. The last time I checked, there was just under $62 million. I really don't know where the rest came from." Penny seemed genuinely confused but unconcerned. "At least it's more money than I thought I had, right?

Maybe there is enough extra for the *slight* raise that you two *may* deserve.

Certainly enough for a new tent…"

She followed her smirk to give me a kiss. She was aiming for my lips, but I had already turned so she only managed to graze my cheek.

"I know her! She works in our bank, our real bank, the Caledonian in Inverness! Her there!" It was the turn of Andy and Penny to follow my hand pointing in the direction of the IBCI. "Her name, what is it…. Wait, I know this… it begins with 'N' maybe…? No, 'M'…, 'Margaret'…, 'Moira'… something like that."

"Melissa?!" The voice called out into the crowded square and came from the direction of the bank.

"Thank you, yes, that's it. *Melissa!*" It was my turn to shout at her. She obviously heard me as her reaction told me I was right. My immediate thought was that she would faint from shock; she looked like she'd seen a ghost. Standing rooted to the spot and staring directly at our table, her eyes drifted from Andy, to me, and then settled on Penny.

I sat back in triumph.

"Penny? Is that you? I am so sorry!" Melissa broke into a short run and made her way directly to our table. Behind her, a man

kept shouting her name and, seeing her run, broke into a jog to catch her.

The faceless masses completely ignored her.

"Melissa, what are you doing here?" Penny pulled out the spare seat at our table and invited her to take a seat. Before she could speak, the man who had been chasing her approached.

Andy sat with his eyes fixed on the stranger, instantly ready for action.

"Melissa, thank you so much for the email. As per your request, I transferred the full amount and took the liberty of extending Miss Munro's overdraft to the maximum 10% as allowed by the bank. Otherwise, it would have left the account with a zero balance and so no charges could be levied. That now means that Mr. Bradley has a whole lot of explaining to do." Robert Bowden spoke only to Melissa and ignored everyone else at the table.

"Mr. Bowden, this is Miss Munro. She was Mrs. Kristy Bradley, and I can now say that I fully understand why she isn't any longer."

"Pleasure to meet you Mrs.... *Miss* Munro." Robert extended a hand that Penny gratefully shook.

"So, Melissa, tell me, what brings you to the Caymans?" We all knew from the

401

tone of Penny's question that this would be a long explanation.

Melissa and Robert both sat down and she began to talk… and talk… and talk.

"…and that's how I ended up sending the email to Robert here. I've been dealing with him on your behalf since you opened your account with our bank. That's why I took a chance at the transfer, hoping that he would read it before Michael could get access to the funds. Thankfully, it worked out."

The table was silent, as each of us tried to let everything sink in.

"I have a question. It may be somewhat impertinent, but as we are all being honest, maybe this is the time I can push my luck a little." Nobody interrupted, so I took that as the okay to continue. "Melissa, you said that the ransom was $34 million, right?"

Melissa nodded.

"Penny, you said that, when you last checked, that the balance on your account here at the IBCI was just under $62 million, right?" I hooked my thumb over my shoulder in the general direction of the bank.

"Yes. Was that your question? In fact, that was two questions. I'd say that was *really* pushing your luck!" Penny knew my question, but was enjoying the game.

"No. Well, yes, it was two questions,

but here is my real question. How did you manage to go from $34 million to $62 million in such a short space of time?" Looking around the table, it was plain to see that this was a question that everyone else was thinking, but only I was asking.

I felt brave and courageous all over again.

"What can I say? I invested wisely!" Penny could barely finish the sentence before she burst out laughing. It was such a wonderful sight; the return of the girl I fell in love with.

Sadly, Robert interrupted my moment. "So, Melissa, it's okay that I call you Melissa, right?" She nodded. "When do you fly home?"

"Hold on a minute please Robert, if I may, but I have one more thing I need to know. Melissa, are you telling me that all of this..., this..., oh, what would you call it? Crusade, quest, or whatever, you did it all *for love?*"

"Well, yes. It was all for love. To be honest, I just thought I could help both you and Michael. Now I know Michael needs a whole lot of different help." Her sincerity made her point even funnier. As we all started to laugh, she could only join in, although I wasn't sure if she was laughing with us, at us, or at her own naivety, or her own stupidity.

Probably all.

"Although I cannot lie, the million-dollar reward was also a factor. It was the only time in my life where I could expect to make that much money. To me, everybody was a winner. Unfortunately, I now know that it was never real. That will teach me to ever believe what I read in the media." A shroud of sadness fell over Melissa as she realized that all of her dreams, real and imagined, had just evaporated.

"So, Melissa, when do you fly home?" Robert asked again. For reasons best known to himself, he was determined to have an answer.

"Well, as soon as possible I guess. Reality beckons." The very thought seemed to weigh heavy on her.

"Well, perhaps you can have dinner with me tonight and maybe stay here on the island for a few days? I would love to get to know you better." *Smooth Robert, very smooth.* It was my turn to throw a knowing wink to Andy. Robert Bowden had proven himself a man of action, now he was proving himself a man of words too.

"I wish I could, but I'm afraid that's impossible. As they say at home, I am what's known as *'financially embarrassed'*. So even if I wanted to, and I most certainly do want to, believe me, I just cannot afford to." At long last, Melissa seemed to understand what Robert was saying – I'd only recently caught on myself. It was heart-breaking to see such an obvious spark between two people quenched before it even had a chance to start.

All over something as vulgar as money.

As Melissa spoke, Penny had reached into her purse and only I could see what she was doing. *That's my girl.* I reached around her shoulders and kissed her on the side of the head. She stopped for a second and whispered into my ear, "I love you."

"Good job." My sincere reply.

"Maybe I can help you with that, if you would permit me Melissa?" Penny passed over the folded piece of paper. Melissa opened it and once again looked like she would faint. She immediately raised her other hand to her mouth, it seemed like she was fighting the urge to be sick. The shock caused heavy sobs that were instantly accompanied by free flowing tears. In between gulps, she was valiantly struggling to speak.

Everyone could see the check was for two million pounds.

"Than… than… thank you." It was the only words Melissa Chisholm was capable of saying.

"Well, now you have to stay to deposit the check. That may take a few days, but I can help you with that. We can discuss your options… *over dinner.*" Robert Bowden was proving himself a man simply impossible to dislike. As Melissa nodded, I feared that his face would explode in delight.

"Two's company, five's a crowd. Let's go." Penny stood and held out a hand for both Andy and I to take.

"Where are we going?" I took her hand, but wondered what else was left for us to do. No doubt, something else that only they knew and I'd discover later.

"Let's go home…"

Epilogue

Scotland, UK

Christmas Eve

It was good to be home. I've lived in different houses for many years now, but only with my parents do I ever truly feel 'home'. A child's sanctuary that only they can create where you truly feel cherished and protected without regard or respect of your age. They have kept my old room much as I left it, clothes from my teenage years still hanging in a closet or folded neatly in the chest of drawers. "They might become fashionable again, and you will be thankful we kept them when they do, as it'll save you a fortune," was all my mum had said when I once asked why they hadn't discarded them.

We both knew they would never fit me again.

I had long thought it laziness on their part, not clearing out my room. It would have meant having to redecorate and hunt for new furniture. Consequently, the freshest room in the house would have been the one that was spare and that would never do. It would also have caused no end of arguments. Mum wanting my dad's input into color schemes, his opinion on furniture, and an agreement on budget. So, for the sake of their marriage, and their sanity, they just left my room as it was. Or, as I perceived it, laziness.

Now I knew different.

Now I understood that, whilst my parents were happy enough for me to leave the home and make my way in the world, it was equally important to them that I should know that my home would always be there and that would never change.

Especially at Christmas.

The plush duvet was more than adequate, but Mum had thrown on a warm blanket on top, *'just in case it gets cold during the night'*. As she had done since I was a child, the window was adorned with fairy lights and fake snow sprayed on the inside. The curtains were held to the side and the blinds turned on the angle. Not that privacy was a concern, for my bedroom window simply framed the most beautiful

Scottish countryside. Always changing with the seasons, it was majestic and elegant, yet wonderfully unspoilt. Looking through the lights and into the darkness, it felt like I was 12 years old again.

As usual, my stocking was hanging from the chest of drawers that sat right next to the door. In my later years of living here, I had to pretend to be asleep when my dad opened the door, so slowly it was painful, in order to take my stocking and hand it to my mum for filling. Not that I could ever be certain it was him, for he had cleverly used the door to guarantee his anonymity. It had seemed so childish and immature then, yet now it was a treasured memory. Tonight, the memory would be the greatest of all. For tonight, my mum – my wonderful, fantastic, loving, and so thoughtful Mum – had placed a new stocking beside my old one.

I held Penny close and gently kissed her forehead, but I could see from the light in the window that she was already asleep.

Merry Christmas my love…

Christmas Day

The wonderful array of smells emanating from the kitchen blended into a single delicious aroma that wormed its way around my heart, mercilessly taunting and teasing me. More than once had I tried to breach the perimeter only to be accosted by my mother and Penny; now I was on my final warning. Another attempt and there would be no dinner for me. Desperately seeking my dad's support had proven fruitless, as his experience had brought enough wisdom to know better than risking his own share of the feast.

I was simply too young to be so wise.

Or so patient.

The knock on the front door gave me the opportunity to drag myself away from the usual Yuletide offerings on the television. It would have been cruel to have expected Dad to answer his own door and drag him away from his traditional viewing of *It's a Wonderful Life*. After all, I was back to being the kid in the home and taking care of random callers was my job. I knew the drill, anyone unimportant or, worse, annoying was to be given short shrift. Just as I was about to draw it open, they chapped the door for the second time.

Who does that?

"Okay, okay. I hear you, I'm *comin...*"

"Merry Christmas!"

"Andy! Wha....what...what a sur...

"Surprise? Yeah, I thought it might be!"

He laughed as he shook my hand and walked passed me. Well, not so much shook my hand as used it to pull himself into the house. He was in the living room by the time I'd realized that I was still stood holding the door open. I threw it closed more in annoyance at being caught by the surprise – I've had about enough surprises to last me a lifetime, good or bad – and returned to find that Andy and my dad had been joined by my mum and Penny from the kitchen.

They were all sharing a knowing smile.

"What's going on?" I returned with my own smile of ignorance and spoke to the room, but was looking directly at Penny. My confusion seemed to be all the more amusing to them.

"Well, darling, I have asked everyone to be here today because…" Penny's eyes held my own as she made her way towards me with her hands held out, looking for mine.

"Yes…?" My smile of ignorance had now set on my face and it was actually beginning to hurt me a little. However, I had to power through the pain to save myself from any embarrassment, at least until I knew what was happening.

Our hands locked and she pulled my arms around behind her. She briefly closed her eyes as she kissed me lightly on the lips. Gently breaking the embrace, her eyes slowly opened and quickly found mine. The words went out into the room as she spoke directly to me. "Well, because I wanted them to be here and share this moment."

Moment? What moment?

Silently and gracefully, Penny held my gaze as she slipped down onto one knee.

"My darling Z, will you marry me?"

It was the most entirely perfect moment of my life. Of course, she had planned it this way for she knew that it would be. *God, I love this girl.* It was ironic that my tears were flowing all too freely, yet my mouth was dry as I fought to speak.

"Yes, absolutely, positively, *YES!*"

As she tried to stand, I lifted her straight up into the air and swung her around, her laughter mixing with her tears. In my periphery I could see my parents and Andy huddled in an embrace that seemed as odd as it felt right. I dropped her down to kiss her, harder this time, and I held her so close that I was certain that we were bound to fuse together.

"Now we have a proper cause for celebration!" My dad never needed much encouragement to start a party and the speed in which he found a bottle of Champagne sparked my curiosity.

"Wait a minute. So you *ALL* knew that this was happening before me?" I was too delighted to actually be upset, but my feigning so had the desired effect. My dad froze just as he was about to pop the cork. Andy looked sheepishly towards Penny and my mum started to make an excuse then quickly saw through my ruse. Of course, Penny was not taken in for a second. Instead, she simply smiled and kissed me on the cheek, taking the opportunity to whisper into my ear.

"There is one surprise that nobody knows, my love." At that, she looked through yet another one of my confused expressions to stare deep into my soul. As she did so, she gave me a nod and smile that only belongs to lovers in love.

She was holding my hand against her womb.

Author's Note

I would take this opportunity to stress
that this novel is a work of fiction and so
nothing, neither express nor implied, is
based upon actual events, places or people.
Any and all mistakes are my own.

Acknowledgements

To my wife, Marie. "I need you more than want you, and I want you for all time…"

To Laura Tait, for redefining the meaning of the word 'friendship' for me. To say 'thank you' seems altogether inadequate to express the true level of my gratitude. I say it anyway – thank you.

To Mark Tait, you can never know what your encouragement and support has meant to me – thank you.

To Brian and Jane Worth – thank you for everything.

To the unsung heroes of every Indie Author – the ARC reviewers, the Book Bloggers, and all the other reviewers who take the time to read, review and promote our books. YOU GUYS ROCK! PLEASE keep up the great work you do in the knowledge that I, for one, am eternally grateful for your input and feedback – thank you.

Finally, thank you for reading my book, I sincerely hope you enjoyed it.

About Alexander McCabe

After graduating with a couple of useless degrees in law, I left my Scottish homeland and wandered nomadically around the globe to experience the rich diversity of culture that the world has to offer. Along the way, I met my wonderful wife. Between us, we have managed to extend our family with the addition of our little boy, Gabriel.

For the moment, we call Toronto 'home', although that is always subject to change…

Other Books by Alexander McCabe

Greater Expectations – *How the story of Z and Penny began…*
Released August, 2014

"It is said that the course of true love never runs smooth – even for us men. Yet it has never been easier to find love than in this modern digital era where the mighty computer has all but rendered Cupid redundant. Love is now to be found, quite literally, at your fingertips. Although love also seems to have changed with the times. This new love is deceitful and manipulative, cunning and untrustworthy. Love has gotten ugly. Thankfully, not all the answers to life's mysteries are to be found in the computer and Cupid – battered and bruised as he may be – proves that he still has some game and a few tricks up his sleeve…"

Click here to find out how to get your copy! www.aasmccabe.com/books

Connect with Alexander McCabe

Check out my website for the latest updates on current projects
www.aasmccabe.com

Facebook:
www.facebook.com/alexandermccabeauthor

Twitter:
@aasmccabe

Instagram:
www.instagram.com/aasmccabe/

13838989R00237

Printed in Poland
by Amazon Fulfillment
Poland Sp. z o.o., Wrocław